Geometric and Solid Modeling
An Introduction

The MORGAN KAUFMANN Series in Computer Graphics And Geometric Modeling

Series editor, Brian A. Barsky *(University of California, Berkeley)*

Richard H. Bartels, John C. Beatty, and Brian A. Barsky, *An Introduction to Splines for Use in Computer Graphics and Geometric Modeling (1987)*

Christoph M. Hoffmann, Geometric and Solid Modeling: An Introduction (1989)

Norman I. Badler, Brian A. Barsky, David Zeltzer, *Making Them Move: Mechanics, Control and Animation of Articulated Figures* (1989)

Geometric
and
Solid Modeling

An Introduction

Christoph M. Hoffmann
Purdue University, Indiana

Morgan Kaufmann Publishers, Inc.
San Mateo, California 94403

President *Michael B. Morgan*
Editor *Bruce Spatz*
Production Manager *Shirley Jowell*
Production Coordination *Maureen Flores*
Text Design *Beverly Kennon-Kelley*
Cover Design *Joy Dickenson*
Copy Editor *Lyn Dupre*

Library of Congress Cataloging-in Publication Data

Hoffmann, Christoph M. (Christoph Martin), 1946-
    Solid and geometric modeling / Christoph Hoffmann.
        p.   cm.
    Bibliography: p.
    Includes index.
    ISBN 1-55860-067-1
    1. Computer graphics 2. Three-dimensional
display systems. I. Title.
    T385.H64   1989
    604.2'028'566--dc20   89-15327
                                                       CIP

Morgan Kaufmann Publishers, Inc.

Editorial Office:
  2929 Campus Drive
  San Mateo, CA 94403

Order from:
  P.O. Box 50490
  Palo Alto, CA 94303-9953

93 92 91 90 89 5 4 3 2 1

Foreword

John E. Hopcroft

Today, our imagination is limited by the computer systems we have built. The demand for sophisticated tools has grown faster than the corresponding developments of the supporting science base.

Written by one of the leading experts in the field of solid-modeling systems, *Geometric and Solid Modeling: An Introduction* provides the start of a scientific basis to support the coming revolution in computer-aided design. It deals with the concepts and tools needed to design and implement solid-modeling systems, and makes this information accessible to the novice, as well as to the experienced designer.

Man has always distinguished himself from other animals with the aid of language, art, and tools. Language and art remain man's way of representing ideas, either for communicating them to other people or for giving them permanence. Tools extend his strength and mobility.

In early society, tools were simple and the ideas behind their function and manufacture were easily communicated, either verbally or by example. As the complexity of tools increased, written drawings and other documents became an essential component of design. In today's technologically advanced society, in which tools have reached the complexity of a spacecraft, the development of a design requires a team of engineers. Writing, and even drawing and sculpting, are found to be inadequate; they are static and of too limited a dimension for expressing complex designs.

Computers are revolutionizing our ability to represent, develop, and communicate knowledge. By abstracting knowledge into procedures, computers provide dynamic and powerful representations, and enhance our ability to manipulate and expand our thoughts.

In the past, a new product was created by investigating a design in the abstract, using paper, pencil and whatever other tools were available. The design was communicated through the medium of engineering drawings to a manufacturer who built the device. In the future, computers will be used to explore much larger design spaces, and designs will be communicated directly to machines manufacturing the product. The result will be a wider selection of products of higher quality and lower cost.

Imagine using a computer model of an object instead of a physical prototype to validate a complex design. The computer prototype would allow changes with a few key strokes, as well as allow engineering analyses to be automatically carried out. For example, a multifingered gripper could be modeled and electronically simulated in various manipulation tasks, exploring the advantage of the number and placement of fingers.

In the early stages of a new technology, the techniques and methods of the older technology are simply simulated. Gradually the full power of the new technology is achieved as new methods utilizing the natural advantages of the technology are developed. Thus it was not surprising that the initial usage of Computer Aided Design systems was in automating drafting. Today, computer-aided-design (CAD) systems provide new representations of objects as three-dimensional entities rather than as two-dimensional projections. Ultimately we will realize that an object is defined by something more intrinsic than its shape.

Solid modeling and computer-aided design are quickly becoming vital to economic productiveness. The sophistication of new products has necessitated a coinciding sophistication in such engineering tools as computer-aided design systems and analysis programs. The Boeing 767 could not have been designed without such automated tools. Similarly, complex parts for spacecraft, robotic workcells and VLSI technology are accelerating this need.

Geometric and Solid Modeling: An Introduction is a welcome introduction to an increasingly sophisticated and fast-growing field.

John E. Hopcroft
Cornell University
Ithaca, NY
1989

Acknowledgements

John Hopcroft has challenged computer science to involve itself in the problems of geometric and solid modeling. I wish to acknowledge his eloquence and persuasiveness as he set forth the foundation for computer science to have a unique and valuable perspective on these problems.

I want to particularly thank Bruno Buchberger, Ray Sarraga, Jarek Rossignac, Kevin Weiler, Dan Gottlieb, Ari Requicha, Mike Karasick, and Chee Yap, for the many focused and precise suggestions they made, and I wish to recognize the significant amount of time they spent to do so. From their valuable feedback, this book benefits greatly.

Thanks to my students, Bill Bouma, Shing-Choei Chiang, Jung-Hong Chuang, Chris Scherbert, Pam Vermeer, Jia-Xun Yu, and Jianhua Zhou, who have checked the manuscript for accuracy, and who served as a "Turing test" for clarity.

My research has been supported by the National Science Foundation under grants DCR 85-12443, CCR 86-12590, CCR 86-19817, and DMC 88-07550; by the Office of Naval Research, under contract N00014-86-K-0465; and by a grant from the AT&T Foundation.

Contents

List of Figures

List of Tables

CHAPTER 1
Introduction

Solid modeling is rapidly emerging as a central area of research and development in such diverse applications as engineering and product design, computer-aided manufacturing, electronic prototyping, off-line robot programming, and motion planning. All these applications require representing the shapes of solid physical objects, and such representations and basic operations on them can be provided by solid modeling.

As a field, solid modeling spans several disciplines, including mathematics, computer science, and engineering. In consequence, it is a broad subject that must accommodate a diversity of viewpoints and has to meet a diversity of goals. Sometimes, this diversity of goals can lead to conflicting demands. Current thinking on the subject views the proper resolution of these conflicts to be application-dependent. That is, it is no longer thought realistic to envision a comprehensive solid-modeling system that satisfies the needs of all potential users. Rather, as it is argued, we should concentrate on constructing a software environment in which many tools for geometric and solid computation are available and can be combined with ease as appropriate for the specific application under consideration.

Whether we seek to build a complete system or wish to accumulate a set of tools, we need to study and implement many geometric algorithms. In this book, we explain what is needed for this task. Of necessity, we must therefore cover techniques from computer science, numerical analysis, symbolic computation, and many other areas. The relevant facts from these areas are brought together as they are needed. Not only do we develop them technically, we also explain their intuitive content as much as possible, for we have found that intuitive explanations accelerate absorbing the material. Moreover, an intuitive understanding of the ideas underlying a particular subject serves as a guide when special topics are pursued further by reading the pertinent literature, be it for research purposes or for specializing certain methods as demanded by some application.

Geometric or *surface modeling* traditionally identifies a body of techniques that can model certain classes of piecewise parametric surfaces, subject to particular conditions of shape and smoothness. It developed as a separate field in several industries, including automobile, aerospace, and shipbuilding, and has some of its intellectual roots in approximation theory. It is our view that the streams of geometric and solid modeling are converging. As solid modeling strives to extend the geometric coverage, there is an emerging need to research the use of surface forms and the techniques to interrogate them. Similarly, as geometric modeling contemplates building complete solid representations from surface patches, the usefulness of traditional solid-modeling techniques is more widely recognized. In anticipation of the growing importance of this convergence, a large part of this book is devoted to geometric investigations of implicit and parametric surfaces.

Although we will develop a lot of machinery to deal with surface geometries, we do not cover the traditional body of knowledge on parametric surfaces developed by classical geometric modeling. Instead, we concentrate on the fundamental issues that are at the focal point of the possible integration of geometric and solid modeling, and develop techniques that have the potential to bridge the current gaps between the two areas of activity. Thus, we understand geometric modeling in the more generic sense.

1.1 A Brief Historical Perspective of Solid Modeling

As a field, solid modeling is the outgrowth of several convergent developments. These include automatic drafting systems, free-form surface design, and graphics and animation.

Computer drafting systems replace manual engineering drawing. Some of the benefits are that electronic drawings can be modified and archived more easily, and that one may verify automatically the validity of a design by a program rather than by human inspection. Complicated engineering drawings may contain errors. Such errors in the electronic counterpart may, in principle, be corrected without the risk of introducing new errors elsewhere. However, programs to verify design validity are nontrivial, and research on this subject continues.

Early efforts in automated drawing resulted in wireframe modeling systems — that is, in systems in which only the edges and vertices of objects are represented. This would be a natural representation, assuming that

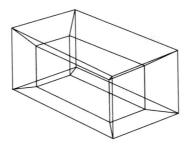

Figure 1.1   Ambiguous Wireframe Object

the objective is to generate line drawings of the design, projected in certain directions. Unfortunately, there may be ambiguities in interpreting the representation. A simple, well-known example of this phenomenon is shown in Figure 1.1. The figure shows a block with a beveled hole through its center. It is not possible to deduce the direction of the hole, since it could lie in any of the three principal directions. For this reason, wireframes are not the preferred object representation. On the other hand, wireframe objects have small storage requirements and can be accessed and displayed quickly. The resulting line drawings constitute an acceptable visualization aid in many situations, and can provide a quick feedback between the modeling system and the designer. For this reason, many modeling systems retain the capability to generate wireframe drawings.

A second contributor to solid modeling has been free-form surface design, using parametric surface patches and, in particular, various types of spline surfaces. Surface design with splines originated in the automobile industry, principally for car body design; in the shipbuilding industry, for the design of ship hulls; and in the aircraft industry, for the design of wings, fuselages, and so on. Free-form surface design in these areas has led to the field of computer-aided geometric design (CAGD), primarily focusing on methodologies for designing curved surfaces subject to aesthetic or functional constraints. Research in CAGD has discovered many useful classes of parametric surfaces and has developed a large repertoire of algorithms for their design, analysis, and manipulation. These surfaces would be most useful in solid modeling. As we stated, we cover basic concepts underlying the use of these surfaces in solid modeling. Many books are available that cover the more classical techniques of modifying the shapes of specific surfaces classes, and we cite some of them at the end of this chapter.

The difficulty of evaluating and representing the intersection of parametric surface patches has hindered the development of solid modelers that incorporate parametric surfaces. Roughly speaking, the topology of a surface patch becomes quite complicated when Boolean operations are performed. Finding a convenient representation for these topologies continues to be a major challenge.

It might seem peculiar to identify computer graphics as an area contributing to solid modeling. Indeed, the primary focus of computer graphics is to render realistic images of objects, and this can be done from data structures that do not represent complete solids. However, there is a need in solid design to obtain visual feedback, so we want to render images from solid representations, and thus an understanding of graphics algorithms and the surface representations used by them can be useful. Conversely, constructing images from solid models is gaining in importance in animation and is also used by rendering algorithms that support image generation in scenes from changing points of view. Thus, computer graphics is beginning to deal with solid models as data and could make useful contributions to visualization techniques and to user-interface design.

1.2 Three Levels of Abstraction

Conceptually, a solid-modeling system spans three levels of abstraction:

1. The user of the modeling system is presented the highest level of abstraction, the *user interface*. He or she interacts with the system through a design language that may be textual, visual, or both. On this level, conceptual tools for constructing, modifying, archiving, and destroying designs are available. Also, there may be various tools for analyzing a design, perhaps even for reasoning about some of its properties.

2. Next, there is a lower level of abstraction comprising the *mathematical and algorithmic infrastructure*. The infrastructure implements the conceptual operations available in the user interface, as well as a wide range of auxiliary tools needed by these operations. Examples include algorithms for constructing the intersection of two objects, or tools for determining whether and how two curved surfaces intersect.

3. On the lowest level, there is the *substratum* of arithmetic and symbolic computations that are used as primitives by the algorithmic infrastructure. In the most basic sense, this substratum consists of the hardware capabilities for integer and floating-point arithmetic, and the logical operations the chosen programming language offers for expressing computations and viewing storage.

Computer science teaches that levels of abstraction should be kept logically separate, and that lower levels must not unduly influence higher levels. Yet, as we shall see, this ideal situation appears to be presently unattainable, except at the great expense incurred by exact arithmetic, so certain operations done at the highest conceptual level take their particular form essentially because of unreliabilities on the lowest level.

1.2.1 User Interfaces

Much of the interest in solid modeling is due to the perceived value of automating the design and analysis of solid objects. If the field is to reap the benefits that good solid-modeling systems could provide, then modeling must be made as widely accessible as possible, and must be developed into as flexible an instrument as possible. Much of this would be the result of having good user interfaces that successfully engage people with minimum training and increase the productivity of experienced designers.

It is widely accepted that user interfaces should have a strong visual component, but clearly a textual interaction is also required; for instance, for the sake of precision. Furthermore, if the modeling system is interfaced to an analysis system, a more machine-oriented interface must also be present.

A major task of the interface is to present the user with a set of operations for solid design and modification. Among these operations are the well-known Boolean operations, global modifications such as rounding and offsetting, and local modifications such as edge beveling or face extrusion. In many cases, the operations are not fully understood. For example, when sweeping an area along a space curve to define a volume, should we allow possible self-intersection?

In doing detail design, we would like to concentrate our effort on local areas of interest and to design them more or less without paying attention to the rest of the design. Having completed the design of such *features*, we could then specify their position and orientation in the larger design through *constraints*. Much current research explores these goals of interface design. It is not clear how best to define features, yet we know that the concept is needed. The notion of features is probably not a static concept; that is, the same geometric design of an object will have different features, depending on the view point. For instance, if we consider how to evaluate stress concentrations, then features such as sharp edges are of interest. If we consider machining operations, we might be interested in the geometry of holes and slots found on the object. The main difficulty, it seems, is to identify a catalog of forms defining a set of features of interest, and to understand how these forms may interact. For example, if a slot is placed at the edge of an object, as shown in Figure 1.2 to the right, should we still consider it a slot?

Current thinking also stresses the need for *conceptual design*; that is, for a coarse design laying out the overall structure without various details. It is argued that a more efficient approach to engineering design is an overall outlay of the rough shape, with rapid visual feedback, exploration of the

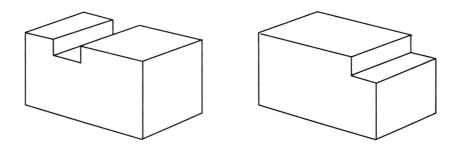

Figure 1.2   Two Slot Positions

suitability of the design through some suite of analysis computations, followed by a computationally intensive detailed design. This approach should not only alleviate some of the delays incurred by certain expensive detailed design operations, but also bring us closer to the long-term goal of *design by functionality*. In the abstract, we may not care about a particular shape, as long as it realizes a certain functionality. For example, in designing a piston engine like the one shown in Figure 1.3, our functional goals might include that the engine develop a certain power while not running too hot or being too heavy. As design parameters, we might wish to vary piston size, stroke length, wall thickness, and cooling-line placement. It seems certain that design by functionality is a possibility, but we have no systematic body of knowledge establishing this connection precisely in a range of applications.

1.2.2 Mathematical and Algorithmic Infrastructure

Infrastructure is traditionally the strongest and most prominent research subject in solid modeling. Among the many questions addressed is the development of efficient and robust algorithms and representations for solving the geometry problems that arise in solid modeling. We mention a few:

1. Given two solid models, test whether they interfere with each other. If so, determine the volume of their intersection.

2. Given two curved faces intersecting in a sharp edge, find a surface that smoothly connects the two curved faces, thereby blending the edge.

3. Given a curved face of a solid model and a point on the surface, determine whether this point lies within the face boundary.

4. Given a closed piecewise algebraic curve in the plane, sweep it along a space curve and determine the surface of the volume so swept.

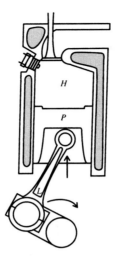

Figure 1.3   Piston Engine

Since efficient algorithms depend on suitable representations for solids and their constituting elements (i.e., for their faces, edges, and vertices), it is crucial to study different schemata for representing them. Moreover, since there are typically no uniform best choices, conversion algorithms between different representations must be designed. In all these algorithms, we must account for efficiency in space and time, as well as for numerical stability and accuracy.

1.2.3 The Substratum Problem

The distinction between substratum and infrastructure may appear arbitrary, and we should clarify why it is made here. When implementing many of the geometric algorithms found in the literature, one encounters a fundamental difficulty: Even though an algorithm may have been meticulously implemented, it need not be completely free from errors. But these errors seem to be due neither to carelessness in the implementation, nor to a mistake in the algorithm design. Rather, the error is due to an oversight — we take for granted that the arithmetic operations in the geometric computation are precise. Of course, we realize that floating-point arithmetic is approximate, but we might have assumed that the errors so incurred are insignificant. This is not always the case, and the distinction between substratum and infrastructure helps to conceptualize the nature of the difficulty.

A computer does two types of computation: symbol manipulation, which can be done exactly, and numerical computation. The latter is exact only for integer and rational arithmetic, and is subject to imprecision in floating-point arithmetic. Floating-point error is due to the limited precision to which the calculations are done and suffers from *roundoff* and *digit-cancellation* errors. The two problems are well known in numerical analysis and have given rise to extensive research into designing algorithms that exhibit greater accuracy and numerical stability, besides solving a problem efficiently.

The vast majority of geometric computations in solid modeling are performed in floating-point arithmetic. Since logical decisions are made based on these calculations, errors incurred by the arithmetic should be of great concern. In particular, since the same logical decision may recur throughout a computation but may have been based on different calculations, there is the possibility of making inconsistent decisions. It is precisely this possible inconsistency that causes solid-modeling systems to fail on certain inputs.

The interplay of symbolic and arithmetic computation is a critical dimension in solid modeling and appears to be unparalleled. It raises fundamental problems of profound mathematical content, and there is a growing sense in the field that these problems need to be addressed urgently. At this time, it appears that there are three choices:

1. Create a substratum implementing exact arithmetic. Typically, this slows down all computations unacceptably, but in some situations a priori precision bounds exist, and then this approach may lead to acceptable speeds.

2. Use an inexact arithmetic substratum, and hope for the best. This is the traditional choice of system designers, and a great deal of effort is subsequently expended to tune the system such that the occasional catastrophic failures do not happen in typical applications.

3. Augment an inexact arithmetic substratum with specific algorithmic steps that avoid catastrophic failure and are capable of delivering valid results for all inputs. This alternative has been proposed only recently and is the subject of much current research.

Note that an exact arithmetic substratum does allow a clean separation of the various levels of abstraction. However, current technology does not have the necessary tools to make this approach attractive in the curved-surface domain, and we have to wait with this alternative until more progress has been made.

The second choice does not permit a clean separation of substratum, infrastructure, and user interface. Systems implemented in this way will fail occasionally, so the first phase of an implementation is usually followed by a second, time-consuming phase in which the system is fine-tuned to avoid failures on common inputs. Although this fine-tuning is often done by trial and error, it can be ameliorated by careful consideration of the geometric significance of each error as it is encountered. Such systems are difficult to maintain and changes to them are risky.

The third alternative, finally, is to redesign a substratum in which operations such as point/surface incidence are supplemented by processing steps that account for inaccuracies. At this time, it is hard to assess the impact this approach may have on the complexity of the algorithm, and whether the approach can achieve a strict separation of the levels of abstraction. Known complexity bounds seem to be overly pessimistic, and much further work will be needed before we can judge the ultimate utility of this approach. Research on this subject is, of course, fueled by the hope that in this way we can reach a middle ground somewhere between the expensive exact approach and the complicated and unsatisfactory traditional approach.

1.3 About This Book

This book deals primarily with the concepts and tools needed to design and implement solid-modeling systems, their infrastructures, and their substrata. Of necessity, this subject requires a considerable amount of mathematical fact and thinking. We have made every effort to make the material accessible even to the novice. The reader should be able to absorb the intuitive content without much difficulty. Going into the details may require some patience, perhaps, but should not be daunting.

Throughout the book, algorithms and the underlying theory needed to design them are in the foreground. Thus, designers, implementors, technical leaders of solid-modeling groups, and academic researchers constitute the primary audience of this book. Nevertheless, a prospective user of a solid-modeling system should read Chapters 1 and 2 to gain an appreciation of the field and of the basic concepts it exercises. Armed with these insights, he or she should then be able to assess the true capabilities of the systems under consideration. Chapter 4 provides an understanding of the finer points, and is useful when judging whether the system can provide the needed accuracy and robustness.

Chapter 2 explains the basic concepts. It discusses first the conceptual operations that one expects to find in a user interface, except for visualization and archiving operations. The presentation is kept conceptual, rather than technical, and is well suited to the casual reader who wishes to gain an overview. The chapter then presents the two dominant representation schemata used in solid modeling — namely, constructive solid geometry (CSG), and boundary representation (B-rep). Basic geometric operations in CSG are also sketched. The section on topological validity presents technical material needed for devising algorithms that test whether a given boundary representation is correct. There are other representation schemata, and they are briefly summarized at the end of Chapter 2.

In Chapter 3, we design an algorithm for Boolean operations on solids given in a boundary representation. This algorithm serves as a useful frame for developing an appreciation of the subtleties of representing and manipulating solids. Representing, analyzing, and manipulating solid models by computer is not a simple matter, and to implement competently modeling operations such as the determination of the intersection of two solids is a project of considerable complexity. For this reason, the intersection operation is discussed in depth. We restrict Chapter 3 to the intersection of polyhedra with nonmanifold boundaries. Except for the treatment of tangencies and singularities, polyhedral intersection requires dealing with virtually all aspects of this operation, so our restriction does not oversimplify the problem. The polyhedral-intersection algorithm can be used as the basis for an extension to curved solids. The added difficulties encountered relate to mathematical issues and accuracy questions that are discussed in Chapters 5 and 6.

Chapter 4 addresses the important substratum problem. There is at present much discussion as to the true origin of the problem; hence, the chapter looks at different manifestations of accuracy and robustness problems and surveys a number of approaches proposed for solving them. It seems that the polyhedral case is already very difficult, and we have restricted our presentation to this case only. As already mentioned, research on this subject is relatively recent and has not yet matured, so the chapter concentrates more on making the problems intelligible rather than on giving recommendations for a "best" solution.

The balance of the book is devoted to the treatment of curved surfaces. Chapter 5 begins this topic by looking at the representational requirements. Surfaces can be represented parametrically or implicitly. Both representation styles have strengths and weaknesses. For example, for an implicitly represented surface $f(x, y, z) = 0$, the problem of testing whether a given point p lies on the surface is simple. If the same surface is represented parametrically, then this question is difficult. On the other hand, it is simple to generate points on a parametric surface. On an implicit surface, this would be much harder. Hence, we will examine methods for converting between parametric and implicit surface forms. Curve and surface singularities add specific subtleties to boundary representations of curved solids. If they are ignored, geometric ambiguities may arise that are due to the fact that, between two points in space, there might be different connecting curve segments, both belonging to the intersection of the same pair of curved surfaces. An example of this phenomenon is also discussed in Chapter 5, along with recommendations on how to avoid it.

When we are dealing with curved surfaces, the evaluation of their intersection is a fundamental operation. Chapter 6 looks at a number of techniques used to implement this operation. Specifically, by combining traditional numerical techniques with symbolic computations from algebraic geometry, it is possible to deal with complicated singularities. For plane curves, these algebraic techniques are simple and effective. Such curves could be trimming curves when intersecting parametric surfaces. For space curves presented as the intersection of two implicit surfaces, complications arise that continue to be research topics. Here, one expects that more sophisticated symbolic computations will be needed.

Since symbolic algebraic computations require a working knowledge of ideal theory, we have added a chapter on Gröbner bases techniques. These techniques include some very powerful algorithms for implicitization and inversion, and provide completely general and comprehensive methods for solving systems of algebraic equations. The great generality of the algorithms make them too slow to be of immediate routine use in production systems. However, they hold much potential for providing specializations that could play a major role in the manipulation and analysis of curved surfaces. We touch on some of these specializations in the section on basis conversion. This section also describes a strategy for implicitizing curves and surfaces that can handle problem sizes that could not be attacked successfully by other techniques known to us.

1.4 Notes and References

As A. Requicha pointed out, the term *solid modeling* is of relatively recent coinage: Early work used the term *geometric modeling* to refer to solid modeling, and reserved the term *surface modeling* to refer to work on parametric curves and surfaces.

There are several surveys dealing with solid modeling, including Requicha and Voelcker (1983). The survey by Requicha (1988) is a recent update. Voelcker, Requicha, and Conway (1988) is another survey of the area that focuses on how solid modeling could be integrated into the manufacturing process and on what the problems raised by this prospect are.

Geometric modeling in the current sense is the subject of the books by Bartels, Beatty, and Barsky (1987), Farin (1988), and Mortensen (1985). These books give good introductions to the rather large literature on the subject.

In his book on solid modeling, Mäntylä (1988) describes how to represent manifold polyhedral objects and how to implement Boolean operations on them. He also describes a facility for storing and undoing previous designs. Chiyokura (1988) describes the implementation of *Designbase*, a specific modeling system with some curved-surface capabilities. Briefly, curved solids can be designed and modified by local operations, such as altering the shape of certain edges and faces, but Boolean operations require that one of the intersecting objects be polyhedral. All objects will have manifold surfaces. Chiyokura's book also discusses several classes of parametric curves and surfaces.

The ambiguity of wireframes shown in Figure 1.1 was found by J. Shapiro at the University of Rochester.

CHAPTER 2
Basic Concepts

This chapter reviews the conceptual operations one expects to be present in the user interface. Also discussed are constructive solid geometry and boundary representation, two major representation schemata used in solid modeling.

In constructive solid geometry (CSG) a solid is represented as a set-theoretic Boolean expression of *primitive* solid objects, of a simpler structure. Both the surface and the interior of an object are defined, albeit implicitly. A boundary representation (B-rep), on the other hand, describes only the oriented surface of a solid as a data structure composed of vertices, edges, and faces. The orientation convention permits us to decide on which side of the surface the solid's interior is located.[1] This suffices to describe the solid's interior and exterior unambiguously, provided the surface and its geometric embedding satisfy certain geometric and topological requirements.

CSG and B-rep have different inherent strengths and weaknesses. For instance, a CSG object is always valid in the sense that its surface is closed and orientable and encloses a volume, provided the primitives are valid in this sense. A B-rep object, on the other hand, is easily rendered on a graphic display system. In consequence, there is a discernible tendency to combine both CSG and B-rep in an effort to take advantage of the different

---

[1] If only objects of bounded volume are represented, then a surface orientation is unnecessary. However, we shall permit unbounded objects.

strong points afforded by each. Such modelers are called *dual-representation* modelers.

To develop an understanding of the properties and algorithmic aspects of these representations, we describe some of the basic operations on them. For CSG, these include classifying points, curves, and surfaces with respect to a solid; detecting redundancies in the representation; and approximating CSG objects systematically. For B-rep, we review the possible surface types, the winged-edge representation schema, and the Euler operators. A more flexible B-rep schema is given later in Chapter 3, where we discuss how to intersect two polyhedra given in this representation.

Given a boundary representation, the question of whether it represents a solid is of obvious practical interest. Algorithms for testing topological validity can be given, but should be based on precise mathematical definitions. We develop formal definitions of what constitutes a valid solid in the topological sense, and derive from it a validity check. This material is intricate and uses methods from algebraic topology. Although the intuitive content is fairly obvious, it is necessary to develop the material carefully, since there are many subtleties that are not apparent at first glance.

There are other solid representation schemata based on spatial subdivision; for example, octrees. We comment on them briefly at the end of the chapter, but do not go into the algorithmic aspects entailed by them.

2.1 Conceptual Operations and Primitives

Irrespective of the representation schema chosen, we must make available conceptual tools for defining objects, for modifying them, and, eventually, for archiving them. We discuss these operations now.

2.1.1 Primitives

A solid design is usually created in several steps that begin with an existing design and modify it, or create a new design from *primitive* objects. The former situation presupposes an earlier design that is retrieved from a database. The latter situation depends on a suitable notion of what constitutes a primitive.

Primitive objects are selected from a universe of possible shapes. A shape is instantiated by assigning values to certain parameters. Some systems allow delaying parameter assignment. We give three examples of primitive object definition.

1. Each primitive is selected from a set of solid shapes and is instantiated by choosing values for certain dimensioning parameters that control the final shape. For instance, a CSG modeler may use blocks, cylinders, spheres, cones, and tori. The parameters in this case include the side lengths of blocks, the diameter and length of cylinders, and so on.

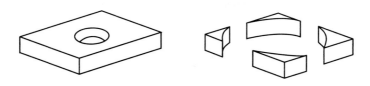

Figure 2.1   Shape Variation Due to Parameter Values

2. A primitive is created by sweeping a contour along a space curve. Both the shape of the contour and the shape of the space curve are defined by parameters. For instance, we can sweep a disk of radius r along a line segment of length l, thus creating a solid cylinder. This approach lends itself to generating and verifying cutting paths for numerically controlled machining.

3. All primitives are algebraic halfspaces; that is, point sets defined as

$$\{(x, y, z) \mid f(x, y, z) \leq 0\}$$

where f is an irreducible polynomial.[2] The coefficients of the polynomial can be considered the shape parameters. This approach has been used in several research systems.

We will discuss the first approach in the section on constructive solid geometry (CSG). Note that, in a pure CSG modeler, the instantiation of the shape parameters can be delayed. It is then possible to construct *generic designs*. However, a generic design cannot be displayed or converted to boundary representation, since different parameter assignments could lead to totally different shapes. See also Figure 2.1, where we have varied the diameter of the cylinder defining the hole. In some modelers, the parameters carry default values that can be used to visualize generic designs.

In the second approach, various elementary operations have been proposed for creating primitive solids. A typical example is *sweeping*: We are given an object to be swept, and a path along which to sweep it, and thereby we define some volume. The object S to be swept could be a finite area delimited by a closed curve, or a solid. The path of the sweep typically would be a segment of a space curve C, and could be open or closed. The

---

[2] As explained in Chapters 5 and 7, a polynomial is *irreducible* if the point set defined in the text cannot be decomposed into the union of simpler components. Technically, the polynomial f is irreducible if it cannot be factored.

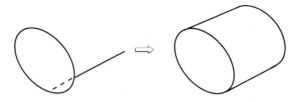

Figure 2.2   A Circular Disk Swept Along a Line

primitive solid created by this operation consists of the volume swept by S as it is moved along C. An example is shown in Figure 2.2.

The mathematics of sweeping is more delicate and demanding than it might seem at first glance. Foremost, it depends on certain conventions. We need to fix a reference point on S that will traverse the curve C. We also must define how, if at all, the orientation of S varies as S moves along C, and what the initial orientation is. These conventions must be determined by default or by suitable parameters to the sweep operations. Then, there could be degeneracy problems: If a planar area S with fixed orientation is moved along a path C that has a tangent parallel to the plane containing S, then the interior of the resulting volume could have self-intersections. In the three-dimensional example shown in Figure 2.3, this is indicated by the crease in the center that is the result of a self-intersection. Figure 6.6 in Chapter 6 shows a two-dimensional example. Moreover, if the entire path C is parallel to the plane of S, then we have defined an area instead of a volume. If such cases are considered an error, we need algorithms for their detection. If they are allowed, we need to give proper meaning to the results.

Usually, there is no closed-form mathematical description of the surface

Figure 2.3   Sweep Degeneracies

bounding the swept volume. For example, the cylinder in Figure 2.2 is bounded by finite areas on two linear surfaces and on one quadratic surface. Moreover, if the surface contains self-intersections or other types of singularities, the areas of interest may not have a simple definition.

Important special cases include sweeping a sphere along a space curve or across a surface of another solid. In the first case, we obtain a partial description of the volume removed by a ball cutter as the cutting tool is moved along the path of the sweep.[3] Thus, this case has applications in numerically controlled machining, and can be used to represent the effect of cutting operations, either for automatic generation of cutter paths or for verification that such paths do not interfere with other parts of the solid to be manufactured.

When a sphere is moved across a surface, we obtain a volume bounded by the *offset* of the surface. Offsetting can be viewed as an operation on solids or on surfaces, and has been used to define global *blending* operations on solids in which all edges are rounded or filleted. We return to the subject of offsets and spherical sweeps in Chapters 6 and 7.

The third approach of using algebraic halfspaces as primitives raises difficult algorithmic problems and is the subject of current research. Unless additional restrictions are placed on f, the generality of the primitives can be overwhelming, and general algorithms such as the ones discussed in Chapter 7 should be considered.

Note that variations of the third approach have also been used. For example, we could require that the polynomial f have degree no greater than 2 or 3. Doing so has the advantage that the specialized techniques discussed in Chapter 5 suffice to manipulate the resulting objects.

2.1.2 Local Modifications

Numerous local modifications to solids have been proposed. Most of them operate on a boundary representation, and can be implemented using Euler operations (see also Section 2.3.4). Figures 2.4 through 2.6 show several examples.

If we operate on boundary representations with simple shape elements, then local modifications could be inexpensive, provided that the geometric shapes we manipulate are sufficiently simple. Local modifications do, however, require validity checks to avoid errors such as the one shown in Figure 2.7. Here, the face is extruded too far and interferes with other parts of the solid.

---

[3]Strictly speaking, a ball cutter cannot physically remove the entire volume swept by the sphere, since we must accommodate the shaft of the cutter.

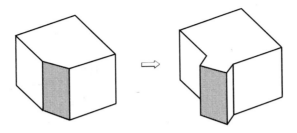

Figure 2.4   Extruding a Face

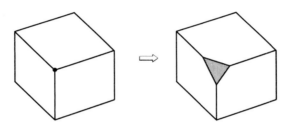

Figure 2.5   Beveling a Vertex

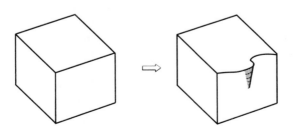

Figure 2.6   Altering Edge and Face Shape

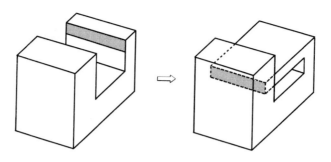

Figure 2.7   Error in Face Extrusion

2.1.3 Global Operations

There are several trivial global operations, including rotating and translating solids. Regularized Boolean operations, explained in Section 2.2, are also considered global operations, as are the operations of offsetting solids, and of rounding all convex and filleting all concave edges.

2.1.4 Undoing and Redoing

Ideally, solid design is an interactive process in which the designer experiments with alternatives, modifies them, corrects errors, and so on. Whereas interactivity demands quick response time, exploring alternative designs and correcting errors requires the possibility of undoing a sequence of operations, or redoing some of them.

Undoing an operation requires minimally a *history* that records all operations leading, in sequence, to the present design. Then, in principle, we could reconstruct the entire sequence of operations, from the beginning up to some prior point. Effectively, this undoes all subsequent operations. If alternatives should be explored and if we wish to return to some of them, then the history record must be a tree. An example of a history tree of designs is shown in Figure 2.8.

Redoing a design from the root up to a specific alternative is inferior to using a more direct *undo* capable of reversing the effect of an operation. The difficulty of the undo will depend on the way objects are represented. The operation is easy in pure CSG. In boundary representation, local modifications are easy to undo, but Boolean operations are not. For difficult undo operations, it is better to *check point*; that is, we store the representation of the design prior to the operation, and then once more after its completion. Then, undoing is simply a retrieval.

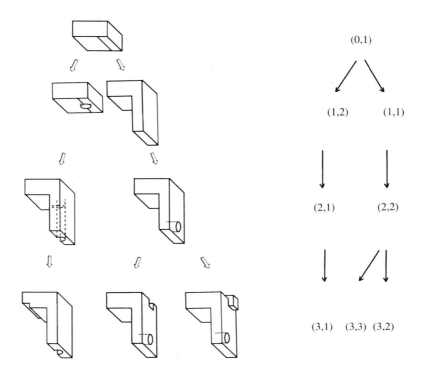

Figure 2.8 History Tree of Design   **Figure 2.9** Indexing a History Tree

The cost of check pointing has to be balanced against the cost of inverting the operation. If an undo is cheap, it is probably better not to check point, especially in B-rep, where the data structures describing the current design may be very large.

Having undone a partial design, we may wish to reconstruct a design alternative previously defined. Since most operations include consistency checking for their results, an explicit *redo* operation has the advantage that such checks are not needed. Thus, a redo operation can be faster. Moreover, for expensive operations such as union or intersection, redo can simply access the check-pointed representation and is therefore also cheap.

The history tree should be presented to the user as an aid to remember the various versions of design already explored. The presentation can be augmented by an indexing scheme that generates default names for the design based on the position in the history tree. Thus, instead of issuing a sequence of undo and redo commands to reach a specific alternative, we can retrieve the alternative directly by giving its name. A simple indexing scheme is as follows:

> Each tree vertex is indexed by a pair of numbers (i, j), where i is the depth of the vertex, and j enumerates all vertices of equal depth in the order of creation.

The *depth* of a vertex is determined as follows: The root has depth 0; if v descends from a vertex w, then $\text{depth}(v) = \text{depth}(w) + 1$. Figure 2.9 shows an example.

2.2 CSG Representation

In the strict sense, CSG is a method of representation, a design methodology, and a certain standard set of primitive objects. So, a CSG object is "built" from the *standard primitives*, using regularized Boolean operations and rigid motions. We will sketch this methodology first, and will present some of the properties and algorithms it entails. Later on, we will consider the possibility of greatly enlarging the set of allowed primitives.

2.2.1 CSG Standard Primitives

The CSG standard primitives are the parallelepiped (block), the triangular prism, the sphere, the cylinder, the cone, and the torus.[4] They are *generic* in the sense that they represent shapes that must be *instantiated* by the user to chosen dimensions. Thus, to obtain a parallelepiped of edge lengths 1, 1, and 3, one might specify `block(1, 1, 3)`, where the lengths are expressed in units depending on conventions, or, perhaps, are given explicitly. Also depending on convention would be the placement of the resulting object in space: With each primitive object there is associated a *local coordinate frame*. Here, we will place this coordinate frame as shown in Figure 2.10. These different local coordinate frames must be related to one another, by placing them with respect to a common *world coordinate frame*, discussed later.

All standard primitives have a finite domain. For example, the cylinder always has a finite radius and a finite length. This convention seems to be rooted in the thought that we always model finite solids. We will see later that it can be convenient to consider infinite solids, at least as intermediate steps, in the process of defining complex, finite solids.

2.2.2 Regularized Boolean Operations

After instantiation, primitive objects can be combined using *regularized Boolean operations*. The operations are the *regularized union*, denoted $\cup^*$;

---

[4]Note that the prism or the parallelepiped is redundant.

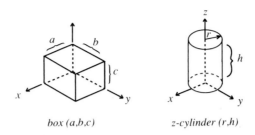

box (a,b,c)   z-cylinder (r,h)

Figure 2.10   Coordinate Frames for Two Standard Primitives

regularized intersection, denoted $\cap^*$; and *regularized difference*, denoted $-^*$. They differ from the corresponding set-theoretic operations in that the result is the closure of the operation on the interior of the two solids, and they are used to eliminate "dangling" lower-dimensional structures. For example, to compute $A \cap^* B$, we proceed conceptually as follows:

1. We compute $A \cap B$ in the set-theoretic sense. The result is a collection of volumes, and additional faces, edges, and vertices. These additional faces, edges, and vertices are lower-dimensional structures that we will eliminate.

2. We now take the *interior* of $A \cap B$. The interior consists of all those points $p \in A \cap B$ such that an open ball of radius ϵ, centered at p, consists only of points of $A \cap B$, for a sufficiently small radius ϵ.

3. We form the *closure* of this interior, by adding all boundary points adjacent to some interior neighborhood. A point q that is not an interior point of $A \cap B$ is *adjacent* to the interior if we can find a curve segment (q, r) of sufficiently small length ϵ, between q and another point r of $A \cap B$, such that all points of this segment are interior points of $A \cap B$, except q. Note that the lower-dimensional structures do not enclose volume and are therefore not adjacent to the interior of $A \cap B$.

The resulting solid is the regularized intersection. Figure 2.11 illustrates the procedure.

Note that, in practice, regularized Boolean operations are not implemented in this manner. Rather, $A \cap^* B$ is implemented by classifying the surface elements of $A \cap B$ and eliminating lower-dimensional structures. This explicit classification is delayed until a geometric query requires it, as explained later, or until a conversion from CSG to B-rep is carried out; see also Section 2.2.6.

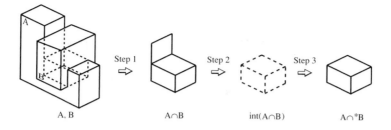

Figure 2.11   Procedure for Regularized Intersection

Eliminating the lower-dimensional structures is desirable for defining solids. However, in some applications, it may be desirable to retain them, possibly even in the interior of objects. For example, when considering solids as *domains* in finite element analysis, interior lower-dimensional structures might represent certain constraints on how to discretize the domain, or might define the domain discretization outright. At present, this is a research topic, and we do not explore this line of thought further.

Before the two objects are intersected, they must be positioned appropriately with respect to each other. This is done by translations and rotations, as needed. To make this positioning meaningful, we must establish a relationship between the local coordinate frames of the objects. A simple method is to identify the local frames with a single, universal coordinate frame. The universal frame is often referred to as the *world coordinate frame*.

Suppose we have positioned the two primitives, and have constructed an intersection. Then, the resulting object should have a local coordinate frame of its own, needed for subsequent positioning operations we might wish to perform. By convention, we will use (a copy of) the world coordinate frame for this purpose.

2.2.3 Construction of a CSG Object

The CSG representation of the simple bracket shown in Figure 2.12 is easily worked out. We think of the bracket as the union of two blocks of respective dimensions (1,4,8) and (8,4,1) with the hole subtracted by a cylinder of radius 1. Without the hole, we can specify the bracket as

$$\texttt{block}(1, 4, 8) \; \cup^* \; \texttt{x-translate}(\texttt{block}(8, 4, 1), 1)$$

The hole is removed by subtracting a cylinder about the z axis, resulting in the expression

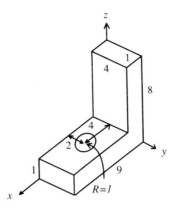

Figure 2.12   Bracket

$$(\texttt{block}(1,4,8) \; \cup^* \; \texttt{x-translate}(\texttt{block}(8,4,1),1)) \; -^*$$
$$\texttt{x-translate}(\texttt{y-translate}(\texttt{z-cylinder}(1,1),2),5)$$

The expression is conveniently drawn as a tree, as shown in Figure 2.13. This tree can be considered to be the *representation* of the object, and is customarily called a *CSG tree*. We see that the leaves of the CSG tree are primitive solids, and the interior nodes are rigid motions and Boolean operations.

In our example, the two blocks joined are touching, and the cylinder length matches the bracket thickness. In practice, this is an unsafe specification for nonintegral dimensions because of the possibility of floating-point inaccuracies. It is thus advisable to allow for a safe amount of overlap when specifying union operations. Here, then, is one place where substratum problems have intruded into the higher design levels.

2.2.4 Point/Solid Classification and Neighborhoods

Having built a CSG object, we might wish to interrogate its geometry in various ways. The most elementary such query is to test whether a point (x, y, z) is inside a solid, is on its surface, or is outside of it. This query is usually referred to as a *point/solid classification*. Other such queries include a classification of how a line intersects a solid, a classification of how a surface intersects a solid, and a test of whether two solids intersect in a nonempty volume. These operations will be discussed later.

Point/solid classification can be done with an algorithm that has a simple conceptual structure. Despite its apparent straightforwardness, however, we soon realize that a difficulty may arise when the point lies on the

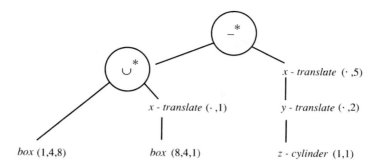

Figure 2.13   Tree Representation of CSG Expression

surface of a primitive, and this difficulty necessitates the introduction of *neighborhoods.*

The basic idea underlying this and other such algorithms is to reduce the point/solid classification to a query of the primitives in the CSG tree. The respective answers, one for each primitive, are then collated at each operation node as appropriate. Thus, the algorithm is based on the *divide-and-conquer* paradigm familiar from the literature.

Downward Propagation

Point/solid classification is naturally implemented as a set of recursive procedures, but it might be simpler to think of it as passing messages between the tree nodes. At the outset, the point coordinates are sent to the root of the tree. From there, they are propagated into the tree down to the leaves, possibly altered. At each leaf, the final coordinates describe the same point, but with respect to the local coordinate frame of the primitive solid that the leaf represents.

At the leaf, we classify the point as one of *in, on,* or *out,* depending on whether the point is, respectively, in the interior, on the surface, or on the outside of the primitive solid. This classification is passed back up the tree, to the root. At an operation node, the results from the subtree are coordinated. So, we specify the first phase of the algorithm as follows.

1. If (x, y, z) arrives at a node specifying a Boolean operation, then it is passed unchanged to the two descendants of the node.

2. If (x, y, z) arrives at a node specifying a translation or rotation, the inverse translation or rotation is applied to (x, y, z), yielding a new point (x', y', z'), which is sent to the node's descendant.

$\cup^*$	in	on	out
in	in	in	in
on	in	$on?$	on
out	in	on	out

$\cap^*$	in	on	out
in	in	on	out
on	on	$on?$	out
out	out	out	out

Table 2.1   Naive Neighborhood Combination for Union and Intersection

3. If (x, y, z) arrives at a leaf, then the point is classified with respect to that primitive solid, and the classification is returned to the parent of the leaf.

When classifying the point $(2, 1, 0.3)$ with respect to the bracket, for instance, we classify the point $(2, 1, 0.3)$ with respect to block$(1, 4, 8)$, the point $(1, 1, 0.3)$ with respect to block$(8, 4, 1)$, and the point $(-3, -1, 0.3)$ with respect to z-cylinder$(1, 1)$. The respective classifications are *out*, *in*, and *out*.

Upward Propagation

In the second phase of the algorithm, the messages contain point classifications that must be combined at the Boolean operation nodes. No work is done at nodes representing translation or rotation. Table 2.1 shows what to do for union and intersection operation nodes.

Neighborhoods

Implemented in this way, the algorithm will be incorrect. For example, classifying the point $(1, 1, 0.5)$ with respect to the bracket yields an incorrect *on*. The problem here is the classification of points that lie on the surface of a primitive solid. These points may lie on a primitive surface area that remains a part of the surface of the solid described by the tree, and then using the table yields the correct result. If, however, the point is on a surface area that is not on the final surface — for example, because it becomes solid interior as the point $(1, 1, 0.5)$ does — then the tables do not suffice. What is needed in addition to the classification as one of *in*, *on*, or *out* is the local geometry of the solid in the vicinity of the point. The additional information is given by a neighborhood of the point, as explained next.

A *neighborhood* of a point $p = (x, y, z)$, with respect to the solid S, is the intersection with S of an open ball of infinitesimal radius ϵ centered at p. We used this concept to define the interior of a solid, and recall that p is *inside* S, iff the neighborhood is a full ball. The point p is on the *outside*, iff the neighborhood is an empty ball. If p is on the surface of S, then the

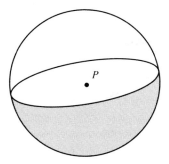

Figure 2.14   Neighborhood of an Interior Face Point

structure of the neighborhood depends on the local topology of S at p. We explain the possible topologies of these neighborhoods by restricting the local geometry to planar surfaces; that is, by considering only polyhedra for the moment.

We decompose the surface of the solid into faces, edges, and vertices. Here, a *face* is a closed subset of the surface all of whose points lie in the same plane.[5] An *edge* is the intersection of two adjacent faces, and a *vertex* is the common intersection of three or more faces. For example, the surface of a cube consists of 6 faces, 12 edges, and 8 vertices.

If a surface point is in the interior of a face, then its neighborhood is a *halfspace* whose surface in the ball is a subset of the face. In Figure 2.14, the ball neighborhood of such a point is shown, and the solid part of the neighborhood has been shaded. Next, consider a point on an edge different from the two vertices. In the simplest case, the edge is adjacent to exactly two faces, so the neighborhood is a *wedge*. For some CSG objects, however, it is possible that an edge is adjacent to an even number of faces that is greater than two. In that case, the neighborhood of the point is a union of such wedges, all with the edge in common, as exemplified in Figure 2.15. Again, the solid part of the neighborhood is indicated by the shading.

Finally, consider a vertex. Again the simplest case is when all faces incident to the vertex are edge adjacent in a single cycle. In that case, the vertex neighborhood is a *cone*. Some possibilities are shown in Figure 2.16. In general, the faces incident to a vertex are organized in several cycles. In this general form, the vertex neighborhood consists of a collection of cones,

---

[5]Strictly speaking, we may have to split the closed subset into two maximal components such that the solid interior lies locally on the same side of the plane, for each component. In this case, each component is a separate face.

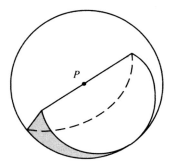
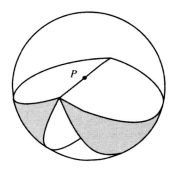

Figure 2.15   Neighborhood of an Interior Edge Point

possibly with conical holes and touching along certain edges. All cones have the vertex as common apex; see also Figure 2.17 for an example. Such a neighborhood can be represented as a set of curves on the surface of a sphere. The curves represent the intersection of the cone surfaces with the sphere, and the resulting map on the sphere is two-colorable, with one color representing solid interior, the other representing solid exterior.

In the case of curved surface elements, the neighborhood structure remains topologically the same as in the polyhedral case, but the geometric structure is more complicated. Often, we can approximate the curved sur-

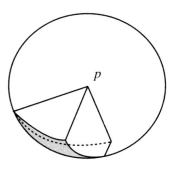
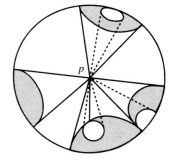

Figure 2.16   Simple Neighborhoods
of a Vertex

Figure 2.17   General Neighborhood
of a Vertex

faces with the tangent planes at p. However, in situations where surface
elements match and combine in ways that alter the topology qualitatively,
we must consider the curved-surface geometry. Some of these situations are
discussed in the next section.

Refined Upward Propagation

The problem with Table 2.1 is that no geometric information on the neighborhood structure is taken into consideration. Thus, although the union
of two halfspaces in general forms a wedge, it may remain a halfspace or
become a full solid ball. Since this geometric information is ignored, the
tables cannot always produce the correct answer.

Thus, to repair our method for processing the information during the
second phase of point/solid classification, we must perform the respective
Boolean operation on the neighborhoods themselves. Only then do we
obtain correct answers. This requires accounting for the local geometry,
devising suitable data structures to represent neighborhoods, and transforming the geometric data appropriately at the rigid motion nodes in the
tree. Again, we consider the polyhedral case first.

Representing the neighborhoods of interior or exterior points is trivial.
So, let p be a point on the surface of the solid defined by a subtree. If p
is in the interior of a face, then the neighborhood can be represented by
the plane equation of the face, oriented such that the plane normal points
to the exterior of the halfspace. If p is on the interior of an edge, then
the neighborhood is represented by a set of sectors in a plane containing
p that is perpendicular to the edge. Vertex neighborhoods, finally, are
inferred from the adjacent edge neighborhoods. When performing Boolean
operations on boundary representations, it will again be useful to think in
terms of neighborhoods, so we will discuss this subject again in the next
chapter.

At a union node, we must compute the union of the two neighborhoods
of p that reach the node from its left and right descendants. Except for the
trivial cases where one or the other neighborhood is the empty or the full
ball, we must merge the two data structures and inspect the result. We
describe this procedure conceptually.

Essentially, the following rules apply for merging neighborhoods at a
union node. Let N_L and N_R be the two neighborhoods at the descendants
to the left and to the right. Then the neighborhood N at the node is as
follows:

1. If N_L is the full ball, then $N = N_L$. If N_L is the empty ball, then
   $N = N_R$.

2. If N_L and N_R are face neighborhoods, then N is an edge neighborhood
   unless the two faces coincide. This case includes coplanar faces; then,
   N will be a face neighborhood or the full ball, depending on how the
   faces are oriented.

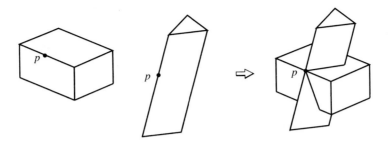

Figure 2.18   Edge-Neighborhood Merge, General Position

3. If N_L and N_R are edge neighborhoods, then N is in general a vertex neighborhood whose cones are formed from the wedges of N_L and N_R; see Figure 2.18. If the edges coincide, N will be an edge neighborhood, unless the wedges match up to form a single face with p in the interior; see also Figures 2.19 and 2.20.

4. If N_L is a vertex neighborhood, and N_R an edge neighborhood, then N is a vertex neighborhood unless each of its solid cones is contained in a wedge of N_R.

5. If N_L and N_R are vertex neighborhoods, then N is a vertex neighborhood, as shown in Figure 2.21, unless the cones match up to form wedges or a face with p in the interior; see also Figures 2.22 and 2.23.

The remaining cases can be worked out easily, and analogous rules are formulated for the other Boolean operations.

Clearly, the geometric processing required to cover all cases is not trivial, even when we restrict our attention to polyhedral objects only. The vertex-

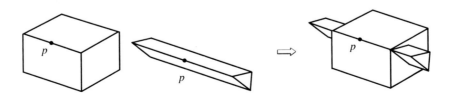

Figure 2.19   Edge-Neighborhood Merge Producing an Edge

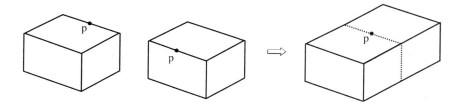

Figure 2.20   Edge-Neighborhood Merge Producing a Face

neighborhood merge is inherently complicated because the neighborhood structure can be complex. The other cases gain in complexity because of the exceptions that arise when the various geometric elements are in special positions with respect to one another.

2.2.5 Curve/Solid Classification

A useful interrogation primitive is the classification of a space curve against a solid. The special case of the straight line can be used to generate shaded images as follows. Consider a line through the view point and a screen pixel. Classify that line against the solid, pick the nearest intersection point, and, recalling which primitive is intersected at that point, compute the intensity from the surface normal and the lighting information. Since this application uses the algorithm a large number of times, it is important to implement it as efficiently as possible. The approximation techniques discussed here provide additional strategies for speeding up the computations.

The algorithm for classifying a line or curve against the solid is organized exactly like the point/solid classification.

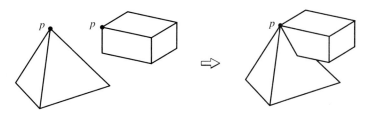

Figure 2.21   Vertex-Neighborhood Merge, General Position

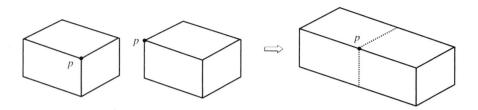

Figure 2.22   Vertex-Neighborhood Merge Producing an Edge

1. Send the line or curve description to the leaves. Partition the curve into segments labeled *inside*, *outside*, or *on* the surface of the primitive.

2. Propagate the segments back upward, and merge them appropriately.

To classify a line against a primitive, we may parameterize the line and substitute the parametric form into the implicit surface equations bounding the primitive, thereby deriving a polynomial in one variable for each surface. The roots of the polynomial define the intersection points. Only those points that lie on the primitive are considered further. The points are then sorted along the line and are paired into segments with the appropriate labeling.

Example 2.1:   We classify a line against a primitive cylinder. The cylinder is z–cylinder$(1, 2)$, and the line is

$$
\begin{aligned}
x &= 2 - 2\lambda \\
y &= 0 \\
z &= \lambda
\end{aligned}
$$

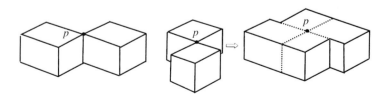

Figure 2.23   Vertex-Neighborhood Merge Producing a Face

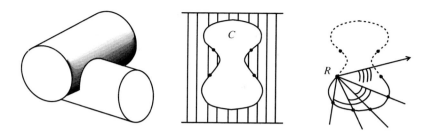

Figure 2.24   Sorting Curve Points on a Parametric Surface

The cylinder's perimeter is given by $x^2 + y^2 - 1 = 0$, so the line/perimeter intersection points correspond to the roots of $(2 - 2\lambda)^2 - 1 = 0$. The two roots are $\lambda = 1/2$ and $\lambda = 3/2$, corresponding to the points $p = (1, 0, 1/2)$ and $q = (-1, 0, 3/2)$. Both points are on the primitive, since they are above the plane $z = 0$ and below the plane $z = 2$ that bounds the cylinder domain. The intersections of the line with these planes are outside the primitive, and hence are irrelevant. We sort and pair the two intersections found, and conclude that the segment (p, q) is inside the primitive, and the unbounded segments with parametric values $(-\infty, 1/2)$ and $(3/2, +\infty)$ are outside. $\diamondsuit$

Classifying a curve against a primitive can be done in the same way, provided the curve has a parametric form. For such curves, we sort the intersection points by their parameter values. However, even when we consider only those space curves that arise as the intersection of two standard CSG primitives, we need not obtain curves that possess a parameterization. For those curves, more complicated sorting procedures are needed.

Briefly, if the curve lies on a parameterizable surface, then we may equivalently sort the points by sorting the corresponding points in parameter space. That is, instead of considering the point $p = (x(s, t), y(s, t), z(s, t))$ in three-dimensional space, we consider the point $q = (s, t)$ in parameter space. If p is on the intersection with another surface, then q is on a plane algebraic curve C in parameter space. This curve C is considered.

The curve C is decomposed into convex segments not containing any singularities. Points P_k on a specific segment may be sorted by the angle between the secant $\overline{RP_k}$ connecting P_k with a suitable reference point R and a reference direction; see also Figure 2.24. All intersection curves between standard primitives can be processed in this way. See Chapter 6 for information on how to deal with singularities on plane algebraic curves. How to sort points on a general space curve is not well understood.

2.2.6 Surface/Solid Classification, Conversion to B-rep

A surface will intersect a solid in a number of areas. Each such area is bounded by curve segments, where each segment is on the intersection of the surface with one of the primitives of the solid. A general strategy for determining the segments, and from them the respective areas, is therefore as follows:

1. Intersect the surface with each of the primitives from which the solid has been constructed.

2. Classify the resulting curves, thereby determining the bounding edges of those surface areas that are inside or outside the solid, or are on the solid's surface.

3. Combine the segments, appropriately oriented, constructing a boundary representation of the respective surface areas.

Elaboration of this conceptual method leads to many details but is straightforward. The resulting algorithms are similar to, or use outright, the algorithms for point/solid and for curve/solid classification.

Surface/solid classification, in turn, can be used to devise a method for converting from a CSG to a boundary representation. Such a conversion algorithm is based on the *generate-and-test* paradigm: We consider all pairs of intersecting primitives in the CSG object A, obtaining for each a set of space curves in which they intersect. By classifying each curve against the solid, we can determine those segments that are on the surface of A. Each segment will be an edge of the boundary representation. These segments now define, on the surface of the primitives, areas that will be the faces of the boundary representation of A. By considering the neighborhoods, we derive the topological information needed to determine the adjacencies and incidences of the various faces.

2.2.7 Redundancies and Approximations in CSG Trees

Since a geometric query of a CSG tree grows at least linearly, and in some cases quadratically, with the number of primitives, we investigate whether a given CSG tree contains redundant subtrees that can be eliminated without altering the object defined by the tree. The most blatant redundancy would be a subtree that represents empty space. Such a subtree is said to define the *null object*, Λ, and a detection algorithm for Λ can be used to test whether two CSG objects interfere: Let T_1 and T_2 be two CSG trees defining the objects. Then the two objects do not interfere iff $T_1 \cap^* T_2$ represents the null object.

More generally, a subtree T' of the CSG tree T is *redundant* if replacing T' with the null object Λ, or with the complement Ω of the null object, does not alter the shape defined by T. In the first case, we say that T' is Λ-redundant. In the other case, we say that T' is Ω-redundant.

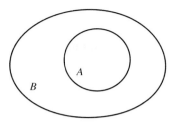 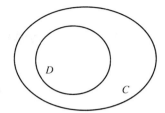

Figure 2.25 A Is Λ-Redundant in $A \cup^{*} B$

Figure 2.26 C Is Ω-Redundant in $C \cap^{*} D$

Example 2.2:   In Figure 2.25, the primitive A is Λ-redundant in the CSG expression $A \cup^{*} B$, because $A \cup^{*} B = \Lambda \cup^{*} B$. In Figure 2.26, the primitive C is Ω-redundant in the CSG expression $C \cap^{*} D$, because $C \cap^{*} D = \Omega \cap^{*} D$. $\diamondsuit$

Redundancies arise in contexts other than interference detection. It is possible that a CSG tree T contains redundancies because it was constructed by modification of another CSG tree T_1. Possibly, the object defined by T_1 contains certain parts that are unnecessary for the object defined by T. In such a situation, the designer may simply obliterate the entire unwanted substructure, say by cutting it away using a differencing operation. If the eliminated structure was defined by a complicated subtree in T_1, then that subtree would be redundant.

A general approach to redundancy detection is to approximate CSG objects by enclosing them in simple geometric shapes, and to derive criteria for redundancy based on the approximations. When the approximating shapes are sufficiently simple and are easily constructed, this approach leads to efficient redundancy tests. Based on approximations, however, it can only yield *sufficient* criteria for redundancy. Hence, certain redundancies would remain undetected.

As approximating shapes, we could use spheres or boxes that are oriented in a particular way. The advantage of spheres is that they are invariant under rotation. This would not be true for boxes, whose edges are parallel to the coordinate axes, but there are elegant data structures for using such boxes, as explained in Chapter 3. We describe an approximation algorithm for CSG objects whose structure is independent of the particular choice of approximating shape. However, we shall assume that the CSG object is completely contained within the approximating shape.

We fix a class Σ of approximating shapes. The algorithm begins by approximating all primitives P in the tree with a shape $\sigma(P) \in \Sigma$. By processing the trees from the leaves to the root, we then determine the

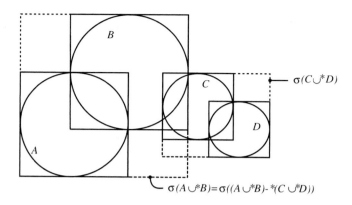

Figure 2.27   Approximation of $(A \cup^* B) -^* (C \cup^* D)$

approximations at all interior nodes by the following three rules.

1. If $T = T_1 \cup^* T_2$, then $\sigma(T) = \sigma(\sigma(T_1) \cup^* \sigma(T_2))$.

2. If $T = T_1 \cap^* T_2$, then $\sigma(T) = \sigma(\sigma(T_1) \cap^* \sigma(T_2))$.

3. If $T = T_1 -^* T_2$, then $\sigma(T) = \sigma(T_1)$.

We eliminate translations and rotations from consideration by distributing them over the leaves. That is, we require that all primitives are positioned with respect to the coordinate system of the final solid. Thus, we need only a method for computing $\sigma(P)$, where P is a primitive, suitably rotated and translated, and an algorithm for approximating the union, intersection, and difference of two approximations. It is now straightforward to show that every point of the object defined by the CSG tree T must be contained in the approximating shape.

Example 2.3:   We let Σ be the class of all rectangles whose sides are parallel to the axes. Then the approximation of $(A \cup^* B) -^* (C \cup^* D)$ is as shown in Figure 2.27. The intermediate approximations are also shown. $\diamondsuit$

The approximation algorithm yields a criterion for when a primitive or a subtree in T is redundant. We noted that the approximation at the root contains the entire object. Hence, if T' is any subtree of T, then only points in $\sigma(T') \cap^* \sigma(T)$ can contribute to the object defined by T. In particular, if $\sigma(T') \cap^* \sigma(T) = \emptyset$, then the subtree T' does not contribute to the final shape and can be deleted from T. For example, the primitive D shown in Figure 2.27 is redundant by this criterion, and can be deleted.

2.2.8 Nonstandard Primitives

We can extend the primitives by adding other shapes to our repertoire. For instance, we might add all quadric halfspaces — that is, ellipsoids, paraboloids, hyperboloids, and cylinders and cones with conic base curves. We could require that infinite halfspaces, such as the hyperboloids, be restricted to finite domains, as we did with circular cylinders and cones, or we could work with infinite halfspaces. Less modest extensions might include various classes of sculptured surfaces, or even all irreducible algebraic surfaces.

We can assess the difficulties this enterprise raises by reviewing the basic CSG algorithms we have presented. Recall that the basic classification algorithms follow the divide-and-conquer paradigm. The attractiveness of such a strategy depends on the ease with which we can do the various classifications with respect to primitives, and the algorithmic complexity entailed by analyzing neighborhoods, sorting points on surface intersections, determining adjacencies, and so on. With greater geometric complexities at the primitive level, the difficulty of these operations quickly increases, and even the classification against primitives can no longer be taken for granted.

In such a situation, a case-by-case analysis may become too complex, and more general algorithms will be needed. Such algorithms are the subject of Chapters 5, 6, and 7. They continue to be research topics. In geometric and solid modeling, these algorithms are exercised many times. Each one of them must be sufficiently fast, yield results of adequate accuracy, and exhibit unfailing robustness. How best to negotiate these sometimes conflicting demands is not clear at this time, and probably depends not only on the geometric coverage, but also on the individual applications for which the modeler is needed.

2.3 Boundary Representations

We can represent a solid unambiguously by describing its surface and topologically orienting it such that we can tell, at each surface point, on which side the solid interior lies. This description has two parts, a *topological* description of the connectivity and orientation of vertices, edges, and faces, and a *geometric* description for embedding these surface elements in space. Historically, the representation evolved from a description of polyhedra.

Briefly, the topological description specifies vertices, edges, and faces abstractly, and indicates their incidences and adjacencies. The geometric representation specifies, for example, the equations of the surfaces of which the faces are a subset. The equations have been written such that, at a point p in the interior of a face f, the surface normal points to the exterior of the solid. More details are given later in Section 2.3.2, in this chapter, and in Section 3.2, in Chapter 3.

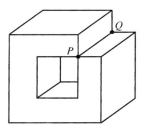 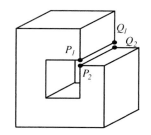 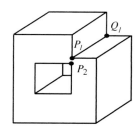

Figure 2.28   A Non-
manifold Object

Figure 2.29   Two Possible Topologies

2.3.1 Manifold Versus Nonmanifold Representation

A large segment of the literature requires that the surface represented by
a boundary representation be a closed, oriented manifold embedded in 3-
space. Intuitively, a *manifold* surface has the property that, around every
one of its points, there exists a neighborhood that is homeomorphic to the
plane. That is, we can deform the surface locally into a plane without
tearing it or identifying separate points with each other. Thus, surfaces
that intersect or touch themselves are excluded.

A manifold surface is *orientable* if we can distinguish two different sides.
The procedure for deciding orientability can be thought of as follows. Pick
any point p, and define arbitrarily a clockwise orientation around it. Maintaining this orientation, move along any closed path on the surface. If
there exists a path such that it is possible to return to p with an opposite
orientation, then the surface is not orientable; otherwise, it is orientable.
Examples of nonorientable surfaces include the Möbius strip and the Klein
bottle. Orientable surfaces include the sphere and the torus. Closed, orientable manifolds partition the space into three regions that we may call
the *interior*, the *surface*, and the *exterior*, respectively. In Section 2.4.2 we
explain these concepts in greater detail.

The topological properties of manifolds are well understood. Thus, restricting attention to manifold solids has the advantage that one can draw
on a rich mathematical theory for such objects. However, systematic work
to relate this topological theory to specific representation schemata is relatively recent.

It is only recently that the requirement for manifold surface objects
in B-rep is being revised, partly because a regularized Boolean operation
on two manifold objects may yield a nonmanifold result. An example is
shown in Figure 2.28, where we have taken the regularized union of two
L-brackets. The problem is the edge (P, Q) that is adjacent to four faces.

Three approaches to treating nonmanifold structures have been developed:

1. Objects must be manifolds, so operations on solids with nonmanifold results are not allowed and are considered an error.

2. Objects are topological manifolds, but their embedding in 3-space permits geometric coincidence of topologically separate structures.

3. Nonmanifold objects are permitted, both as input and as output.

Not much needs to be said about the first approach. It is straightforward and appears to be satisfactory in many applications. Note, however, that it unduly restricts modelers carrying out Boolean operations. Moreover, depending on the internals of the modeling system, operations that produce a nonmanifold object as an intermediate result might be disallowed even when the final result would be a manifold object. Such restrictions might not be convenient for the user.

In the second approach, we must give a topological interpretation of the nonmanifold structures. In the example of Figure 2.28, we must interpret the nonmanifold edge as two separate edges that happen to coincide. Two possibilities exist, and Figure 2.29 shows them side by side. Which interpretation should be chosen is discussed in Section 2.4. In this example, the left interpretation is more natural. Briefly, we choose an interpretation in which the surface is triangulable without degenerate triangles. Note that such a triangulation is possible for the left, but not for the right, interpretation shown in Figure 2.29: In the right interpretation, the triangulation of the front face must include an edge (P_1, P_2), since those two points are topologically distinct. They are, however, geometrically coincident; hence, this edge has zero length — that is, the adjacent triangles are degenerate.

From a robustness point of view, the second approach is likely to lead to difficult geometric problems, and analyzing them in the presence of geometrically coincident but topologically separate surface elements could be intricate. These difficulties would be further exacerbated in the curved-surface domain, in which the numerical problems are more severe. Moreover, no efficient general algorithm for triangulating curved faces is known.

In the third approach, nonmanifold edges and vertices are accepted. It is our experience that this approach ultimately leads to the simplest algorithms because it requires neither testing for the presence of the disallowed configurations, nor special processing that derives topological disambiguations. The algorithm for Boolean operations on polyhedra described in the next chapter is based on this approach.

2.3.2 Winged-Edge Representation

The oldest formalized schema for representing the boundary of a polyhedron and its topology appears to be the *winged-edge* representation. It describes manifold polyhedral objects by three tables, recording information about

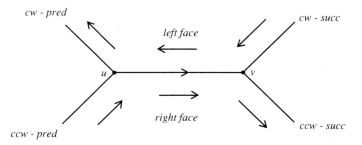

Figure 2.30   Winged-Edge Data Structure

vertices, faces, and edges. We will describe a nonmanifold representation scheme in Chapter 3.

The topological information is as follows. Each face is bounded by a set of disjoint edge cycles, one of which is the outside boundary of the face, the others bounding holes. In the face table, therefore, a representative edge of each cycle is recorded. Each vertex is adjacent to a circularly ordered set of edges, so the vertex table specifies one of these edges for each vertex. Finally, for each edge, the following information is given:

1. Incident vertices

2. Left and right adjacent face

3. Preceding and succeeding edge in clockwise order (explained later)

4. Preceding and succeeding edge in counterclockwise order

The edge is oriented by giving the two incident vertices in order, the first being the *from* vertex, the second the *to* vertex. Left and right, as well as clockwise and counterclockwise, are interpreted with respect to viewing the oriented edge from the solid exterior. The information is shown schematically in Figure 2.30. Various restrictions may be placed on faces. For example, we may require that each face be bounded by a single cycle of edges, or even that each face be triangular. Such restrictions might be imposed to increase the uniformity of data structures, or to simplify processing for certain operations on B-rep objects.

The geometric information consists typically of coordinates of the vertices and plane equations for the faces. Each face equation has been written such that its normal, at an interior face point, is directed toward the outside of the solid. Thus, if two faces lie on the same plane $p = 0$, but in opposite orientation, then both $P = 0$ and $-P = 0$ must be specified.

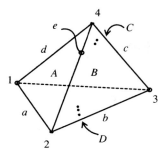

Figure 2.31   Tetrahedron

The geometric information may also include parametric equations for specifying the edges in 3-space. In the case of curved solids, other information may be required to avoid ambiguities, as discussed in Chapter 5.

Figure 2.31 shows a tetrahedron, where vertices, edges, and faces are labeled as shown. The topological data in its winged-edge representation is summarized in Table 2.2.

2.3.3 The Euler–Poincaré Formula

As we have seen, the topological data of a B-rep solid is symbolic information. Unless care is exercised, this prescribed topology might be inconsistent in the sense that there cannot exist a manifold solid whose vertices,

Edge	Vertices		Faces		Clockwise		Counter-clockwise	
Name	from	to	left	right	pred	succ	pred	succ
a	1	2	A	D	d	e	f	b
b	2	3	B	D	e	c	a	f
f	3	1	C	D	c	d	b	a
c	3	4	B	C	b	e	f	d
d	1	4	C	A	f	c	a	e
e	2	4	A	B	a	d	b	c

Table 2.2   Edge Table of the Tetrahedron, Winged-Edge Methodology

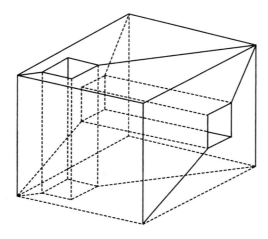

Figure 2.32   An Object with Two Holes and with Faces Homeomorphic to Disks

edges, and faces satisfy the prescribed incidence relationships. This problem becomes especially acute when the topological data are derived from geometric information that is only approximate, due to floating-point errors. Hence, there is interest in maintaining consistent topological data, and a number of formulae have been found that must be obeyed by the number of vertices, edges, and faces. Note that these formulae provide necessary conditions, but not sufficient ones. In Section 2.4, we will derive necessary and sufficient conditions.

From a topological viewpoint, the simplest solids are those that have a closed orientable surface and no holes or interior voids. We assume that each face is bounded by a single loop of adjacent vertices; that is, the face is homeomorphic to a closed disk. Then the number of vertices V, edges E, and faces F of the solid satisfy the *Euler* formula:

$$V - E + F - 2 = 0$$

This fact is easily proved by induction on the surface structure. Extensions to this formula have been made that account for faces not being homeomorphic to closed disks, the solid surface not being without holes, and the solid having interior voids, as reviewed next.

We consider the possibility that the solid has holes, but that it remains bounded by a single, connected surface. Moreover, each face is assumed to be homeomorphic to disk. For example, the torus has one hole, and the object in Figure 2.32 has two. It is a well-known fact that such solids

Figure 2.33   A Surface of Genus 2

are topologically equivalent, i.e., *homeomorphic*, to a sphere with zero or more handles. For example, the object of Figure 2.32 is homeomorphic to a sphere with two handles, the latter shown in Figure 2.33. The number of handles is called the *genus* of the surface. In general, with a genus G, the numbers of vertices, edges, and faces obey the *Euler–Poincaré* formula:

$$V - E + F - 2(1 - G) = 0$$

Next, we further generalize by adding the possibility of internal voids. These voids are bounded by separate closed manifold surfaces, called *shells*. The number of shells will be denoted by S. Finally, we relax the requirement that a face is bounded by a single loop of vertices, but require that each face can be mapped to the plane. Thus, a sphere missing at least one point can be a face. In Figure 2.34, a face is shown with four bounding loops. Note that one of these loops consists of a single vertex, and another one of two vertices connected by an edge. To account for faces of this complexity, we must count, for each face, the number of bounding vertex loops. For

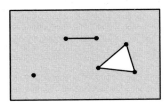

Figure 2.34   A Face with Four Bounding Loops

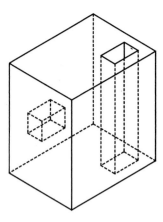

Figure 2.35   Solid with 24 Vertices, 36 Edges, 16 Faces, 18 Loops, 2 Shells, and Genus Sum 1

the face in Figure 2.34, this number is four. With L the total number of loops, the relationship among the number of faces, edges, vertices, loops, and shells, and the sum G of each shell's genus, is then

$$V - E + F - (L - F) - 2(S - G) = 0$$

An example solid illustrating this relationship is shown in Figure 2.35.

We may think of the quantities V, E, F, L, S, and G as existing in an abstract six-dimensional space. The relationship among them is then the equation of a hyperplane. Since the values of the variables must be nonnegative integers, we might view the relation as defining a lattice on this hyperplane. For each solid with a given topological structure, there corresponds a point in this lattice.

Although a manifold solid must satisfy the extended Euler–Poincaré formula, not every surface satisfying the formula will be the surface of a manifold solid. For example, the cube is a manifold object with 6 faces, 12 edges, and 8 vertices. It has a single shell surface of genus zero. However, the surface shown in Figure 2.36 has the same number of faces, edges, and vertices, yet it is not the surface of any manifold solid, since it has a "dangling" pentagonal face attached to the pyramidal part by a nonmanifold edge.

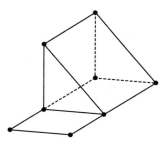

Figure 2.36   Surface with 8 Vertices, 12 Edges, and 6 Faces

2.3.4 Euler Operators

Conceptually, *Euler operators* can be thought of as creating and modifying consistently the topology of manifold object surfaces. In particular, they can create closed surfaces, and modify these surfaces by adding or deleting faces, edges, and vertices. They also modify the surface genus by adding or deleting handles. Euler operations are traditionally named by a string of the form *mxky*, where *m* stands for *make*, and *k* stands for *kill*. The strings *x* and *y* name the topological element types that are created or destroyed. The types are vertex, edge, loop, face, and shell. Ordinarily, only one new element of each type is created or destroyed, but sometimes several elements of the same type are created or destroyed. For example, *mekfl* adds an edge and deletes a face and a loop, whereas *mefl* adds an edge, a face, and a loop.

Euler operators are used as an intermediate language in some modeling systems. Using them has the advantage of insulating, to a degree, the operations implemented on top of them from details of the data structures used to represent the surface topology. Thus, in principle, the underlying representation could be changed with minimal impact on the modeling system's implementation. Another advantage is that Euler operators ensure topological consistency throughout the modeling process. This can be advantageous when the precise topology of the result of a modeling operation may be in doubt because of imprecision of the numerical model data, as discussed in Chapter 4.

As example of specific Euler operators, consider the operation of adding an edge between two existing vertices. Depending on the two vertices designated, this operation has differing topological effects. In consequence, different Euler operations would be used to implement the operation. The possibilities are as follows.

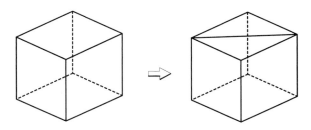

Figure 2.37   *mefl* Operation

1. The new edge closes off one part of a face from the rest. In this case, the operation is called *mefl*. Its effect is to increase the number of edges, faces, and loops by one each. An example is shown in Figure 2.37.

2. The new edge connects two different loops bounding the same face. In this case, the operation is called *mekl*. Here we have added one edge and deleted one loop; see also Figure 2.38.

3. The new edge connects two vertices on two different shells. In this case, the operation is called *meks*. It merges the two shells, which includes deleting a face on each shell and creating a new face that makes a connection between the two surfaces. Figure 2.39 shows an example of the *meks* operation. The interior shell is connected with the exterior shell, opening the interior void to the outside by a conical face. Note that for polyhedra, more than one edge would have to be created.

Note that these operations need additional specifications to ensure an unambiguous placement of the new constructs. For example, in the *meks* operation, it is not clear which faces should be deleted on each shell. Suitablè conventions for communicating this geometric information to the operation are readily worked out, say via certain parameters.

The implementation of Euler operations increases in difficulty with the geometric coverage of the modeling system. We mentioned that there are no efficient general algorithms that triangulate curved faces. Clearly, triangulation of curved faces can be based on the *mefl* operation. Hence, this operation will be difficult to implement unless the geometric coverage is suitably restricted.

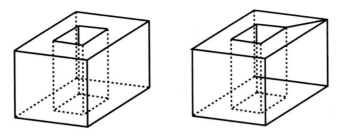

Figure 2.38   *mekl* Operation

2.4 Topological Validity of B-rep Solids

A basic assumption underlying solid modeling is that we deal with topologically valid solid objects. The meaning of *topological validity* needs to be made precise, for otherwise we cannot be assured that the computer representations of solids and the algorithms using them are correct. This task is especially important in B-rep, where we must infer, from a description of the two-dimensional boundary, that a solid is defined. In this section, we give a definition of topological validity. Based on this definition, it is possible to derive an algorithm that tests whether a given data structure, intended as a boundary representation of a solid, does in fact describe a solid. Such an algorithm is also sketched, but no deep consideration has been given to its implementation. Rather, it serves to elucidate the various aspects of topological validity.

Initially, we consider manifold solids. Thereafter, we discuss how to char-

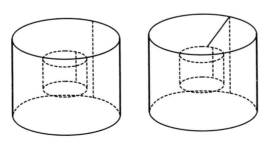

Figure 2.39   *meks* Operation

acterize nonmanifold solids topologically. The material is fairly detailed, as is necessary: The tools provided by topology are very general, and their naive use can lead to subtle errors. Hence, it is important to develop the material carefully and explicitly.

Checking topological validity has a geometric dimension. For instance, each face in a B-rep must consist of manifold points. In the case of planar faces, this condition is trivial; for curved faces, however, it is by no means a straightforward computation. Moreover, the geometric dimension naturally suggests broadening the topological-validity problem to a proper mathematical definition of the term *solid* that encompasses the other aspects as well. Although we do not develop such a comprehensive definition, we discuss some of the issues that are needed for for such a task. These issues arise from the interaction of geometric and topological factors.

2.4.1 Topological Polyhedra

Our objective is to characterize a solid as a topological polyhedron. We initially think of a solid as a 3-manifold with boundary, and then impose a triangulation to grasp better the structure of these manifolds. The resulting definition of a topological solid is preliminary because we characterize the solid as an object without accounting for the surrounding space. By characterizing subsequently the relationship between the solid and Euclidian 3-space, we refine this definition to a definition of manifold solids in the sense discussed in Section 2.3.1.

Topological Spaces

A *topological space* (X, T) is a set X along with a system of subsets T, called the *open sets* of X. The system T must satisfy the following two properties:

1. The intersection of finitely many sets in T is again in T.

2. The union of sets in T is also in T.

Note that infinite unions of open sets are permitted. Therefore, T must be closed under finite intersection and arbitrary union. A subset of X is *closed* if its complement is open.

In the following discussion, we specialize the set X and assume that it is the n-dimensional Euclidian space $\mathbf{E}^n$ or a subset thereof. $\mathbf{E}^n$ consists of all points $(x_1, ..., x_n)$, where the coordinates x_k are real numbers. In $\mathbf{E}^n$, we consider the *natural* topology, using as our system of open sets all those sets that can be obtained as the union of *open balls*. The open ball $B(p, r)$, of radius $r > 0$ centered at the point $p = (x_1, ..., x_n)$, is defined as

$$B(p, r) = \{q = (y_1, ..., y_n) \mid d(p, q) = \sqrt{\sum_{k=1}^{n}(x_k - y_k)^2} < r\}$$

That is, $B(p, r)$ consists of all points whose Euclidian distance from p is less than r.

A *neighborhood* of a point p is any open set U that contains p. Note that this definition of neighborhood has a different meaning from that introduced in Section 2.2.4. It can be shown that a subset of $\mathbf{E}^n$ is open precisely when X contains a neighborhood of every point p in X.

The *interior* of a set U, denoted $int(U)$, consists of all points $p \in U$ such that U contains a neighborhood of p. The *closure* of a set U, denoted $cl(U)$, is the complement of the interior of the complement of U. Let $\neg U$ denote the set-theoretic complement of U. Then

$$cl(U) = \neg int(\neg U)$$

A map f from a topological space (X, T) to another topological space (X', T') is *continuous* if every neighborhood of $f(p)$ in (X', T') is also a neighborhood of p in (X, T). If f is *bijective* (i.e., is one to one and onto), and if both f and its inverse f^{-1} are continuous, then f is a *homeomorphism*. Two topological spaces are *topologically equivalent* if there is a homeomorphism between them.

In $\mathbf{E}^n$, we identify topological subspaces. A subspace is a subset Y of $\mathbf{E}^n$ along with the *relative topology* consisting of the intersection of the open sets of $\mathbf{E}^n$ with Y. Examples include open balls of any radius, but also closed sets such as the unit cube consisting of all points $p = (x_1, ..., x_n)$ such that, for $k = 1, ..., n$, we have $0 \leq x_k \leq 1$. Note that an open set in the relative topology need not be open in the containing topological space. For example, the (relatively) open set U in the unit cube in $\mathbf{E}^3$, obtained as the intersection with the open ball of radius 1 centered at $(1, 1, 1)$, is not an open set in $\mathbf{E}^3$ since no neighborhood of $(1, 1, 1)$, in $\mathbf{E}^3$, is contained in U.

An *n-manifold* M in $\mathbf{E}^m$, where $m \geq n$, is a subspace that is *locally* homeomorphic to $\mathbf{E}^n$. That is, for every point p of M, there exists a neighborhood U of p that is homeomorphic to $\mathbf{E}^n$. An *n-manifold with boundary* is a subspace that is locally homeomorphic to the positive halfspace

$$\mathbf{E}^{n+} = \{(x_1, ..., x_n) \in \mathbf{E}^n \mid x_1 \geq 0\}$$

The hyperplane $x_1 = 0$ is the *boundary* of $\mathbf{E}^{n+}$.

Note that, in an n-manifold M with boundary, we can distinguish between interior and boundary points: A point $p \in M$ is an *interior point* if there is a neighborhood U of p that is homeomorphic to $\mathbf{E}^n$. A point $p \in M$ is a *boundary point* if it has a neighborhood U that is homeomorphic to a neighborhood of the point $(0, ..., 0)$ in $\mathbf{E}^{n+}$. In contrast, an n-manifold consists of only interior points.

The boundary of an n-manifold with boundary can be shown to be homeomorphic to an $(n-1)$-manifold without boundary. A manifold is *connected* if it cannot be decomposed into two disjoint manifolds.

A set in $\mathbf{E}^n$ is *bounded* if it is contained in an open ball. When a set is both closed and bounded, it is *compact*.

We wish to define a solid as a connected 3-manifold with boundary where, in addition, the boundary is compact. This definition is too restrictive in that it excludes nonmanifold solids. At the same time, it is also too general, because it places no requirements on the space surrounding the solid.

Simplicial Complexes

We explain how to construct 3-manifolds combinatorially. The basic building blocks are simplices of various dimensions that are put together in particular ways to obtain manifolds. We explain how this is done.

Let p_0 and p_1 be two distinct points. The *convex combination* spanned by p_0 and p_1 is the set

$$\langle p_0, p_1 \rangle = \{\lambda p_0 + (1 - \lambda)p_1 \mid 0 \leq \lambda \leq 1\}$$

Geometrically, $\langle p_0, p_1 \rangle$ is the closed line segment $[p_0, p_1]$ in Euclidian space. Similarly, we define the convex combination spanned by three distinct points as

$$\begin{aligned}
\langle p_0, p_1, p_2 \rangle &= \{(\lambda p_0 + (1 - \lambda)p_1)\mu + (1 - \mu)p_2 \mid 0 \leq \lambda, \mu \leq 1\} \\
&= \{\mu q + (1 - \mu)p_2 \mid q \in \langle p_0, p_1 \rangle, 0 \leq \mu \leq 1\}
\end{aligned}$$

If the p_i are not collinear, then $\langle p_0, p_1, p_2 \rangle$ is a triangle with vertices p_0, p_1, and p_2. The notion of convex combination generalizes to arbitrary dimension: The convex combination of the points $p_0, ..., p_{d+1}$ is

$$\langle p_0, ..., p_{d+1} \rangle = \{\lambda q + (1 - \lambda)p_{d+1} \mid q \in \langle p_0, ..., p_d \rangle, 0 \leq \lambda \leq 1\}$$

We say that $d + 1$ points in d-dimensional real space $\mathbf{R}^d$ are *linearly independent* if none of the points is contained in the convex combination of the others. It is not difficult to show that we can define $\langle p_0, ..., p_{d+1} \rangle$ equivalently as

$$\langle p_0, ..., p_{d+1} \rangle = \{\sum_{k=1}^{n} \lambda_k p_k \mid \lambda_k \geq 0 \text{ and } \sum_{k=1}^{n} \lambda_k = 1\}$$

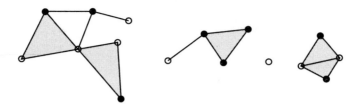

Figure 2.40   A Simplicial Complex C

Here, the numbers λ_k are the *barycentric coordinates* of the point $\sum_{k=1}^{n} \lambda_k p_k$. If the p_k are linearly independent, then it can be shown that the barycentric coordinates of every point in $\langle p_0, ..., p_{d+1} \rangle$ are unique.

A *d-simplex* is the convex combination of $d + 1$ linearly independent points. Moreover, d is the *dimension* of the d-simplex. Clearly, a 0-simplex is a point, a 1-simplex is a line segment, a 2-simplex is a triangle, and a 3-simplex is a tetrahedron.

The *boundary* of a d-simplex S consists of all $(d-k)$-simplices contained in S, where $k > 0$, and is denoted ∂S. Every simplex in the boundary of S is a *face* of S. A k-simplex that is a face is also called a *k-face*. The following theorem is elementary.

Theorem

A d-simplex contains exactly $\begin{pmatrix} d+1 \\ k+1 \end{pmatrix}$ k-simplices as faces.

Moreover, two d-simplices are homeomorphic.

A *simplicial complex C* is a finite set of simplices satisfying the following restrictions:

1. Let S be a simplex in C, and let S' be one of its faces. Then S' is also in C.

2. Let S_1 and S_2 be two simplices of C. Then their intersection is either empty or is a simplex of C.

Figure 2.40 shows a simplicial complex; Figure 2.41 shows a set of simplices that do not form a simplicial complex.

The *dimension* of the simplicial complex C is defined as the maximum dimension of the simplices in C. The dimension of the simplicial complex in Figure 2.40 is 2. It can be proved that the dimension of a simplicial complex is invariant under continuous maps. If S is a d-simplex and $d > 0$, then the boundary ∂S of S is a simplicial complex of dimension $d - 1$.

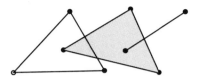

Figure 2.41   Simplices Not Forming a Simplicial Complex

A subset of $\mathbf{E}^n$ is *triangulable* if it is homeomorphic to a simplicial complex. A triangulable set is also called a *topological polyhedron*. Note that the term is not used in a geometric sense, because a homeomorphism may map a linear surface to a curved surface. Hence, the closed unit ball in $\mathbf{E}^3$ is a topological polyhedron since it is homeomorphic to a 3-simplex. Figure 2.42 shows several topological polyhedra of dimension 2. Moreover, given a topological polyhedron M, the homeomorphism from a simplicial complex onto M is a *triangulation* of M.

Abstract Simplicial Complexes and Geometric Realization

Since we defined simplices as convex combinations of points, it is conceivable that this definition is too narrow. That is, when constructing a simplicial complex, can we obtain more complicated structures using simplices that are only homeomorphic to convex combinations? From a topological point of view, the answer is no, and is justified as follows.

We define an *abstract* simplex S as a finite set of points, called the *vertices* of S. Every proper subset of S is a face of S. If S consists of $d + 1$

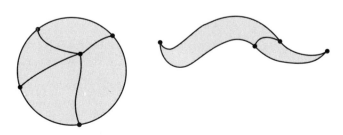

Figure 2.42   Topological Polyhedra of Dimension 2

points, then we say that it has the dimension d. An *abstract* simplicial complex C is defined as follows:

1. There is a finite set of *vertices* V.

2. C is a set of subsets S of V with the property that all subsets of S are in C.

Intuitively, the subsets S are the simplices in C.

It can be proved that every abstract simplicial complex C has a geometric realization $|C|$ in Euclidian space as a complex of simplices that are convex combinations. That is, given an abstract complex C with vertices $\{v_1, ..., v_m\}$, we can find m points in Euclidian n-dimensional space E such that, for every abstract simplex $S = \langle p_0, ..., p_d \rangle$ in C, the points in E corresponding to the p_k are linearly independent and hence define a simplex $|S|$ in E that is a convex combination of those points.

Theorem

If C is an abstract simplicial complex of dimension n, then C can be realized by a corresponding concrete simplicial complex $|C|$ in $\mathbf{E}^{2n+1}$, where the vertices are points and the simplices are convex combinations of them.

In other words, the abstract complex C has a "nice" piecewise linear realization in a Euclidian space of sufficiently high dimension. Thus, we do not lose generality by using the concrete definition of simplices as convex combinations.

Manifold Triangulations

We return to the problem of characterizing manifolds as topological polyhedra, and describe the local structure of a simplicial complex triangulating the manifold. Because of the above, we may assume that the simplicial complexes are piecewise linear in a suitable Euclidian space.

Let S be a d-simplex with vertices $p_0, ..., p_d$. A proper subset $q_0, ..., q_r$ of the vertices of S defines an r-simplex that is a face S_1 of S. Let $q_{r+1}, ..., q_d$ be the remaining vertices of S. Then these vertices define another face S_2. We say that S_1 and S_2 are *opposite faces* of S. Figure 2.43 shows examples in the case of $d = 3$. Let S and S' be two simplices in a simplicial complex. Then S and S' are *adjacent* if they have a common face. If S'' is a face in which S and S' are adjacent, then S and S' are *incident* to S''. Finally, a simplicial complex C is *connected*, if for all pairs of simplices S and S' in C, we can find a sequence of simplices $S_1, ..., S_r$ in C such that, for $1 \leq k < r$, we have $S = S_1$ and $S' = S_r$; and S_k is incident to S_{k+1}, or vice versa.

Let S be a simplex in some simplicial complex. S will be incident to a finite set of simplices $S_1, ..., S_r$ in C. For each simplex S_i of which S is a face, let T_i be the face of S_i opposite S. The set of all such opposite faces is the *link* of S in C; see Figure 2.44 for an example. We are now in a position to

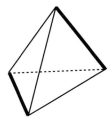
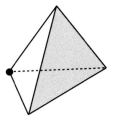

Figure 2.43   Opposite Faces in a 3-Simplex

characterize 2- and 3-manifolds in terms of simplicial complexes. Although stated as definitions, these characterizations can be proved formally.

A *2-manifold without boundary* is homeomorphic to a simplicial complex C of dimension 2 satisfying the following restrictions:

1. Every 1-simplex in C is incident to exactly two 2-simplices.

2. The link of every 0-simplex in C is a triangulation of the circle.

See also Figure 2.45 for an illustration of the vertex structure in a 2-manifold without boundary.

Similarly, a *3-manifold without boundary* is homeomorphic to a simplicial complex C of dimension 3 satisfying the following restrictions:

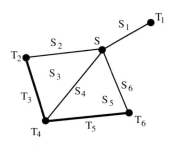

Figure 2.44   Link of S

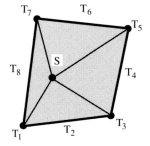

Figure 2.45   Vertex Structure in Triangulated 2-Manifold

1. Every 2-simplex in C is incident to exactly two 3-simplices.

2. The link of every 0-simplex in C is a triangulation of the sphere.

To so characterize 3-manifolds with boundary, we need to distinguish between simplices that are on the boundary of the manifold and ones that are interior. We discuss only 3-manifolds with boundary.

Let S be a 2-simplex in the complex C. Then S is an interior face if it is incident to exactly two 3-simplices of C, and is a boundary face if it is incident to exactly one 3-simplex. Similarly, a 0-simplex is interior if its link is a triangulation of the sphere, and is a boundary point if its link is a triangulation of the disk. Note that we do not give an analogous characterization of 1-simplices; such a characterization is not needed.

Formally, then, a *3-manifold with boundary* is homeomorphic to a simplicial complex C of dimension 3 satisfying the following restrictions:

1. Every 2-simplex is adjacent to one or two 3-simplices.

2. The link of every 0-simplex is a triangulation of the disk or the sphere.

This completes the explanation of the polyhedral structure of 2- and 3-manifolds.

2.4.2 Manifold Solids

We wish to define a topological solid as a 3-manifold with boundary, where, in addition, the boundary should be compact. The intuition is that we should have a finite surface, but that infinite volumes are permitted. As pointed out before, this definition will not constrain the relationship between the topological solid and the surrounding 3-space. Moreover, since in B-rep a solid is implicitly described by a specification of its surface, we must also clarify the relationship between a topological solid and its surface. We do this now.

Embeddings in $\mathbf{E}^3$

We consider the relationship between a 3-manifold with boundary and the surrounding space. This relationship needs to be examined because there are "unreasonable" 3-manifolds in $\mathbf{E}^3$ that are homeomorphic to well-behaved topological polyhedra. For example, a manifold can be unreasonable because it has a fractal-like surface. The difficulty is rooted in the fact that the characterization of manifolds as topological polyhedra requires only that there be a homeomorphism from a simplicial complex of suitable structure onto the manifold, without consideration of whether this homeomorphism can be extended to the surrounding Euclidian space.

An *embedding* of the topological space (X, T) into a topological space (Y, T') is a homeomorphism between (X, T) and a subspace Y' of Y. In particular, let X and Y' be subspaces of $\mathbf{E}^n$. Depending on whether and

Figure 2.46   A Wildly Embedded Simple Arc

how the homeomorphism extends to a homeomorphism of the entire surrounding space we call embeddings *tame* or *wild*. Wild embeddings lead
to unreasonable 3-manifolds in $\mathbf{E}^3$. A simple example is depicted in Figure
2.46, which shows a wildly embedded arc in $\mathbf{E}^3$. By giving "thickness" to
the arc, we obtain a 3-manifold with compact boundary that can be shown
to be homeomorphic to a sphere. Clearly, this would not be a reasonable
solid.

In view of this fact, we require, in addition, that a topological solid be
tamely embedded into $\mathbf{E}^3$. Rather than giving a formal definition, we will
argue later on that the primitives used in CSG and in B-rep guarantee that
we are working with tame embeddings.

Orientability

So far, we have characterized a topological solid in its entirety; that is, as
a three-dimensional object. In B-rep, however, we have only a description
of the boundary. We need to make a connection between the topological
structure of the solid and the topological structure of its boundary. This
connection requires the concept of *orientability*. Briefly, we can prove the
following theorem.

> **Theorem**
> Let M be a connected 3-manifold with boundary embedded in
> $\mathbf{E}^3$. Then the boundary of M is an embedded orientable 2-
> manifold without boundary.

Note that we do not need to assume a tame embedding. A converse of
this theorem can be formulated which allows us to conclude from boundary
properties that a topological polyhedron is enclosed. However, such a theorem requires additional assumptions. These additional assumptions will
involve geometric properties of the embedding and are explained later.

Orientability is best visualized in terms of a triangulation of the manifold. It can be shown that the orientability of a manifold is independent
of the particular triangulation. That is, if the manifold is orientable, then
every one of its triangulations is orientable. Conversely, if the manifold

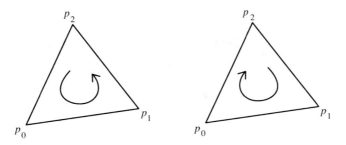

Figure 2.47   Orientations (p_0, p_1, p_2) and (p_0, p_2, p_1) of a 2-Simplex

has an orientable triangulation, then the manifold is orientable. So, we explain orientability of 2-manifolds by orienting simplicial complexes that are a triangulation of the manifold.

We orient a 2-simplex by cyclically ordering its vertices. For example, the simplex $\langle p_0, p_1, p_2 \rangle$ can be oriented (p_0, p_1, p_2). Figure 2.47 shows the two possible orientations of the 2-simplex. Note that the orientation of a 2-simplex induces an orientation of every one of its 1-faces. More generally, any d-simplex can be oriented in exactly one of two ways.

Let S and S' be two adjacent 2-simplices in a complex C, and assume that they are adjacent in a 1-face S''. Then S and S' are *coherently oriented* if the orientations of S'' induced by the orientations of S and S' are opposite. Figure 2.48 shows two pairs of adjacent 2-simplices. The left pair is oriented coherently, whereas the right pair is not.

Let C be a triangulation of a connected 2-manifold with or without boundary. Then C is orientable iff all of its adjacent 2-simplices can be oriented coherently. It can be shown that, if C is orientable, then it can be

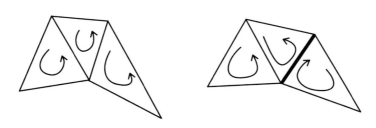

Figure 2.48   Coherent and Incoherent Orientations

oriented in exactly two ways, and for this reason there is a simple algorithm for testing orientability. Roughly speaking, we pick any 2-simplex and orient it arbitrarily. Thereafter, we orient an adjacent 2-simplex coherently, continuing iteratively until the manifold has been coherently oriented, or until we reach a 2-simplex S adjacent to two other simplices that are already oriented in a way that precludes orienting S coherently with both.

We return to the problem of formulating the converse of the preceding theorem. We would like to obtain a characterization that is roughly as follows.

Theorem

Let M' be a compact, connected 2-manifold without boundary that is tamely embedded into $\mathbf{E}^3$ and is oriented. If M' satisfies a property $\mathcal{P}$, then M' is the boundary of a connected 3-manifold that is tamely embedded in $\mathbf{E}^3$.

Sufficient properties $\mathcal{P}$ are readily formulated. One possibility is to require that $\mathbf{E}^3$ is triangulated in its entirety such that this triangulation also triangulates M'. However, rather than making $\mathcal{P}$ a global property, we formulate a more local property of the embedding.

Intuitively, wild embeddings (and some tame embeddings) are unsatisfactory because the manifold is "ruffled." It appears that there is no purely topological characterization of this intuitive notion, and we need to introduce geometry to make the idea precise. Let M be an embedded 3-manifold with compact boundary in $\mathbf{E}^3$. We say that M is of *bounded variation* if every line in $\mathbf{E}^3$ intersects M in finitely many segments and every plane in finitely many areas. Analogously, we say that a compact 2-manifold in $\mathbf{E}^3$ is of bounded variation if every line intersects it in finitely many points and every plane in finitely many curves.

Throughout this book, we assume that the boundaries of solids can be described by finitely many subsets of algebraic surfaces. It is easy to show that algebraic surfaces are always of bounded variation;[6] hence, we do not have to make additional requirements on B-rep to achieve embeddings of bounded variation. This simplifies verifying topological validity. Note also that embeddings of bounded variation are always tame.

Topological Validity of Manifold Solids

Consider a 3-manifold M with boundary embedded in $\mathbf{E}^3$. Its boundary is an embedded orientable 2-manifold M' without boundary, but M' need not be connected. Thus, when given an embedded oriented 2-manifold M' without boundary, we need to satisfy a compatibility condition so that its connected components will collectively define a solid. The compatibility condition depends on the given orientation of the components.

---

[6]Cf. Bezout's theorem in Section 5.3.3 of Chapter 5.

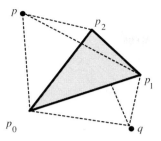

Figure 2.49   Interior Point p and Exterior Point q

Let M be an oriented, connected 2-manifold in $\mathbf{E}^3$. We call a point p not on M *interior* to M if there is a triangulation C of M satisfying the following conditions:

1. There is a 2-simplex S of C oriented as (p_0, p_1, p_2) such that the corresponding points on M are seen from p in a counterclockwise orientation.

2. There is a point q in the image of S such that the line segment (p, q) does not intersect M except at q.

Figure 2.49 illustrates the definition. It is not difficult to show that, with this definition, the manifold partitions $\mathbf{E}^3$ into two open sets, one consisting of all points that are interior, the other consisting of points that are neither interior nor on M. The latter set is the set of *exterior* points.

Note that the definition of interior and exterior points agrees locally with the convention of outward-pointing normals explained in Section 3.2 of Chapter 3. Let (p_0, p_1, p_2) be an oriented 2-simplex. For an acute angle, say at p_0, define a normal direction as the cross product of the vectors $\overline{(p_0, p_2)}$ and $\overline{(p_0, p_1)}$. Then this normal direction points locally to the exterior.

Given this definition of interior and exterior points, we can define a manifold solid as follows:

Definition
A *single-shell manifold solid* A is a connected 3-manifold with boundary embedded in $\mathbf{E}^3$. The boundary A' of A is a compact, connected 2-manifold without boundary, embedded in $\mathbf{E}^3$ with bounded variation, and is oriented such that A consists of the set of interior points of A' along with A'.

Now assume that we have two disjoint connected oriented 2-manifolds, M_1' and M_2', in $\mathbf{E}^3$. Each defines a set of interior points. We say that M_1'

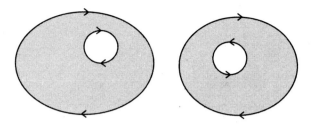

Figure 2.50   Inconsistently and Consistently Oriented Boundaries of Orientable 2-Manifolds

and M_2' are oriented *consistently* if M_1' consists of interior points of M_2' whenever M_2' consists of interior points of M_1'. Figure 2.50 illustrates the definition for the two-dimensional case. The bounding cycles on the left are inconsistently oriented, those on the right are consistently oriented. Consequently, the following is a definition of a multishell manifold solid.

Definition
A *multishell manifold solid* A is a 3-manifold with boundary in $\mathbf{E}^3$. The boundary A' of A is a compact, oriented 2-manifold without boundary, embedded in $\mathbf{E}^3$ with bounded variation. Let $A_1', ..., A_r'$ be the connected components of A'. Then, for each pair (i, k), where $1 \leq i < k \leq r$, the components A_i' and A_k' are consistently oriented.

Topological validity of a manifold B-rep solid is verified as follows. We assume that we are given a boundary representation specifying finitely many vertices, edges, and faces. Moreover, we assume that each face is a compact subset of an algebraic surface, and that edges and vertices are intersections of faces. These assumptions guarantee that the surface is of bounded variation and that it is compact.

Let $A_1', ..., A_r'$ be the connected surface components described by the representation. Perform the following steps.

1. Verify that the A_k' are pairwise disjoint and that they do not self-intersect.

2. Triangulate each A_k' and verify that it is a 2-manifold without boundary, using the triangulability conditions explained previously.

3. For each pair A_i' and A_k' of components, verify that their orientation is consistent.

A topologically valid B-rep must satisfy all these criteria.

Step 1 tests that the geometric embedding into $\mathbf{E}^3$ makes sense. Self-intersections create nonmanifold points on the boundary; hence, they must not occur. This is primarily a geometric property of the embedding. Step 2 verifies that the boundary is a 2-manifold without boundary. The assumptions on faces imply that the boundary is compact. It can be proved that a closed 2-manifold embedded in $\mathbf{E}^3$ must be orientable. Hence, orientability need not be tested explicitly. Note, however, that the triangulation of the surface is computationally easy only for planar faces. Step 3, finally, tests whether the individual shells are oriented such that they collectively define the solid's interior and exterior.

All algebraic surfaces have bounded variation, and a B-rep describes finitely many compact subsets of algebraic surfaces. Therefore, the theorem above implies that a B-rep satisfying the conditions checked for in the algorithm defines a topologically valid solid.

2.4.3 Nonmanifold Solids

We sketch how to characterize nonmanifold solids from a topological perspective. Briefly, we consider a nonmanifold solid as an *immersion* of several manifold solids; that is, we allow the manifolds to intersect in $\mathbf{E}^3$. However, we restrict intersections to sets of dimension 1 or 0. This point of view was explained in Section 2.3.1 as the second approach to defining valid boundary representations. That is, each such intersection is considered a geometric coincidence of topologically different parts of the manifold boundary.

To identify the various manifold solids, we triangulate the nonmanifold solid and consider the interior points of the resulting simplicial complex. They decompose into several connected, open sets, each of which can be understood as the interior of an immersed 3-manifold with boundary.

Reversing this process, we *define* a nonmanifold solid as homeomorphic to an oriented simplicial complex of dimension 3, such that the interior points are an embedded 3-manifold of bounded variation. The closure of the set creates a boundary that is compact and of bounded variation. In particular, this implies that the surface of a nonmanifold solid can be triangulated without degenerate 2-simplices of zero area.

We adapt the validity test for manifold solid boundary representations to test whether a given B-rep describes a valid nonmanifold solid. Briefly, we must "split" nonmanifold edges and vertices by locally considering the solid interior, as implied by the given surface orientation. In effect, we construct a set of surface components, each a 2-manifold without boundary. Each of these components are then tested as described previously.

Intuitively, the splitting process "shrinks" the volume of the solid infinitesimally. After shrinking, the nonmanifold edges and vertices disappear. See also Figure 2.51 for a two-dimensional example. Note, however, that this topological resolution of nonmanifold edges and vertices will be different in a solid A and its complement solid, $\neg A$, because we shrink the

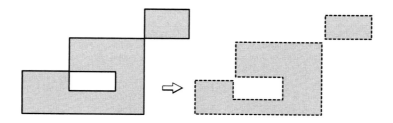

Figure 2.51   Resolution of Nonmanifold Structures

interior of the solid. Hence, shrinking the complement solid $\neg A$ is equivalent to expanding the solid A.

2.5 Spatial Decomposition

Apart from CSG and B-rep, there exist a number of solid representation schemata, based, loosely speaking, on spatial decomposition. We briefly mention these schemata now. Most of them play a peripheral role in solid modeling because of certain limitations. Nevertheless, many of them have important special applications, including numerical analysis and geographic databases.

The simplest decomposition schema is a *uniform subdivision* of space into a grid of cubes of specified size, and *marks* all cubes that intersect the solid interior. The solid would thus be represented by all marked cubes. Figure 2.52 illustrates the idea in two dimensions. This representation is approximate, and the size of the cubes will define the degree of accuracy. In principle, only the marked cubes need to be stored. Adjacency of two cubes could be represented explicitly, or could be inferred from a cube's location in space. Representations of this type are used in numerical analysis for domain discretization.

When a high degree of accuracy is required, the number of cubes may be too great for this data structure to be considered convenient. *Octrees* ameliorate this problem by aggregating certain marked cubes into larger ones. Conceptually, we partition space by several grids, each with mesh size twice that of the previous one. Eight adjacent marked cubes are combined into a larger marked cube, provided the larger cube lies in the next larger mesh. Figure 2.53 illustrates the idea in two dimensions. Octrees are stored as trees that essentially record this adjacency information. The interior nodes represent cube aggregations where not all component cubes are marked, whereas the leaves represent cubes that are marked or that do

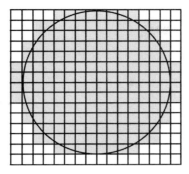

Figure 2.52   Circle Represented by Uniform Subdivision of Space

not intersect the solid interior at all.

So far, we have discussed space decompositions in which the space elements are in a specific implicit relationship with the coordinate system. This makes it unattractive to rotate objects so represented. At the expense of more complex adjacency and shape processing, we can drop this relationship and allow irregular shape elements. In finite element analysis,

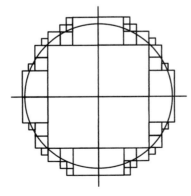

Figure 2.53   Octree Subdivision of Space

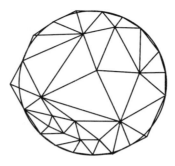

Figure 2.54   Irregular Subdivision of Space

triangular and tetrahedral space elements are used, as illustrated by Figure 2.54.

2.6 Notes and References

Early work on constructive solid geometry includes the work on TIPS by Okino, Kakazu, and Kubo (1973), and the work on PADL by Voelcker et al. (1974) and Requicha and Voelcker (1977). Most of the CSG material presented here follows the various publications by that group, which relied heavily on an algebraic formulation of the algorithms. See the bibliography under the author names Brown, Tilove, Requicha, Rossignac, and Voelcker.

The approximation algorithm to CSG objects is due to Cameron (1985). By considering different approximation strategies, including approximating only some of the primitives, Cameron devises several redundancy tests. Cameron's algorithm also includes a downward phase in which the approximation at the root of the CSG tree is propagated downward toward the leaves, possibly further refining the approximation. Rossignac and Voelcker (1988) consider redundancy determination without approximating primitives. Their idea is to identify those surface areas of a primitive P that contribute to the surface of the final solid defined by a CSG tree T. By analyzing the volumes defined by the subtrees descending from the nodes on the path from P to the root of T, they derive a description of a volume that must contain the surface area of interest. They call this volume the *active zone* of P, and show how knowledge of the active zone can be used to improve conversion from CSG to B-rep, detection of redundancies, and other operations on CSG trees. The relationship between the active zone and the approximation approaches to redundancy testing is described in Cameron and Rossignac (1988).

The winged-edge style of boundary representation is due to Baumgart (1975). Many variants of the method, as well as several alternatives, have been proposed and used in B-rep–based modeling systems since then. For a survey of the various representation schemata, see Weiler (1986). Weiler's thesis also contains much material on Euler operators, and on the problem of whether a specific representation method is minimally topologically complete. Nonmanifold boundary representations were apparently first proposed by Wesley (1980). They were again advocated by Weiler (1986) and by Hoffmann, Hopcroft, and Karasick (1987). In each case, the motivation seems to have been the observation that the internals of a number of geometric operations on polyhedra simplify when nonmanifold structures are permitted.

Paoluzzi et al. (1986 and 1988) implement Boolean operations on B-rep solids by disambiguating the topology, as discussed in Section 2.3.1. They assume that all faces have been triangulated before constructing the intersection or union of two polyhedra. With this restriction, they obtain a uniform data structure representing polyhedra. They show that the needed storage is at most 50 percent more than that of a winged-edge representation with untriangulated faces.

Mäntylä (1984) proves that Euler operations form a complete set of modeling primitives for manifold solids. That is, every topologically valid polyhedron can be constructed from an initial polyhedron by a finite sequence of Euler operations. In Mäntylä (1988), the use of Euler operations to implement Boolean operations on polyhedra is explained. The explanation of Euler operators in Chiyokura (1988) is more explicit on the interaction of the topological and geometric aspects.

The section on topological validity reviews standard material from algebraic topology. Good sources on the subject include Aleksandrov (1956), Hocking and Young (1961), Schubert (1964), and Seifert and Threlfall (1947). Hocking and Young (1961) give pictures of wildly embedded manifolds, including Alexander's horned sphere and Antoine's necklace.

The Euler–Poincaré formula can be generalized to manifolds of arbitrary dimension; it is then called the Euler–Poincaré characteristic of the manifold. It is related to the dimensions of the homology groups of the manifold.

Requicha (1977) defines solids not only topologically but also geometrically. The topological characterization is similar to ours. Requicha also shows how the Euler–Poincaré characteristic can be derived from homology computations. Octree and other spatial subdivision schemata are presented in depth in Samet (1989a,b).

CHAPTER 3

Boolean Operations on Boundary Representation

Algorithms for determining the regularized union, intersection, or set difference of two solids can be used in B-rep and dual-representation modelers. They can be used also to convert solids represented by CSG trees to an equivalent B-rep. Thus, algorithms for Boolean operations on B-rep are sometimes called *boundary evaluation and merging* algorithms.

These algorithms are not difficult conceptually, but their implementation requires substantial work for several reasons. Layers of primitive geometric and topological operations to implement them have to be designed. Finding a good structure for these layers is not simple, and accounting for the many special positions of incident structures in three dimensions can be tedious. Moreover, the presence of curved surfaces introduces nontrivial mathematical problems, and, since most of the algorithms require numerical techniques, there is inevitably the problem of numerical precision and stability of the calculations.

In this chapter, we consider the regularized intersection of two nonmanifold polyhedral solids given in B-rep. This avoids presenting up front the mathematical problems arising from nonlinear geometric objects. The algorithm presented here has not been specialized to the point where its structure makes it unsuitable for extension to the curved case. Moreover, the majority of geometric operations to be formulated will, with certain extensions, apply to the curved-surface case. However, the need for high precision is more exacting in the curved-surface case, and the possibility of curve and surface singularities is a new dimension that necessitates additions to the algorithm.

It is desirable to use a B-rep in which the topological information is separated from the geometric representation of the surfaces elements. Moreover, as far as possible, the algorithm ought to be made independent of the specific details of the geometric representation, since then extensions of the coverage or alternatives to the chosen representation can be explored with minimum programming. This is especially important in the curved-surface domain, where different geometric representations offer different advantages.

3.1 Chapter Organization

The intersection algorithm to be described has many details and depends on many conventions. We begin the description by explaining the representation, and introducing a number of low-level operations used repeatedly throughout.

The heart of the algorithm is a method for intersecting two polyhedra, A and B, each of which has one shell. Conceptually, the method subdivides the faces of the two polyhedra along the curves in which their surfaces intersect. This subdivision is refined to faces of the output polyhedron, and the adjacencies of these faces are determined. Thereafter, the surface of the intersection is completed by adding certain faces of A and of B. Two aspects complicate this description:

1. The analysis and subsequent transfer of results must account for many special cases that come about when surface elements on the two polyhedra align in specific ways.

2. The face subdivision does not proceed independently, face by face, on each solid. Rather, each intersecting face pair is subjected to a neighborhood analysis whose results are immediately transferred to all adjacent surface elements.

The first complication is intrinsic to the problem. Often, descriptions in the literature will omit many of these details to simplify the narrative, leaving the reader to invent his or her own methods for handling them. The second complication trades programming effort against robustness, and is discussed later on. Our organization increases robustness, but at the price of additional programming.

After the description of how to intersect single-shell polyhedra, we explain how to intersect polyhedra with multiple shells. This requires fairly easy extensions. We also mention how the union and difference operations can be implemented by a simple modification of the intersection algorithm.

In the form first sketched, the intersection algorithm requires testing of each face pair for intersection. This is not efficient, and there should be a preceding computation that filters out face pairs that cannot intersect. A simple way to do this is to enclose each face in a box whose sides are aligned with the coordinate axes, and to construct a list of intersecting boxes. Clearly, if two enclosing boxes do not intersect, the faces inside them cannot intersect and need not be considered together. A fast algorithm for box intersection is described at the end of the chapter.

Note that such preprocessing steps cannot speed up certain cases of intersecting polyhedra. However, they do speed up the algorithm on average and should therefore be incorporated.

At first reading, it may be advisable to skim or skip parts of the chapter. Section 3.4, which describes how to intersect single-shell polyhedra, is the key part. It requires a conceptual understanding of the representation and of some of the geometric subroutines; this understanding can be obtained by skimming Sections 3.2 and 3.3. Section 3.4.4 may be skipped, postponing the various situations arising in neighborhood analysis. On subsequent reading, Sections 3.5 and 3.6 explain multishell polyhedra and the reduction of other Boolean operations to intersection.

Section 3.7 is self-contained. It presents box-intersection techniques without assuming any background in computational geometry. The algorithm is developed in stages, reviewing the needed data structures and discussing first the simpler problems of interval and rectangle intersection.

Subsection 3.4.4, on neighborhood analysis, maps out the many positional special cases that are encountered when implementing Boolean operations. It is included for the less experienced system developer who may become stymied by the many details. There is a second, less obvious purpose to this subsection. When we study the various cases carefully, we form a conceptual understanding of positional degeneracy as a cumulative impression, and we develop a valuable ability to organize the algorithm concisely.

3.2 Representation Conventions

We assume that polyhedra have nonmanifold surfaces of *finite* area. The topological representation fixes the following information:

1. For each vertex, the adjacent edges and faces are given.

2. For each edge, the bounding vertices and the adjacent faces are specified. Moreover, the adjacent faces are cyclically ordered according to how they intersect a plane normal to the edge, and pairs of adjacent faces that enclose volume in between are identified.

3. For each face, the bounding edges and vertices are given. They are organized in a set of cycles locally enclosing the face area to the right.

Ordering information is given that specifies how the boundary graph is embedded in the face plane.

The logical structure of this information is as described later. In the description, we do not distinguish between, for example, a face and a *reference* to that face, since this distinction is unnecessary for understanding the algorithms.

For the sake of specificity, we describe how the geometric information is stored. However, in the subsequent algorithm description, the exact format of the geometric data is not essential. The geometric information is *irredundant*, specifying only the equations for the planes containing faces. These equations are oriented by the convention that the normal direction points locally to the solid exterior. Edges are defined geometrically as the line segment connecting the bounding vertices. Note that an edge may be adjacent to more than two faces. Vertices are given as the intersection of specific planes containing incident faces.

Irredundancy of the geometric information reduces the possibility of contradictory data and therefore increases robustness. Moreover, since the planes containing the faces of $A \cap^* B$ are a subset of the face planes of A and B, no new geometric data are ever constructed. Hence, no inaccuracy can be introduced through computed geometric information. On the other hand, irredundancy of geometric data in the curved-surface domain must be weighed against the computational cost of deriving coordinates for vertices.

Note that faces may consist of disjoint areas, provided these areas lie in the same plane with the same orientation. Some Boolean algorithms have been proposed that require that each face be a connected region, or a region homeomorphic to a disk, or a convex polygon, or a triangle. Typically, such constraints simplify the algorithms. However, one would then have to devise an algorithm that subdivides certain surface areas of the result polyhedron, since inputs with restricted face topologies do not always yield results that satisfy these constraints as well. Thus, the work is shifted from the intersection algorithm to a postprocessing step that constructs legal faces for the result object.

In the polyhedral case, this strategy is not without merit, even though it may lead to unnecessary edges in repeated Boolean operations on an object. It is unclear, however, whether the approach remains viable in the curved-surface domain, because in that case triangulation or other forms of face subdivision can be quite difficult.

3.2.1 Face Representation

A *face* is a finite, nonzero area in a plane, bounded by one or more cycles of vertices and edges. Edges are directed such that the face area locally lies to the right, as seen from the exterior of the solid. Face planes have been written such that the normal vector points locally to the solid's exterior.

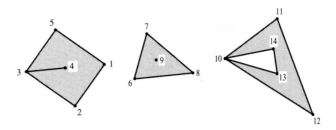

Figure 3.1   Legal Face Cycles $(1, 2, 3, 4, 3, 5)$, $(6, 7, 8)$, (9), and $(10, 11, 12, 10, 13, 14)$

We refer to this as the convention of *outward-pointing normals*, and use it, for example, when determining the face direction vector as explained in Section 3.3.1.

A bounding cycle may be *degenerate*, containing the same vertex more than once, or containing only one or two vertices. In these cases, the cycle should not enclose zero face area. Thus, a single vertex may bound a zero-area puncture in a face, but may not lie outside the face area. In particular, edges must bound a nonzero area immediately to the right.

Example 3.1:   Figure 3.1 shows several legal degenerate face cycles; Figure 3.2 shows illegal ones. ◇

Together, the edge cycles form an embedded directed, planar graph. Separate connected components may be nested. This nesting structure is recorded in a separate forest of trees. Each tree node corresponds to a connected boundary component. Nested components are in subtrees. For example, for the face shown in Figure 3.1, we have three trees in the forest. Two trees consist of a single vertex each, and represent the cycles $(1, 2, 3, 4, 3, 5)$ and $(10, 11, 12, 10, 13, 14)$, respectively. A third tree has two nodes. Its root represents the cycle $(6, 7, 8)$, and its descendant represents the cycle (5).

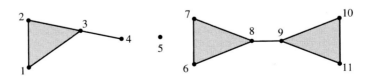

Figure 3.2   Illegal Face Cycles $(1, 2, 3, 4, 3)$, (5) and $(6, 7, 8, 9, 10, 11, 9, 8)$

Consider a vertex u of the face f. The incident edges of u define sectors in the face plane that are alternately inside and outside the face f. Since edges are oriented, the incident edges must alternate in direction, one being oriented away from u, the other being oriented toward u. We order the edges clockwise about u and consider them paired such that each pair encloses a sector in f. Each pair is called an *area-enclosing pair*. Note that the clockwise orientation is with respect to the solid exterior; that is, it depends on the face-plane normal. We think of this pairing as a representation of the two-dimensional neighborhood of u in the face plane.

Example 3.2:   In the face cycle $(1, 2, 3, 4, 3, 5)$ shown in Figure 3.1, the vertex 3 is incident to the four directed edges $(3, 5)$, $(4, 3)$, $(3, 4)$, and $(2, 3)$. There are two area-enclosing pairs at u; namely, $(3, 5), (4, 3)$ and $(3, 4), (2, 3)$. $\diamondsuit$

Recall from Section 2.4 that the surface of a solid should be orientable. Since all faces are planar, the orientation of the edge cycles ensures that every triangulation of a face can be coherently oriented, assuming the orientation is consistent. Here, consistency is exactly analogous to consistency of orientation of the boundary components of topological solids.

3.2.2 Edge Representation

Consider an oriented edge $e = (u, v)$. The adjacent faces define wedges of volume that are alternately inside and outside the solid. We order the adjacent faces clockwise about e as seen in the direction (u, v), and pair adjacent faces that enclose a wedge of solid interior. Each pair is called a *volume-enclosing pair*. Again, we think of this pairing as a representation of the three-dimensional neighborhood of points in the *interior* of the edge. Representing this information explicitly, we thus give the following information for each edge:

1. Beginning and ending vertices, establishing a default orientation

2. An ordered, circular list of adjacent faces

3. A pairing establishing which face pairs enclose volume

The circular ordering and pairing can be represented by a single structure.

Note that the adjacent faces use the edge in alternating direction. We explicitly annotate the face reference, indicating whether the edge is used in the default orientation (u, v) or in the opposite orientation (v, u). This alternation of edge directions implies that locally the surface of the solid can be oriented coherently in the sense of Section 2.4 of Chapter 2.

3.2.3 Vertex Representation

Given a vertex, we must know all incident edges and adjacent faces. As discussed in the previous chapter, the adjacent faces form cones that can be nested, and the logical structure is a spherical map. Instead of representing this structure explicitly, we let the algorithm infer it when needed; see also Section 3.3.4.

3.2.4 Surface Structure

We require finite surface area for polyhedra, but permit infinite volume. This is convenient for reducing the union operation to an intersection and several complementation operations. A polyhedron can have internal voids, and is thus, in general, an object with several surface components. Each surface component is a collection of vertices, edges, and faces that are adjacent. These components are its *shells* and are organized into a forest of trees reflecting spatial containment and shell orientation.[1] A face consisting of two or more disjoint areas must not belong to different shells.

Each shell is given as a list of faces and an indication of whether the shell, taken separately, represents a polyhedron with finite or infinite volume. This information is stored at the nodes of the shell trees. A node s is a descendant of another node t if the shell stored at s is spatially contained by the shell stored at t. Consider the shell structure of a cube with two internal voids. The exterior surface is the shell s represented at the root. By itself, it describes a solid of finite volume, and is marked as such. The two shells bounding the interior voids are t_1 and t_2. Separately, each describes a polyhedron of infinite volume. Both shells are nested in s, but not within each other. In consequence, the shell forest is a single tree whose root is s and whose two leaves are t_1 and t_2.

3.3 Geometric Operations

The intersection algorithm is developed in terms of simpler geometric operations that are used as subroutines. The most trivial ones, such as computing vertex coordinates and testing point/line incidence are not described here. Note, however, that in the context of robustness they will have to be considered in some detail, as discussed in the next chapter.

3.3.1 Face Direction Vector

Given an edge e of a face f, we will need to know the orientation of the edge and the direction in the plane of f in which the interior of f lies. Suppose the edge is defined by two incident vertices u and v, and we know an equation $ax + by + cz + d = 0$ for the plane P containing an adjacent face f. The orientation of the edge with respect to f is determined from the topological data that specify how the edge is referenced by f.

---

[1] Each shell is a connected component of the 2-manifold bounding the solid, as discussed in Section 2.4 of Chapter 2.

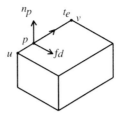

Figure 3.3   Face Direction Vector

The *face direction vector* is a vector *fd* in the plane P. The vector is perpendicular to the edge tangent vector t_e and points to the interior of f (Figure 3.3). It is defined for every point p on the edge. Since the edge is a line segment, the vector does not depend on p. It is computed from the edge orientation as referenced by f and from the normal vector $n_P = (a, b, c)$ of the plane P as the cross-product $t_e \times n_P$. Here, t_e is the edge tangent vector, oriented by the edge direction. This computation also works for curved edges, but then the surface normal n_P and the edge tangent t_e depend on the point p.

It is possible that the same edge is referenced twice by f, once in each direction. In this case, we know that there is face interior on both sides of the edge, and which of the two sides is needed must be determined from the context; see also Section 3.3.3.

3.3.2 Splitting an Area- or Volume-Enclosing Pair

In the neighborhood analysis, we have to determine whether a face locally extends to the interior or exterior of the other solid. This question is reduced to determining whether a certain vector splits two paired vectors. Similarly, in two dimensions, we may determine whether a line segment extends into the interior of a face, which we do by determining whether the segment splits an area-enclosing pair of edges.

Given an area-enclosing pair of edges (v_1, u) and (u, v_2), we wish to determine whether a vector $t = \overline{(u, w)}$ lies in the area enclosed by the pair. If so, we say that t *splits an area-enclosing pair*; see Figure 3.4 for an example. To determine this, we order clockwise the three vectors t, $\overline{(u, v_1)}$, and $\overline{(u, v_2)}$ about u, beginning with (u, v_2). If, after sorting, t lies between the pair, then it splits the pair.

Given a volume-enclosing pair of adjacent faces, we determine whether the vector t lies inside the volume so bounded. If so, we say that t *splits a volume-enclosing pair*. The test can be reduced to a test for splitting area-

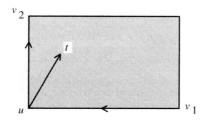

Figure 3.4   Splitting an Area-Enclosing Pair

enclosing pairs by projecting t onto the plane spanned by the face direction vectors of the faces.

3.3.3 Ordering Points Along a Line and Pairing Them

The transversal intersection of two faces is a set of segments on a line. The segments are obtained by first intersecting each face with the plane containing the other face, followed by intersecting the segments. We address how to intersect one face with the plane containing the other face.

Given a line representing the intersection of two face planes P and Q, containing, respectively, the faces f and g, we order sequentially the points in which the bounding edges of g intersect the plane P. Assuming no arithmetic problem, the ordering of points is straightforward and can be done by sorting them by one of the coordinates, depending on the slope of the line.

Having ordered the points, we now pair consecutive points such that the line segment bounded by each pair represents an intersection of the face g with the plane P (Figure 3.5). Since faces have finite area, there cannot be infinite line segments, and so we pair consecutive points in sorted order. For curved surfaces P and Q, the problem is much more complicated because their intersection may be a complicated space curve.

We orient the line $P \cap Q$ (arbitrarily) by the cross-product of the plane normals, $t = n_P \times n_Q$, and order the intersection points accordingly. Complications arise from special positions where vertices of g lie on the line $P \cap Q$, and from intersections with edges that must be considered in both orientations.

Let (u, v) be an *oriented* edge of g. If u is below P while v is above it, then the intersection point is paired with the subsequent point in sorted order; otherwise, it is paired with the previous point. If both (u, v) and (v, u) must be considered, then the two intersection points must not be paired with each other.

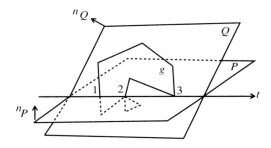

Figure 3.5   Intersection-Point Sorting and Pairing

If a vertex of g is on the line $P \cap Q$, it is considered as a double intersection point. Call the two intersections u_1 and u_2, in sorting order. Then, u_1 is paired with the preceding point if $-t$ splits an area-enclosing pair of edges incident to u, and u_2 is paired with the succeeding point if t splits an area-enclosing pair of incident edges. If $-t$ or t is collinear to an incident edge of g, then that edge is used to connect the respective copy of u with its predecessor or successor. If neither t nor $-t$ split an area-enclosing pair, then u is an isolated point.

For example, in Figure 3.5, the first copy 2_1 of point 2 is paired with the preceding point 1, but the second copy is not paired and is therefore ignored. The intersection point 3 is isolated. Note that isolated points must be recalled in later stages of the algorithm, and cannot be discarded outright.

3.3.4 Line/Solid Classification

A general method for determining possible containment of two nonintersecting bounding structures A and B is to connect a point on the boundary of A by a line segment with a point on the boundary of B, and then to analyze how this line segment intersects the boundaries of the two structures. However, the structure A may consist of several disconnected components, as may B. Therefore, any containment conclusions drawn apply to only those components of A and B that the line segment actually intersects. For example, the line segment (p, q) in Figure 3.6 allows us to conclude that both the component containing p and the component containing q will bound the intersection of the two areas A and B, but it cannot reveal that the other component of A is not part of the final boundary. For the final boundary, the components are assembled by a sequence of the tests now described; see also Section 3.5 on multishell objects. We explain the test

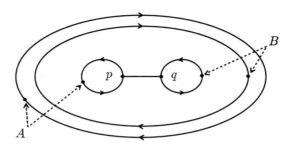

Figure 3.6   Classification of Multiple-Boundary Components

first in the case of faces.

Consider a face f and a face g, both in the same plane and oriented the same way. We assume that the boundaries of f and g do not intersect, and wish to test whether one face boundary contains the other. We select a point p on the boundary of f and a point q on the boundary of g, and connect them with a line segment (p, q). The segment intersects the boundaries of f and g in a number of points that must be ordered linearly and that then partition the line (p, q) into intervals. Each interval is classified as being outside of f or in f, and, likewise, as being outside of g or in g. Since p is on the boundary of f and q is on the boundary of g, there is some interval with one endpoint that is an intersection of the line (p, q) with the boundary of f, and the other endpoint that is an intersection with the boundary of g. We pick the first such interval encountered, scanning the intervals in order beginning at p. There are four possible classifications of this interval, as shown in Table 3.1. Associated with each is a position of the two faces relative to each other. Figures 3.7 and 3.8 illustrate the four cases, with the interior as implied by the orientation of the bounding cycles.

Test	Example	Action
in f, in g	f and g intersect	both components are kept
in f, out g	g is contained in f	the g component is kept
out f, in g	f is contained in g	the f component is kept
out f, out g	f and g do not intersect	neither component is kept

Table 3.1   Containment Classification for f and g

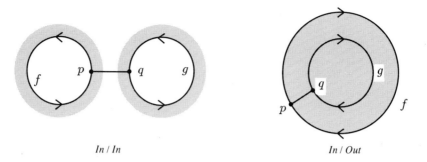

Figure 3.7   The Classifications "in *f*, in *g*" and "in *f*, out *g*"

The interval classification is essentially the same operation that was done in the intersection-point pairing along the line $P \cap Q$ described previously. As with that operation, care has to be exercised when the segment (p, q) intersects a boundary at a vertex.

Now consider testing the possible containment of two solids A and B whose boundaries do not intersect. In spirit, we proceed exactly as for faces, selecting a point p on the surface of A and a point q on the surface of B, and connecting these two points with a line segment. As before, the intersection of (p, q) with the boundaries of A and B induces an interval partition, and the individual intervals are again classified as being inside or outside of the solids. Again, Table 3.1 governs the outcome of the test, based on the first interval encountered, going from p to q, that is bounded by an intersection with the boundary of A and an intersection with the boundary of B.

The classification of intervals in the solid case is more complicated, however, and we explain it further. Conceptually, it is an analysis of the neigh-

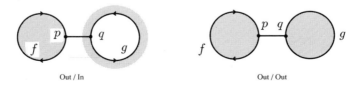

Figure 3.8   The Classifications "out *f*, in *g*" and "out *f*, out *g*"

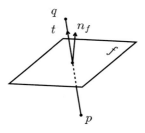

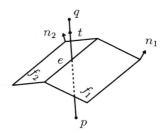

Figure 3.9   Classification for Face
Interior

Figure 3.10   Classification for Edge
Interior

borhood of the intersection points. Thus, it is easiest for interior face points, more complicated for interior edge points, and hardest for vertices.

First, if the segment intersects in the interior of a face f of A, then the direction vector $t = \overline{(p,q)}$ is compared in angle against the face normal n_f of f. If the angle is less than 90° — that is, if the dot product $n_f \cdot t$ is positive — then the interval preceding the intersection is in A, and the interval succeeding it is outside of A. Otherwise, the preceding interval is outside, and the succeeding interval is inside, of A; see also Figure 3.9.

Next, assume that (p, q) intersects at the interior of an edge e of A. Here we must determine whether t and $-t$ split volume-enclosing pairs. That is, if t splits a volume-enclosing pair of the faces adjacent to e, then the succeeding interval is inside of A. If not, it is outside of A. The same analysis of the vector $-t$ classifies the preceding interval with respect to A; see also Figure 3.10. Note that both t and $-t$ must be classified.

Finally, assume that (p, q) intersects at the vertex u of A. Here we must determine whether t, and $-t$, are in the interior of a solid cone defined by the faces incident to u. Since this neighborhood is not explicitly represented, we investigate the structure by intersecting it with a suitable plane. We pick a plane R that contains the line (p, q) and an interior point w of some face adjacent to u. Since u is in the plane R, the vertex appears on R as a point with lines radiating outward. Each line represents the intersection of some adjacent face of u with R.

The sectors defined by these lines are classified as inside or outside of A. Since R contains w, there is at least one nonempty sector. Then t and $-t$ are classified by the sector in which they lie. Accordingly, we now classify the interval on (p, q). See Figure 3.11 for an illustration of the process.

Since the classification is fairly complex and expensive for vertex intersections, we may wish to choose a different point q to avoid this case. Thus, it is a good idea to choose p and q to lie in the interior of faces. Although this does not guarantee that all other intersection points are located favorably,

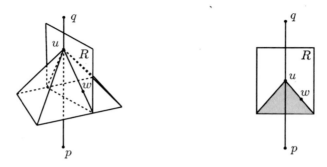

Figure 3.11   Classification for Vertex Intersection

subsequent random perturbations of the positions of p and q will usually succeed in creating well-behaved intersections everywhere. Typically, one or two perturbations suffice.

Recall from Section 2.4 that the connected components of the boundary of a multishell solid should be consistently oriented. The shell-containment test just described can be used to test whether the components are consistently oriented. It is not difficult to prove that two components are consistently oriented iff the containment test determines an "in/in" or an "out/out" classification.

3.4 Intersection of Two Shells

We consider first the intersection of two polyhedra, A and B, each with a surface consisting of a single shell. The intersection of multishell polyhedra will be considered subsequently. We conceptualize the process of intersection as follows:

1. Determine which pairs of faces $f \in A$ and $g \in B$ intersect. If there are none, test shell containment only and skip steps 2 through 4.

2. For each face f of A that intersects a face of B, construct the cross-section of B with the plane containing f. Then determine the surface area of $A \cap^* B$ that is contained in f.

3. By transferring the relevant line segments discovered in step 2, determine the faces of B that contain some of the surface area of $A \cap^* B$ and must be subdivided. Subdivide these faces, and by exploring the face adjacencies of B, find and add all those faces of B contained in the interior of A.

4. Assemble all faces so found into the solid $A \cap^* B$.

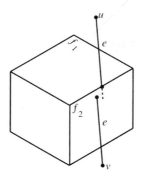

Figure 3.12   Locally Inconsistent Intersection Analysis

This conceptual structure is also suited to the curved-surface domain.

3.4.1 Robustness Considerations

A drawback of the organization just presented is its sensitivity to failure because of numerical imprecision. If step 2 considers each face of A independently, certain intersection structures may be inconsistently analyzed for adjacent faces. In consequence, the algorithm could fail for legitimate inputs.

    Example 3.3:   Figure 3.12 illustrates the problems numerical error could cause when implementing the proposed conceptual algorithm. We analyze whether and how the edge $e = (u, v)$ of B intersects two adjacent faces f_1 and f_2 of A. When considering these faces, the edge e is intersected with the respective face planes. When this is done independently, the intersection-point coordinates could have different precision. In consequence, it is possible that e will be judged to intersect the edge between f_1 and f_2 when considering face f_1, but that e will not be recognized to intersect the edge when considering f_2. This apparent inconsistency could cause a catastrophic failure of the implemented algorithm. $\diamondsuit$

    Similar robustness problems are endemic to the following popular algorithm for Boolean operations. First, mark on the surface of A the curves in which B intersects A. Then, reverse the roles of A and B, and repeat this step. Thereafter, assemble the surface of $A \cap^* B$ by adjacency exploration. This method is attractive because it reduces the programming effort. However, the independent subdivision of the surfaces of A and B gives many opportunities for inconsistencies due to numerical error. Thus, this paradigm is also not robust.

We refine the conceptual structure of our algorithm with the goal of achieving local consistency and avoiding problems such as the one illustrated in Figure 3.12. Our strategy is to avoid asking the same geometric question more than once. That is, all intersection information is immediately posted to all adjacent faces:

1. Determine which pairs of faces $f \in A$ and $g \in B$ intersect. If there are none, then do a shell-containment test only and skip steps 2 through 4.

2. For each intersecting pair of faces, f of A and g of B, construct the points and curves in which they intersect. For each intersection, analyze the three-dimensional neighborhood and transfer its elements to all adjacent faces of A and of B.

3. By exploring the face adjacencies of A and of B, find and add all those faces of either solid that are in the interior of the other.

4. Assemble all faces into the solid $A \cap^* B$.

3.4.2 Intersecting-Pairs Determination and Shell Containment

We elaborate on step 1 of the algorithm, detecting pairs of intersecting faces. The obvious method for determining whether the face $f \in A$ intersects the face $g \in B$ is actually to intersect these faces. Since all face pairs would be so tested, there is no hope that the algorithm could perform well in those situations where A and B have many faces but only a few of them actually intersect. Instead, it is convenient to enclose each face in a box whose sides are parallel to the coordinate planes, and to ask whether the box containing f intersects the box containing g. If the boxes do not intersect, then the faces cannot intersect. If the boxes do intersect, then the faces may or may not intersect, and we continue with the remaining steps.

There is an $O(n \log^2(n) + J)$ algorithm for intersecting the boxes, where n is the number of boxes and J is the number of intersecting box pairs found. Since J may be quadratic in n, we cannot improve the worst-case running time for polyhedral intersection, but we can significantly improve the average running time. A box-intersection algorithm with this time performance is described later in this chapter.

Since box intersection can determine only that two faces do not intersect, we may arrive at a situation where some boxes intersect, yet later in step 2, we determine that the surfaces of A and B do not intersect after all. In this case, we must run the shell-containment test following step 2.

Assuming that the surfaces of A and B do not intersect, we distinguish four possibilities:

1. The surface of $A \cap^* B$ consists of both the surface of A and the surface of B.

2. $A \cap^* B = B$.

3. $A \cap^* B = A$.

4. $A \cap^* B$ is empty.

These four situations are precisely the four possibilities of the line/solid classification, discussed previously, corresponding, respectively, to "in A, in B," "in A, out B," "out A, in B," and "out A, out B."

3.4.3 Face Intersection and Neighborhood Analysis

Having found all candidates of intersecting face pairs, we proceed to step 2 of the algorithm and construct their intersection. Although this step is conceptually not hard, the details tend to get in the way. Moreover, it requires intermediate data structures that are incomplete edge and face subdivisions. Conceptually, we repeat the following tasks for the intersecting faces f of A and g of B:

1. Construct and analyze the points and line segments of their intersection.

2. Transfer the results to all adjacent faces of A and of B.

3. Link up the intersection elements into complete face and edge subdivisions.

After this operation has been performed for all intersecting faces, we know implicitly the surface area of $A \cap^* B$ that lies on the surface of A and of B, except the faces of A that lie inside B and the faces of B that lie inside A.

Example 3.4: Consider the intersecting boxes A and B shown in Figure 3.13. Four faces of B and one face of A are subdivided in the process of face-pair intersection. In the end, we have discovered five of the six faces bounding $A \cap^* B$. The sixth face is discovered in a later step of the algorithm. The important point is that, when intersecting the faces f and g, both f and g are subdivided by a line segment. A technical difficulty is that the intersection line segment introduced on f does not yet define a valid subdivision of f. The subdivision of f is completed only after f has been intersected with four faces of B. $\diamondsuit$

Determining and Placing Intersecting Elements

Let g be a face of B that we suspect intersects the face f of A. We intersect the bounding edges of g with the plane P containing f. Excluding for the moment the case that g is contained in P (i.e., that every edge of g is contained in the plane), the edges will intersect P in a number of points that lie on a line l. The line l is the intersection of the plane Q containing g and the plane P. If an edge e of g is contained in P but g is not, then

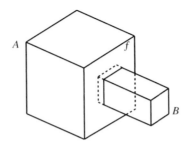

Figure 3.13   Two Intersecting Boxes

the vertices of e are considered the intersection points of the edge with
P. The intersection points are sorted along l and are paired as described
previously. Thereafter, we intersect the line l with f, obtaining a second set
of segments. The two sets are then intersected, and the resulting segments
are placed on f, g, and, possibly, other adjacent faces, as appropriate.

If f and g are in the same plane, then they must be intersected as
polygons. The result area is on the surface of $A \cap^* B$, provided both faces
have the same orientation. If the faces have opposite normals, then $f \cap g$
will be a lower-dimensional structure that is eliminated by regularization.
See Figure 3.14 for an example.

The intersection of f and g consists of line segments and points. Seg-

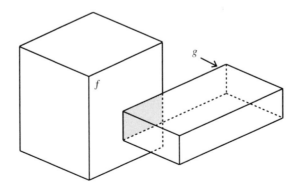

Figure 3.14   Coplanar Faces with Opposite Orientation

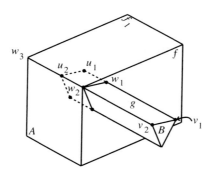

Figure 3.15   Placing Points and Segments

ments are either edges or edge segments, or they represent the intersection of two face interiors. Note that there may be isolated vertices. Points and lines both are analyzed. In particular, the points bounding a segment are analyzed, as is the segment interior. The results of this analysis are

1. The placement of oriented segments on faces

2. The segmentation of edges

3. The placement of certain points on faces and edges

4. The creation of adjacency constraints between points and segments

Placing points on an edge defines a segmentation of the edge. Segments so defined may have to be refined later, when other points on the edge are discovered.

Example 3.5:   Consider Figure 3.15, assuming that the faces f and g are intersected first. Here, the segment (w_1, w_2) is placed on f in the orientation (w_2, w_1) and on g in the opposite orientation. The edge (u_1, v_1) of g is subdivided by placing the point w_1 on it. The resulting segment (u_1, w_1) would have to be further subdivided if another face of A intersected it. This is not the case in the figure. Similarly, the segment (u_2, w_2) is created by placing w_2, and is not further subdivided later.

Now assume we intersect next the faces f_1 and g. Then the edge (u_2, v_2) of g is collinear with the edge (w_3, w_2) of f_1. Both edges are subdivided by placing the segment (w_2, u_2). Here we know that the segment cannot be further subdivided, since the two edges overlap. On g, the segment is placed in the orientation (w_2, u_2), consistent with the orientation in which g uses the edge (u_2, v_2). An analysis of the three-dimensional neighborhood

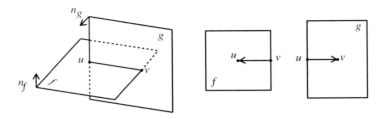

Figure 3.16   Line-Segment Orientation

reveals, moreover, that the segment should not be placed on f_1, since the area of f_1 adjacent to the segment lies in the exterior of B. ◇

Segment Orientation

A segment that is placed on a face f represents part of the boundary of the intersection $A \cap^* B$. It will be oriented such that the interior of the face of $A \cap^* B$ bounded by it is locally to the right. The correct orientation is deduced from the orientation of the two face planes. Figure 3.16 shows a simple example. In some cases, two oriented line segments are placed on f, indicating that the final bounding cycle of edges is degenerate.

3.4.4 Neighborhood Analysis

To analyze the intersection of face pairs, we consider the three-dimensional neighborhoods of the intersection line segments and points in the subdivision. We recall that the interior and the endpoints of a segment must be analyzed. There are six major cases, indexed by the intersecting structures:

1. A face of one solid intersects the face of another solid at a point interior to both.

2. An edge of one solid intersects a face of the other solid at a point interior to both edge and face.

3. An edge of one solid intersects an edge of the other solid at a point interior to both edges.

4. A vertex of one solid intersects a face of the other solid in the interior.

5. A vertex of one solid intersects an edge of the other solid in the interior.

6. A vertex of one solid intersects a vertex of the other solid.

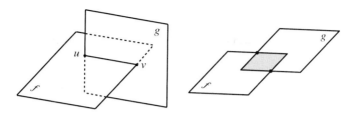

Figure 3.17   Face/Face Intersection

All cases exhibit a conceptual similarity in that the progression from face to edge and then to vertex entails similar processing, but involves more and more faces.

Face/Face Intersection

The generic case arises from a transversal intersection of two faces, shown on the left in Figure 3.17. The segment (u, v) generates two oriented line segments, one on f, the other on g. The orientation is computed from face normals. See also Figure 3.16. The interior of (u, v) will be only on f and on g, but the endpoints require further analysis as described later, and this analysis involves additional faces.

For the degenerate case, arising when f and g are in the same plane, we analyze the interior of a region by comparing the face normals. Normals of equal direction mean that the area is on the surface of $A \cap^* B$. Normals of opposite direction mean that the area is not on the surface of $A \cap^* B$. See also Figure 3.16.

Edge/Face Intersection

Assume that the edge $e = (u, v)$ of B intersects the interior of the face f of A. Ordinarily, the edge intersects the face in one point, as shown in Figure 3.18 on the left. We assume this point is in the interior of f. The edge is subdivided by w. There must be a segment of e, bounded by w, that lies inside A. Whether this segment is contained in (u, w) or in $\overline{(w, v)}$ is determined by computing the dot product of the direction vector $\overline{(u, v)}$ and the face normal n_f. We also know that the faces of B adjacent to e all intersect f, so we must make sure that the respective segments are recognized as adjacent to w.

In the degenerate case, the edge e lies in the plane of f, as shown in Figure 3.18 on the right. The edge is then subdivided by the boundary

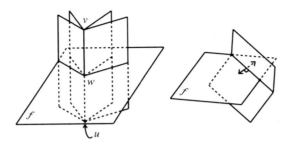

Figure 3.18   Edge/Face Intersection

of f into a number of segments. These segments must be transferred to f and to all faces g adjacent to e. Transfer and orientation is determined as follows.

For the face f, we consider vectors perpendicular to e in the plane of f, in each direction. We ask whether these vectors split a volume-enclosing pair of faces adjacent to e. If so, the segment is transferred to f with the appropriate orientation. In consequence, f receives zero, one, or two directed lines for each segment of e contained in f. Figure 3.19 shows an example in which two segments of opposite orientation are transferred.

Next, consider the face g adjacent to e. By computing the dot product of the face direction vector of g with the normal of f, we determine whether g extends locally into the interior of A. If so, every segment of e is transferred to g, in the same orientation as e has on the boundary of g. Otherwise, no segment is transferred. See also Figure 3.20.

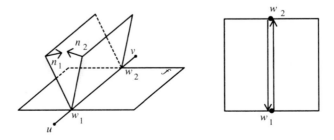

Figure 3.19   Transfer for Degenerate Edge/Face Intersection to f

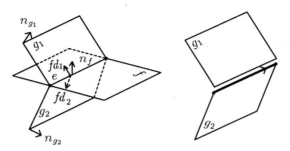

Figure 3.20   Transfer for Degenerate Edge/Face Intersection to g_i

Edge/Edge Intersection

Assume that edge e of A intersects edge e' of B. In the generic case, shown on the left of Figure 3.21, the edges intersect in a single point w that subdivides both edges. This case can be considered as several edge/face intersections, one for each face f adjacent to e. At most two of these cases can be degenerate. Thereafter, we determine whether e and/or e' contain segments bounded by w that lie in the interior of the other solid. This requires the line/solid classification described previously.

The degenerate edge/edge intersection case arises when the two edges are collinear and overlap, as shown in Figure 3.21 to the right. The case generalizes degenerate edge/face intersection. The segment of overlap is transferred in the appropriate direction to each of the adjacent faces whose face direction vector(s) split a volume-enclosing pair of faces of the other solid. See also Figure 3.22.

Figure 3.21   Edge/Edge Intersection

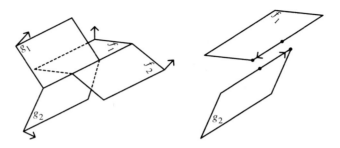

Figure 3.22   Transfer for Degenerate Edge/Edge Intersection

Vertex/Face Intersection

When a vertex u is in the interior of a face f, we have to satisfy adjacency constraints. Figure 3.23 shows an example. The faces g_k adjacent to u may intersect f in segments that must be incident to u. In addition, certain edges incident to u will extend into the interior of f. They are determined by computing dot products, and define edge segments interior to the other solid. Note that such segments may be further subdivided, as discussed before. Here u plays the role of w in the edge/face intersection analysis.

Vertex/Edge Intersection

Assume that vertex u of A intersects the interior of edge e of B. This case is conceptually a collection of vertex/face intersections, one for each face adjacent to the edge. The analysis of which edges of u extend into the interior of B is more complicated and is done as described in the edge/edge

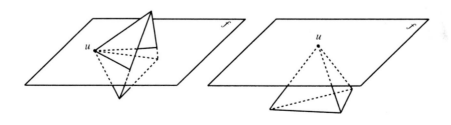

Figure 3.23   Vertex/Face Intersection

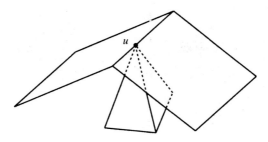

Figure 3.24   Vertex/Edge Intersection

intersection analysis. In addition, the edge $e = (v, w)$ is subdivided by u, and we need to determine whether the segments (v, u) and (u, w) extend into the interior of A. See also Figure 3.24.

Vertex/Vertex Intersection

Assume that vertex v of A coincides with vertex u of B, as in Figure 3.25. We determine all edges incident to u that extend into the interior of B and, conversely, all edges incident to v that extend into the interior of A. This is essentially a line/solid classification; see Section 3.3.4. However, since the line is induced by the position of the intersecting solids, we cannot simplify the classification procedure by perturbing its position. In addition, we must make sure that all intersection segments of adjacent faces are incident to u and v.

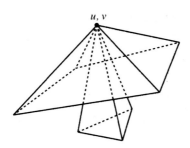

Figure 3.25   Vertex/Vertex Intersection

3.4.5 Face Subdivision

We have placed points and line segments subdividing edges and faces. We think of the points and segments as vertices and edges of a graph. We continue to refer to the graph vertices as points and to the graph edges as segments, to distinguish them from the edges and vertices of A and B. The purpose of neighborhood analysis has been to embed the graph consistently on both surfaces, and to obtain correct incidences at its points. After all face pairs have been intersected, the graph has the following properties:

1. If (u, v) is a segment that is not a complete edge, then the incidences at the points u and v are completely known.

2. If (u, v) is a segment and the incidences at u are not completely known, then u is a vertex of, say, A, and the missing incidences at u are initial segments of all edges of A incident to u.

Property 1 follows from the neighborhood analysis. For property 2, observe that (u, v) must be an edge of A that is included in the graph because v intersects the surface of B and (u, v) extends into the interior of A. Since (u, v) is not subdivided further, no other point of it can intersect the boundary of B. Hence the vertex u must be an interior point of B. Let (u, w) be any edge of A. Since u is in the interior of B, either (u, w) is contained in B, or an initial segment (u, w_1) of it is in B. In the latter case, the point w_1 is an intersection with the surface of B, and has already been discovered.

Thus, we can subdivide all faces of A and of B that intersect the boundary of the other solid by exploring the subgraph consisting of all points and segments contained in f, adding, when needed, undivided edges (u, w) of f adjacent to a vertex u that is not a point in the subgraph:

1. Initialize a list L of all points in f.

2. If L is empty, stop. Otherwise, initialize the stack S to contain a point u in L.

3. If S is empty, return to step 2. Otherwise, pop u from S and delete it from L. Mark u as explored.

4. Let E_1 be the set of all segments incident to u contained in f. If u is not a point, then let E_2 be all edges of f not containing a point; otherwise, E_2 is empty.

5. Order the edges and segments in $E_1 \cup E_2$ cyclically about u in the plane of f, and construct area-enclosing pairs.

6. For each (u, w) or (w, u) in $E_1 \cup E_2$, stack w if it is unexplored. Then return to step 3.

When the exploration is finished, we have a complete subdivision of f from which we obtain faces of $A \cap^* B$ by organizing into cycles the segments and edges considered and determine how they may be nested. Note that the algorithm is organized as a depth-first search.

3.4.6 Adjacencies in the Result

After completion of step 2, we are now ready to find the missing faces of $A \cap^* B$. The missing faces are those faces of A that are in the interior of B, and, vice versa, the faces of B that are in the interior of A. They are found by considering edge adjacencies.

We recall from the neighborhood analysis that the face adjacencies of each segment must be known, since at least one point of the segment is on the boundary of one of the solids. Hence, missing faces are precisely those faces that are edge adjacent to an undivided edge (u, w), added in the face-subdivision phase just described, or faces that are vertex adjacent to an undivided edge (u, v) that is a segment with u not being a point. Again, by exploration of the adjacency structure, all such faces can be found:

1. Let F_1 be the set of all faces of $A \cap^* B$ constructed by the subdivision given previously, and mark them as unprocessed. Set F_2 to the empty set.

2. If all faces in $F_1 \cup F_2$ have been processed, then stop. We have found all faces of $A \cap^* B$.

3. For all unprocessed faces f in $F_1 \cup F_2$, mark f as processed. For each edge (u, v) of f where u is not a point, add to F_2 all faces incident to u in A or in B that have not been subdivided, and mark them as unprocessed.

Note that F_2 accumulates all faces of A and of B that are contained in the interior of the solid. When implementing the algorithm, it is useful to remember which vertices u have already been considered, to avoid redundant processing.

3.4.7 Single-Shell Intersection Summary

By analyzing the three-dimensional neighborhoods of face-pair intersections, we have found segments and points making up the curves of intersection. The complete neighborhood analysis implies that the graph is consistently embedded on the two surfaces, and that the adjacencies have been correctly determined, except for certain adjacencies that are inherited from the boundary cycles of the faces. Considering each face intersecting the boundary of the other solid, we have completed the graph and have constructed a consistent subdivision of those faces of each solid that are not completely in the interior of the other solid. Finally, by considering certain undivided edges, we completed the surface of $A \cap^* B$, adding those faces that are completely in the interior of the other solid.

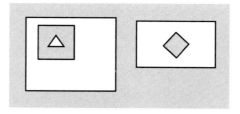

Figure 3.26   A Multishell Polyhedron in Two Dimensions

3.5 Multishell Objects

In general, a multishell polyhedron A consists of several disjoint polyhedra $P_1, P_2, \ldots P_m$. At most one of these polyhedra has infinite volume, and the remaining ones have finite volume, since we required that solids have a finite, bounded surface. Figure 3.26 illustrates this in two dimensions.

Consider the infinite polyhedron P_1. It fills the entire space except for a finite number r of voids that contain the remaining polyhedra $P_2, \ldots P_m$. Each void is bounded by a shell S that, taken separately, bounds a single-shell infinite polyhedron; see also Figure 3.27. Moreover, the forest of shell trees of A contains r trees, each root representing one of the voids of P_1. We think of such a polyhedron as the intersection of r single-shell polyhedra with disjoint shells.

The finite polyhedra P_i are bounded by an *exterior*, positive shell and may have internal voids in turn. Again, we think of each polyhedron as the intersection of several single-shell polyhedra. One of them, bounded by the external shell, has finite volume. The others are of infinite volume and are bounded by the shells of the internal voids.

We therefore write $A = P_1 \cup P_2 \cup \ldots \cup P_m$, where each component is the intersection of single-shell polyhedra. Likewise, $B = Q_1 \cup Q_2 \cup \ldots \cup Q_r$. Since the P_i are pairwise disjoint, as are the Q_i, the intersection of A and B is

$$A \cap^* B = (P_1 \cap^* Q_1) \cup (P_1 \cap^* Q_2) \cup \ldots \cup (P_1 \cap^* Q_r) \cup (P_2 \cap^* Q_1) \cup \ldots \cup (P_m \cap^* Q_r)$$

Each intersection $C_{ik} = P_i \cap^* Q_k$ is the intersection of a set of single-shell polyhedra. Moreover, the polyhedra C_{ik} must be disjoint; thus, their union is trivially determined. It follows that the intersection of multishell polyhedra reduces to the simultaneous intersection of several single-shell polyhedra.

Figure 3.27   Polyhedron as Intersection of Single-Shell Polyhedra

Now it is simple to modify the single-shell intersection algorithm to intersect more than two shells at once, because the algorithm makes no essential use of the fact that the surface of single-shell polyhedra is connected, except for the conclusion that two shells either intersect or else must be analyzed with a shell-containment test. In the more general setting, therefore, the algorithm is run as before, subdividing the appropriate faces of intersecting shells and merging these shells through surface exploration. Thereafter, we consider the remaining, nonintersecting shells, classifying them by the shell-containment test, adding or deleting shells as required.

3.6 Complement, Union, and Difference

To complement an object, we must reverse the surface orientation. This is done as follows:

1. Multiply each face equation by -1, thereby inverting the orientation of the face interior.

2. Reverse the orientation of every boundary vertex cycle of a face.

3. Change the pairing of volume-enclosing pairs by moving it over by one entry, reverse the edge direction, and reverse the cyclic order of adjacent faces. Thus, the pairing $((a, b), (c, d))$ in the cyclical order (a, b, c, d) is changed to $((a, d), (c, b))$.

The forest of shell trees is modified by complementing at each node the indication of whether the shell at that node encloses finite or infinite volume. Note that complementation takes time proportional to the size of the boundary representation; that is, it is linear in the number of faces.

To compute the union of two objects, we apply de Morgan's law and compute instead $\neg(\neg A \cap^* \neg B)$. The difference $A -^* B$ is computed as $A \cap^* \neg B$.

3.7 Face-Boxing Techniques

An *iso-oriented box* is a parallelepiped whose sides are parallel to the coordinate planes. We seek a fast algorithm for reporting all intersecting pairs among a set of iso-oriented boxes, so as to reject as nonintersecting certain face pairs in polyhedral intersection. For each face, the smallest iso-oriented box is used that completely contains the face. For a planar face, the box is found by determining the maximum and minimum coordinates of the vertices of the face, and each box can be specified as three intervals, $[x_0, x_1]$, $[y_0, y_1]$, $[z_0, z_1]$, that specify the extreme coordinate values. The algorithm developed here solves the following problem:

> **Problem**
> Given n iso-oriented boxes, report in $O(n \log^2(n) + J)$ steps all intersecting pairs of boxes, where J is the number of pairs reported.

First, we develop the algorithm by considering one- and two-dimensional versions. In the two-dimensional case, we seek a fast algorithm for reporting intersections among iso-oriented rectangles. This problem can be solved in $O(n \log(n) + J)$ steps, as can the one-dimensional interval-intersection problem.

After giving an $O(n \log(n) + J)$ algorithm for rectangle intersection, we then develop an $O(n \log^2(n) + J)$ algorithm for the same problem. Although slower, this algorithm then allows us to intersect boxes within the same time bound. Various data structures will be needed, and these are explained first.

3.7.1 The Static Interval Tree

This section develops an algorithm for the interval-intersection problem:

> **Problem**
> Given a set S of intervals $I_1, ..., I_n$ of the real line, store them in a data structure such that, for any given query interval Q, we can determine all intervals in S that intersect Q. Moreover, the time needed to find the intersecting intervals is proportional to $\log(n)$ and to the number of intersecting intervals.

This problem is *static* in the sense that the set S is fixed. Eventually, the solution is adapted to a situation in which the set S changes, thus solving a *dynamic* version of the problem. This change will be easy after the static solution has been understood.

The algorithm for interval intersection uses a tree as basic data structure, to direct the search for intersecting pairs. The nodes of the tree are annotated with various additional data structures. The underlying tree will be called a *range tree*. After suitable embellishments, we obtain from it an *interval tree*. We explain the structure and construction of these trees in stages. The algorithm will integrate these stages.

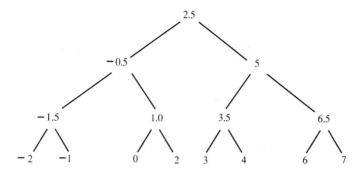

Figure 3.28 Range Tree T

Assume that the intervals are given as the pairs of numbers

$$[a_1, b_1], \ldots, [a_n, b_n]$$

The range tree T carrying the interval information is a binary tree whose leaves are the distinct values a_k and b_k, in ascending order. Let u be an interior node of T, with left subtree T_1 and right subtree T_2. Then the node u contains a number x that lies between the maximum leaf value in T_1 and the minimum leaf value in T_2. This number is called the *split value* of u, and will be denoted $\texttt{split}(u)$.

Example 3.6: Assume we have intervals $I_1 = [-1, 6]$, $I_2 = [-2, 3]$, $I_3 = [0, 4]$, $I_4 = [2, 7]$, $I_5 = [3, 4]$, and $I_6 = [-2, -1]$. The range tree T is shown in Figure 3.28. As split values, we have chosen the arithmetic mean of the maximum and minimum leaf values in the left and right subtrees, respectively. $\diamondsuit$

Recall that the half-open interval $(x, y]$ is the set $\{z | x < z \le y\}$. Each node in the tree represents a half-open interval $(x, y]$ of the real line, called its *range*. The tree root represents the half-open real line $(-\infty, \infty]$. Let u be a node in the tree representing the range $(x, y]$, and assume that $\texttt{split}(u) = s$. Then the left child of u represents the range $(x, s]$, and the right child represents the range $(s, y]$. In the preceding example, the root represents the range $(-\infty, \infty]$. The left child, with split value -0.5, represents the range $(-\infty, 2.5]$, and the right child, with split value 5, represents the range $(2.5, \infty]$. The interior node with split value 3.5 represents the range $(2.5, 5]$.

Given a set S of intervals, the range tree is easy to construct: Sort all interval endpoints in ascending order into a list $L = (x_1, x_2, \ldots, x_m)$, where

$m \leq 2n$. For L we construct a range tree top-down by splitting L into two lists of equal size, $L_1 = (x_1, \ldots, x_p)$ and $L_2 = (x_{p+1}, \ldots, x_m)$, where $p = \lceil m/2 \rceil$. The tree's root has the split value $(x_p + x_{p+1})/2$. The left and right subtrees are now constructed from L_1 and L_2, respectively, in the same way. Note that the range-tree construction requires $O(n \log(n))$ steps.

At the nodes of the range tree, we store the intervals of S. The interval $[a, b]$ is stored at the unique node u satisfying the following:

1. $[a, b]$ is contained in the range of u.

2. $[a, b]$ contains `split`(u), but does not contain the split value of any ancestor of u.

All intervals at u are stored in two lists, with the left endpoints in the list `left_search`(u), sorted in ascending order, and the right endpoints in the list `right_search`(u), sorted in descending order.

Example 3.7: In the range tree of Example 3.6, the intervals I_1, I_2, I_3, and I_4 are all stored at the tree root, the interval I_5 is stored at the node with split value 3.5, and the interval I_6 at the node with split value -1.5. $\diamondsuit$

The intervals are stored in the tree in two phases. In the first phase, the left search lists are constructed. Then, by an obvious modification, the right search lists are constructed.

1. Sort all intervals of S by the left endpoint a_k in ascending order into a list L.

2. Propagate the list down into the tree, beginning at the root.

3. At each node u, break the incoming list L into the lists L_1, L_2 and L_3, where L_1 contains the intervals $[a, b]$ with $b <$ `split`(u), L_2 contains the intervals containing `split`(u), and L_3 contains the intervals $[a, b]$ with `split`$(u) < a$.

4. Propagate the list L_1 to the left descendant of u, propagate the list L_3 to the right descendant of u, and store the intervals in L_2 at u.

The list L is split by sequentially scanning it. Each entry in it is scanned once at each node at which the containing list is considered. Thus, it is scanned at most $\log(n)$ times. Therefore, all intervals are added to the range tree in $O(n \log(n))$ steps.

Recall that in a *preorder* traversal of a binary tree, the root of a subtree is visited, followed by its left and right subtrees being visited. By applying this rule recursively, beginning with the root of the tree, all nodes are visited in *preorder*.

The data structure, as developed, is not sufficiently flexible. The problem, briefly, is that the intervals may be clustered at very few tree nodes, so

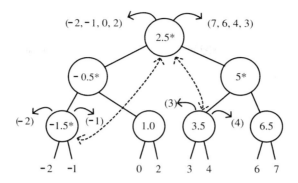

Figure 3.29   Interval Tree T

locating nodes with stored intervals may require too much searching. Thus, we link all nodes containing stored intervals in a doubly linked list. In this list, the nodes are in preorder. Furthermore, each tree node is marked if it, or any descendant of it, contains stored intervals. It is clear that these annotations can be added in $O(n \log(n))$ steps. After we add these annotations, we have now constructed an *interval tree*. The interval tree for the intervals of the example is shown in Figure 3.29. The node marks are represented by asterisks. The doubly linked list of nonempty tree nodes is shown by dashed arrows.

3.7.2 Static Interval Query

The problem of static interval query is solved using an interval tree. Let S be the set of intervals, $Q = [a, b]$ the query interval. We construct an interval tree for S.

In the interval tree, we identify a node set P, consisting of all nodes u whose range has a nonempty intersection with the query interval but is not completely contained in Q. We also identify a set C of nodes each of whose range is contained in Q. Since, at each level in the tree, the set of represented ranges is a partition of the root range, the set P has at most two nodes at each depth, and consists of three paths, P_1, P_2, and P_3. Here P_1 consists of all nodes whose ranges contain Q. The path P_1 begins at the root and ends at the node u_1 whose split value is in Q; the path P_2 consists of all nodes whose range contains the left endpoint a of Q, but not all of Q; and the path P_3 consists of all nodes whose range contains the right endpoint b of Q, but not all of Q. Figure 3.30 shows these node sets schematically. Note that the nodes of C are in subtrees rooted in right descendants of nodes in P_2, or in subtrees rooted in left descendants of

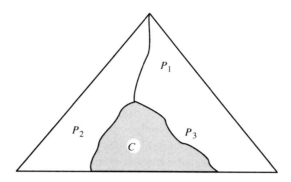

Figure 3.30   Node Sets Used for Querying for Interval Intersection

nodes in P_3. If the query interval is a point (i.e., if $a = b$) then the sets P_2, P_3, and C are empty.

Example 3.8:   Let $Q = [2, 5.5]$ be a query interval to be tested against the intervals I_1 through I_6. In the interval tree of Figure 3.29, the root is the only member of the set P_1, since its split value is in Q. The set P_2 consists of the nodes with split value -0.5 and 1, and the leaf labeled 2. The set P_3 consists of the nodes with split value 5, 6.5, and the leaf labeled 6. The set C contains only those nodes in the subtree whose root has split value 3.5. $\diamondsuit$

The overall structure of the algorithm for reporting all intersections with the query interval is now as follows:

1. Construct an interval tree for S.

2. Identify the path P_1.

3. Identify the paths P_2 and P_3.

4. By processing the path nodes and their descendants appropriately, identify all intersecting intervals.

Step 2 is performed as follows. With u initially the tree root, identify the path P_1 by selecting the left (resp., right) descendant of u provided the split value $s = \mathtt{split}(u)$ satisfies $b < s$ (resp., $s < a$). We continue until we encounter the first node u_1 whose split value is contained in the interval Q.

At u_1, we initiate construction of P_2 and P_3. The path P_2 begins at the left descendant of u_1 and is identified as follows. At node u, select the left (resp., right) descendant of u as the next node provided that $a \leq \mathtt{split}(u)$ (resp., $a > \mathtt{split}(u)$). The path P_3 begins at the right descendant of u_1. To identify the remaining nodes, pick at node u the left (resp., right) descendant provided that $b \leq \mathtt{split}(u)$ (resp., $b > \mathtt{split}(u)$). For degenerate query intervals $[a, a]$, the paths P_2 and P_3 are empty. In this case, care must be exercised if $a = \mathtt{split}(u)$ for an interior node u.

We now discuss how to identify intersecting intervals along the paths P_i, $i = 1, 2, 3$. Let u be a node on one of the paths and $s = \mathtt{split}(u)$. If $s < a$, then an interval stored at u intersects Q iff its right endpoint y satisfies $a \leq y$. Hence, by scanning the right endpoints of intervals stored at u, in descending order, we identify all intersecting intervals in time proportional to their number. If $b < s$, then an interval at u intersects Q iff its left endpoint x satisfies $x \leq b$. These intervals are found by scanning the left endpoints in ascending order, in time proportional to their number. Finally, if s is in Q, then all intervals at u intersect Q.

The nodes in C are in subtrees rooted in right descendants from nodes in P_2, and in left descendants of nodes in P_3. They are characterized by the fact that the range represented at any node in C is completely contained within Q. Hence, all intervals stored at such nodes will intersect Q. For the sake of speed, we must avoid searching through all nodes of these subtrees. Intuitively, we find the first node in the set C that contains intervals, using the node marks. To do so, we examine the nodes in P_2, beginning at the leaf and ending at the left descendant of u_1, until we find a marked node that has a marked right descendant not contained in P_2. If no such node can be found, we try the analogous procedure with the nodes in P_3, beginning at the right descendant of u_1 and ending at the leaf, searching for a left descendant not in P_3. If no such node can be found, then C contains no intervals. Otherwise, we have found the leftmost node in C that contains intervals. The remaining nodes in C containing intervals are found by following the linked list. It is not difficult to see that the entire procedure requires $O(n \log(n))$ steps for constructing the interval tree, plus $O(\log(n) + J)$ steps to report all intersections, assuming J intervals intersect Q.

3.7.3 Rectangle Intersection

We are given a set of rectangles whose intersecting pairs we want to find. Each rectangle is given as the pair of intervals $[x_0, x_1] \times [y_0, y_1]$, the rectangle's projection on the x and y axis, respectively. The algorithm will use interval intersection as one of its operations.

Rectangle intersection will be based on the *line-sweep paradigm*: By sweeping a line that is parallel to the x axis, in increasing y direction, any intersecting rectangle pair must appear as an intersecting pair of x intervals. These intervals are the intersection of the rectangles with the line. As the line sweeps upward, the interval $[x_0, x_1]$ of the rectangle $[x_0, x_1] \times [y_0, y_1]$ appears at the line position y_0, and disappears at the line position y_1.

We sort the numbers x_i and build an interval tree from them that initially

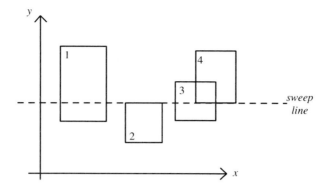

Figure 3.31   Interval Insertion During Rectangle Intersection

does not contain any stored intervals. In this way, we will be able to store each interval at some time during rectangle intersection. Next, we sort the numbers y_i in ascending order, and consider them in sequence. For each particular number y, we have a set of rectangles $[x_0, x_1] \times [y, y_1]$ beginning at y, and another set of rectangles $[x'_0, x'_1] \times [y_0, y]$ ending at y.

The beginning rectangles define a set of x intervals that must be inserted into the interval tree. Before insertion, each of these intervals is tested for intersection with the intervals already in the tree. Intersecting intervals correspond to rectangle intersections. Thereafter, the x intervals of ending rectangles are deleted from the tree. It is clear that the outlined algorithm is correct, and that it does not report an intersecting pair of rectangles more than once. Moreover, rectangle intersection can be reported quickly, based on the algorithm for interval intersection, provided we can insert and delete intervals efficiently.

Example 3.9: In Figure 3.31, we are at a y position at which we must insert the interval I_4 corresponding to rectangle 4, and delete the interval I_2 corresponding to rectangle 2. Before deleting I_2, we use I_4 as query interval and report all intersections. Then we delete I_2 and insert I_4. $\diamond$

To support quick interval insertion and deletion, we must modify the `left_search` and `right_search` lists, organizing them as balanced search trees rather than as lists. These trees must support logarithmic-time insertion and deletion, and they must allow linear-time sequential access to the stored values in sorted order. For example, a 2-3 tree will satisfy these requirements.

An interval $Q = [a, b]$ is inserted as follows: The interval is added to the node u_1 that is last in the path P_1. Note that P_1 was found as part of finding all intervals in the tree that intersect Q. Insertion into the `left_search` and right_search trees is routine. If there are already intervals stored at u_1, we are now done. Otherwise, we must update the linked list of nonempty tree nodes and, possibly, the node marks on the path from u_1 to the tree root. Clearly, updating the node marks is trivial.

Recall how to visit the nodes of a binary tree in *inorder*. Beginning at the root of the tree, a node v is visited as follows: If v is a leaf, then visit it; otherwise, visit recursively all nodes of the left subtree, then visit v, and finally visit the nodes of the right subtree. The order in which the tree nodes are encountered is called inorder.

To locate where to insert u_1 into the list of nonempty tree nodes, we search for the first nonempty node succeeding u_1 in inorder. This node is found using the node marks. If u_1's right descendant u_R is marked, then the needed nonempty tree node is found by exploring the leftmost marked path beginning with u_R. If that node is not marked, we must back up toward the root until we find a marked ancestor who is not empty or whose right descendant is not in P_1 and is marked. Clearly, locating this node requires no more than $O(\log(n))$ steps.

Now consider deleting an interval Q. We first find the node u_1 at which the interval is stored, and delete its endpoints from the search structures unless other intervals at u_1 share that endpoint. If Q was the only interval at u_1, we must delete u_1 from the linked list of nonempty nodes, and, possibly, delete the node mark of u_1 and some of its ancestors. Because the node list is doubly linked, node deletion is simple.

In summary, we have shown that intervals can be inserted and deleted in time proportional to $\log(n)$. In consequence, intersections among a set of n rectangles can be reported in $O(n \log(n) + J)$ steps, where J is the number of intersecting pairs. The simplicity of the algorithm makes its implementation quite practical.

3.7.4 The Segment Tree

The rectangle-intersection algorithm described previously is based on dynamic interval intersection. In principle, a similar extension to three dimensions is possible: Sweep a plane in the z direction and test, at certain positions, whether there are intersections among the rectangles in which the boxes intersect the sweep plane. We do not use the $O(n \log(n) + J)$ rectangle intersection for this purpose, since the recursive line sweeps for finding intersecting rectangles would consume too much time. Instead, we develop a more flexible data structure that supports rectangle intersection without a line sweep. This data structure is called a *segment tree*, and is an annotated balanced binary search tree, recording a set of intervals.

We are given n intervals $[a_k, b_k]$ with distinct endpoints c_i, where $1 \leq i \leq m$ and $m = 2n$. We assume that the c_k are enumerated in ascending order. The underlying binary search tree has $2m + 1$ leaves representing,

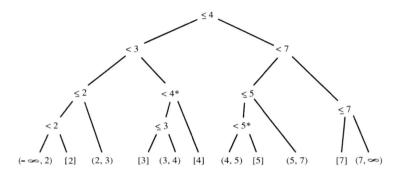

Figure 3.32   Segment Tree T_{seg}; Nodes Storing [3,5] Are Marked with Asterisks

from left to right, the partition of the real line induced by the endpoints.

$$(-\infty, c_1), [c_1], (c_1, c_2), [c_2], \ldots, [c_m], (c_m, +\infty)$$

The tree is constructed in much the same way as the range tree. Like the range tree, the interior nodes have split values to support binary search, only now we must indicate, at each node, whether the left descendant is chosen if the query value is less than, or not greater than, the split value. An interior node represents a segment that is the union of the segments of its descendants. We store an interval $I_k = [a_k, b_k]$ in this tree at a node u provided I_k contains the range of u but not the range of u's ancestor. When we have completed this annotation, we have constructed a segment tree. Note that I_k can be stored at more than one tree node, but not at more than $2h$ nodes, where h is the tree height. The ranges at which a given interval is stored are a partition of the interval. It is not difficult to see that a segment tree can be constructed in $O(n \log(n))$ steps.

    Example 3.10:   The segment tree for the intervals $I_1 = [2,3]$, $I_2 = [5,7]$, $I_3 = [2,4]$, and $I_4 = [3,5]$ is shown in Figure 3.32. The interval [3,5] is stored at the two nodes marked with asterisks. ◇

    Now consider the problem of locating all those intervals in a set S that contain a query point q. We proceed as follows. From S, we construct a segment tree. Using this tree as a binary search tree, we locate the leaf in whose range q lies. Clearly, all intervals stored at the nodes on the path from the tree root to the leaf containing q will contain q. Furthermore, since leaves represent disjoint segments, no other interval of S can contain q. Note also that no interval stored along the path is repeated. Therefore, all containing intervals can be found in $O(\log(n) + J)$ steps, ignoring the time for constructing the segment tree.

3.7.5 Interval, Rectangle, and Box Intersection

In the one-dimensional case, we are given a set S of n intervals and $Q = [a, b]$, the query interval. We observe that an interval Q' in S intersects Q iff one of the following is true:

1. a is in Q'.

2. The left endpoint of Q' is in the half-open interval $(a, b]$.

We will need two search structures, one for each intersection criterion.

The first search structure is a segment tree T_{seg} for the intervals in S. The second search structure is a balanced binary search tree T_{bin}, built with only the left endpoints of intervals in S. Let x be a left endpoint of an interval in S, and l be the leaf at which x is stored. Then we store the interval belonging to x at every node of the path from the root to l. Thus, at each interior node u, we have stored all intervals whose left endpoints are the leaves of the subtree rooted in u.

We test interval intersection as follows. All intervals intersecting Q by the first criterion are found by searching T_{seg} for the intervals containing a. To find intersections by the second criterion, we locate in T_{bin} the search paths for a and for b. The intervals at the point of path bifurcation intersect Q by the second criterion, excluding those intervals that have the left endpoint a. Since the two intersection criteria are mutually exclusive, we have found all intersecting intervals without duplication. Clearly, the trees can be constructed in $O(n \log(n))$ space and time. So, $O(\log(n) + J)$ steps suffice to report all intersections with a query interval.

Example 3.11: Figure 3.33 shows the segment tree for the interval set S of Example 3.10, and Figure 3.34 shows the binary search tree. Assume a query interval $Q = [4, 6]$. The search of the segment tree with the left endpoint 4 ends at the leaf [4]. So, the intervals I_3 and I_4 intersect Q by the first criterion. Next, we search the tree T_{bin} with the arguments 4 and 6. The search paths bifurcate at the leaf labeled 5; hence, the interval I_2 intersects Q by the second criterion. $\diamondsuit$

Now consider locating all those rectangles in a set S that intersect the query rectangle $Q = [x_0, x_1] \times [y_0, y_1]$. The rectangles in S define a set of y intervals and a set of x intervals. We proceed as follows. For the y intervals, we construct the trees T_{seg} and T_{bin}. Consider the rectangles that correspond to a set of y intervals to be stored at each node in these trees. They induce, for each node u, a set of x intervals X_u. With X_u, we construct at each u a *nested* pair of trees $T_{seg}(u)$ and $T_{bin}(u)$.

We use these data structures as follows. With the y interval $[y_0, y_1]$, we locate all intersecting y intervals induced by S. Then, we solve separately

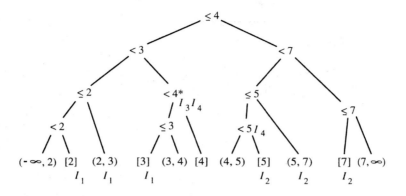

Figure 3.33   Segment Tree T_{seg} with Intervals

the intersection problem for $[x_0, x_1]$ at each node. Clearly, we thus identify all intersecting rectangles.

Let S contain n rectangles. To understand space and time requirements, we recall that each interval is stored at no more than $O(\log(n))$ different nodes, in each tree. Thus, there are $O(n \log(n))$ x intervals for which we construct the nested pairs of trees initially. From this, it follows that the needed data structures can be built in $O(n \log^2(n))$ space and time, and that the query time for reporting all intersections with the query rectangle is $O(\log^2(n) + J)$.

Finally, consider box intersection. We can build a doubly nested data structure, or adopt the sweep paradigm. The first approach yields an $O(n \log^3(n) + J)$ box-intersection algorithm; the second one yields the slightly faster $O(n \log^2(n) + J)$ method. In the sweep paradigm, we now have to enter and delete rectangles dynamically into the nested tree pairs. This can be done in a manner analogous to that used for the dynamic version of the interval tree.

3.7.6 Red-Blue Intersection

When enclosing faces with iso-oriented boxes, the boxes enclosing adjacent faces will intersect. However, intersections among boxes enclosing faces of the same polyhedron are not of interest. We discuss a way of excluding such intersecting pairs.

Given the polyhedra A and B, we color the boxes enclosing faces of A red, and color boxes enclosing faces of B blue. The *red-blue intersection* problem is to report intersecting pairs of red and blue boxes without spending time on finding, and ignoring, blue-blue and red-red intersecting pairs. Clearly,

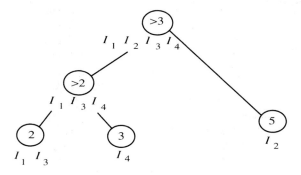

Figure 3.34   Search Tree T_{bin} with Intervals

rectangle and interval intersection have analogous problem variants. We solve the red-blue box intersection problem using the static version of box intersection. Briefly, from the set of blue boxes we construct the needed data structures. Then, we use the red boxes to query the blue data structure for intersection. The details are straightforward, as are the details for red-blue rectangle intersection, and for red-blue interval intersection.

3.7.7 Implementation Remarks

Some form of box intersection should be incorporated into every solid modeler. However, many asymptotically fast algorithms have a considerable start-up cost and are intricate to program. Thus, simpler versions may be contemplated. For example, it may suffice to implement only rectangle intersection and to accept the lower resolution of nonintersecting face pairs. In our experiments, this strategy was satisfactory.

If we replace the balanced search trees at the nodes of the dynamic interval tree with lists, the programming required is further reduced. In small applications, there is no appreciable running-time difference. However, when many intervals are stored at the same node, then this simplification spoils the performance of the algorithm. Ultimately, the attractiveness of these compromises depends on the mix of applications.

The box-intersection algorithm is somewhat harder to implement than is rectangle intersection based on line sweep. Moreover, the segment tree appears to be less robust because of the many leaves that represent point intervals. For this reason, the boxes to be tested for intersection should be enlarged by a small tolerance ϵ. This will make box intersection robust.

3.8 Notes and References

The conceptual topological data structures explained in Section 3.2 have been designed for convenience of accessing various adjacencies. Irredundant representations will store less information. See Weiler (1986) for a study of irredundant topological data structures. Irredundancy of the geometric data is motivated by robustness considerations. As mentioned, geometric irredundancy for curved solids might not be cost-effective, but perhaps an attractive alternative would be to annotate the data structures with *approximate* geometric data to be made precise by a suitable numerical computation when needed.

Boolean operations on polyhedra in B-rep have been implemented many times. Descriptions include Braid (1975), Hillyard (1982), Mäntylä (1986), Okino et al. (1973), Voelcker et al. (1974), and Wesley et al. (1980).

The brief description in Requicha and Voelcker (1985) stresses the important role of local neighborhood analysis. The description does not assume manifold boundaries. Mäntylä (1988) describes an intersection algorithm in considerable detail, but restricts himself to manifold solids. Moreover, his algorithm is based on a symmetric design in which the role of A and B is interchanged for the purpose of face subdivision; hence, one should expect robustness problems. Chiyokura (1988) describes a similar algorithm, also restricted to manifold polyhedra. Both methods use Euler operators to implement surface subdivision.

Paoluzzi et al. (1986) describe a polyhedral modeler for which all faces must be triangles. Although the surfaces topologically are manifolds, surface structures may coincide geometrically. Thus, the algorithm must disambiguate the topology in the manner described in Section 2.3.1 of Chapter 2. Laidlaw et al. (1986) describe a method in which all faces must be convex polygons, but the solid surfaces need not be manifolds. By carefully observing properties of convex polygons, their algorithm attempts to increase local robustness. However, no global processing is done to ensure consistency of the resulting surface structures, and they experience algorithm failures for certain inputs. The observation that two or three random perturbations suffice to eliminate complicated vertex intersection cases in line/solid classifications is due to Laidlaw et al. (1986).

Hoffmann, Hopcroft, and Karasick (1987) and Karasick (1988) describe an algorithm based on the conceptual structure discussed at the beginning of Section 3.4. For robustness purposes, the algorithm was subsequently modified, adding a form of local neighborhood analysis to achieve a consistent subdivision of adjacent faces. The processing is somewhat more complicated, because the underlying structure of the algorithm requires more special-case processing than the version we give here. However, the Karasick modeler also includes *global* consistency computations that explore the consequences of, say, nonincidence between a vertex v and a face f along a path of edges beginning at v. See Karasick (1988) for a detailed description.

Euler operations are often mentioned as a conceptual infrastructure with which to implement higher-level geometric operations, including solid intersection. In our view, operations such as line/solid classification or sorting and pairing points along a line should also be considered part of the infrastructure. Implementing the placement of points and segments with help of Euler operations has the advantage that at all times A and B have valid boundary description. However, the orientation information needed to later interpret points and segments as part of face subdivisions would require extensions to Euler operations or a subsequent separate neighborhood classification. We prefer to combine this classification with the placement of points and lines, for robustness reasons.

Box intersection and related techniques are described in the computational geometry literature. Our description of these algorithms follows Mehlhorn (1984). Many of the technical concepts in that section are standard in the literature on algorithms. See, for example, Aho, Hopcroft, and Ullman (1974) for tree traversals, balanced binary search trees, and other basic techniques. The method to solve the red-blue version of the problem was suggested to me by M. Sharir. Rectangle intersection was implemented by J. Sasaki in 1986 for the Karasick modeler. Karasick (1988) reports that it speeds up polyhedral intersection to almost an $O(n \log(n))$ behavior when intersecting several hundred randomly positioned cubes.

CHAPTER 4

Robust and Error-Free Geometric Operations

Despite much work and great advances in geometric and solid modeling, practical implementations of geometric modeling operations remain error-prone, and the goal of implementing correct, efficient, and robust systems for carrying them out has not yet been attained. This fact seems to originate from an underlying characteristic that sets geometric computations apart from other application areas in computer science and engineering. There is agreement that the problem is serious, but what strategy has the best chance of solving it is not agreed on. The difficulty seems to be rooted in the interaction of approximate numerical and exact symbolic data.

Geometric objects belong conceptually to a *continuous* domain, yet they are almost always analyzed by algorithms doing *discrete* computation. These algorithms typically treat a very large discrete domain — for instance, the set of all representable floating-point numbers — as though it were a continuous domain. This approach may lead to acceptable results in many cases, but it does not work in all situations. In particular, when implementing Boolean operations on solids in B-rep, the problem manifests itself in occasional failures of the implemented algorithm.

We now examine these problems in detail restricting attention to the linear case. Polyhedra and other piecewise linear geometric objects, in three dimensions, consist of points, edges and polygonal faces that are in specific spatial relationship to one another. The specification of such objects consists of two parts: numerical information, recording vertex coordinates or plane equations; and symbolic data specifying face and edge boundaries, adjacencies, and incidences.

Usually, the numerical data describing a geometric object are given only approximately, using floating-point numbers. In consequence, there may be imprecision that leads to contradictory information about the represented object. For instance, the representation may require that four adjacent faces meet in a common vertex, yet the numerical plane coefficients for the faces may specify four planes that intersect in four closely spaced points, rather than in a single point.

Most implementors are well aware of this imprecision and make allowance for it by suitably relaxing incidence tests. However, this approach does not succeed in all cases, because it is difficult to control the implications of approximate incidence tests. In particular, using limited-precision numbers often has the consequence that the outcome of a numerical computation is sequence-dependent and inaccurate. If the computation is to decide symbolic facts — for example, whether a vertex is incident to a face — the imprecision constitutes incomplete or erroneous information.

Geometric algorithms typically make many such decisions, and all decisions so made must be logically consistent, whether based on correct or incomplete information. This is not always a simple matter. For instance, the same decision can sometimes be determined by different computations that yield contradictory information. Given these possibilities, we must ask what it means for a geometric algorithm to be correct, and for it to deliver an acceptable result for all legitimate inputs.

4.1 Chapter Overview

Since the implementation of geometric algorithms is commonly based on floating-point arithmetic, we show in Section 4.2 some of the consequences that the various numerical inaccuracies can have. Even for line-intersection problems in the plane, floating-point errors may result in geometric contradictions that are usually not anticipated by the algorithm. As we demonstrate, these problems increase in seriousness when we iterate and/or compound geometric operations.

Polyhedral intersection can be implemented correctly when using fixed-precision rational arithmetic. Such implementations can achieve acceptable efficiency provided we correctly anticipate the needed internal precision at which all intermediate calculations are carried out, but they also necessitate reexamining some elementary operations that are commonly taken for granted. This approach is discussed in detail in Section 4.3.

We cannot understand the central core of the robustness problem unless we make a clear distinction between ideal Euclidian geometry and its discrete representation in the computer. In Section 4.4, we discuss this distinction by defining what constitutes a suitable *model* for a representation, and what might be a good *representation* for an ideal geometric object. In the discussion of these concepts, we will see that a recurrent theme in increasing robustness is to achieve consistent interpretations of noisy numerical data and computations. In this framework, we can distinguish several basic approaches to achieving robustness:

1. Restructure the algorithm such that all interpretations of noisy numerical data and computations are logically independent.

2. Make interdependent logical decisions by respecting the symbolic data exactly, but possibly perturbing the numerical data somewhat.

3. When making interdependent logical decisions, give priority to the numerical data, possibly altering the meaning of the symbolically represented topological problem data.

The first approach assumes that inconsistencies in the representation are probably not fatal unless they lead to contradictory topological conclusions. Thus, this approach tries to devise geometric algorithms in which, for example, an incidence determination is made by only one numerical computation, and all consequent incidences and nonincidences are explicitly recorded at that time. The algorithm of Chapter 3 for performing Boolean operations on polyhedra has been designed based on this concept.

Philosophically speaking, the second approach assumes that the symbolic data have, in principle, an exact representation, and so we should trust them implicitly. This approach is discussed in Sections 4.4.1 and 4.4.4. The technical problems entailed by this approach are how to interpret the numerical data consistently and how to limit the numerical perturbations needed to achieve this consistency.

The third approach, discussed in Section 4.4.5, tries to obtain smaller perturbations by altering the meaning of geometric elements such as lines. Roughly speaking, a line may be replaced by a curve, possibly piecewise linear, with certain properties, such as monotonicity in specific directions or a maximum deviation from a straight line. The technical challenges faced by the third approach include how to use the results of such an algorithm in subsequent geometric computations. Sections 4.5 and 4.6 summarize this material and give references to the literature.

4.2 Floating-Point Arithmetic

Geometric computations customarily use floating-point arithmetic, since it offers both efficiency and flexibility. However, floating-point arithmetic has a number of subtleties that need to be understood. Without a careful accounting for these subtleties, floating-point computations may be the source of unexpected program failure.

4.2.1 Numerical Errors in Floating-Point Arithmetic

A floating-point number consists of an *exponent* and a *mantissa*. Both are fixed-length integers, which implies that they constitute a discrete set of representable rational numbers. Three types of errors must be considered when analyzing the accuracy of floating-point numbers:

1. *Conversion errors*: Since input numbers are usually decimal, whereas the machine operates with binary numbers, we cannot always represent exactly the number desired. For example, the decimal 0.6 is equal to the periodic binary fraction 0.1001 1001... because $3/5 = \sum_{i=1}^{\infty} 9/16^i$.

2. *Roundoff errors*: Since $a \cdot b$ in general requires higher precision to represent exactly than does either a or b, the representation of the product may be inexact in the last represented digit. For example, with five-digit mantissas, the product $0.24665 \cdot 0.63994 = 0.1578412010$ would be rounded to 0.15784, thereby incurring an error of approximately $1.2 \cdot 10^{-6}$.

3. *Digit-cancellation errors*: The difference of two nearly equal numbers a and b has fewer significant digits than does either a or b. For instance, the difference of $0.90905 \cdot 10^2$ and $0.90903 \cdot 10^2$ is $0.20000 \cdot 10^{-2}$. Assuming a five-digit mantissa, 0.20000 clearly has only one significant digit, unless a and b happen to be exact numbers.

Moreover, if a geometric shape is expressed by means of a graphical user interface, it may not be possible to specify numerical data precisely.

Since geometric operations usually require extensive numerical calculations, the propagation of these errors is of great concern and influences the accuracy and validity of the geometric operations profoundly. We will demonstrate with several examples that elementary geometric computations are sensitive to such errors, and that elementary geometric conclusions can be invalidated in consequence.

4.2.2 Geometric Failures Due to Floating-Point Arithmetic

We discuss several ways in which a geometric algorithm may fail, assuming that the numerical computation is done using floating-point arithmetic. In the examples, we assume double-precision IEEE standard floating-point computation. The crucial fact is that the computation is carried out with limited-precision arithmetic. We can extend the precision to triple or quadruple precision. This has the effect of *narrowing* the range of inputs for which the geometric algorithm will fail, but it cannot eliminate such failures completely as long as a priori bounds are placed on the precision.

Many geometric questions of incidence can be answered by different sequences of numerical computation. The different sequences of computation are equivalent when exact arithmetic is used. When using floating-point arithmetic, however, these computations may yield different answers. The following examples illustrate this fact and show how it can affect solid modeling operations.

Incidence Asymmetry

Consider implementing a test of whether two points in the plane are equal. Specifically, assume that the point u is the intersection of the pair of lines (L_1, L_2), and that the point v is the intersection of the lines (L_3, L_4). The line equations are the input to the following algorithm:

1. Compute the coordinates of u.

2. By substitution into the line equations L_3 and L_4, conclude that $u = v$ if both $L_3(u)$ and $L_4(u)$ are smaller than some tolerance.

Intuitively, this algorithm ought to be equivalent to a second version in which the roles of u and v are reversed. We demonstrate that this need not be the case. We assume the following:

1. The intersection (u_x, u_y) of the lines

$$a_1 x + b_1 y + c_1 = 0$$
$$a_2 x + b_2 y + c_2 = 0$$

is computed as follows:

$$D = a_1 b_2 - a_2 b_1$$
$$u_x = (c_2 b_1 - c_1 b_2)/D$$
$$u_y = (a_2 c_1 - a_1 c_2)/D$$

2. The point (u_x, u_y) is assumed to lie on the line $ax + by + c = 0$ if the distance is small; that is, if $|au_x + bu_y + c| < \epsilon\sqrt{a^2 + b^2}$.

We assume $\epsilon = 10^{-10}$, a reasonable bound for double precision. We ask whether u and v are incident using two different methods:

1. Compute the coordinates of u; conclude that $u = v$ iff u is on both L_3 and L_4.

2. Compute the coordinates of v; conclude that $u = v$ iff v is on both L_1 and L_2.

The line coefficients follow. Since $2^{-23} \approx 10^{-7}$, they differ from 1 and 0 by amounts that are several orders of magnitude larger than ϵ.

$$
\begin{array}{lll}
a_1 = -1 & b_1 = 1 & c_1 = 0 \\
a_2 = -(1 + 2^{-23}) & b_2 = 1 - 2^{-23} & c_2 = 2^{-22} \\
a_3 = 1 & b_3 = 0 & c_3 = -(1 + 2^{-15}) \\
a_4 = 0 & b_4 = 1 & c_4 = -(1 + 2^{-15})
\end{array}
$$

These coefficients can be represented exactly in double precision. The coordinates of the points are now computed to be

$$
\begin{aligned}
u &= L_1 \cap L_2 &= (1.0, 1.0) \\
v &= L_3 \cap L_4 &= (1.000030517578125, 1.000030517578125)
\end{aligned}
$$

They are both exact. Moreover, since $(a_i^2 + b_i^2)$ is approximately between 1 and 2, the evaluation of the line equations after substituting point coordinates yields an error that can be compared directly with ϵ. We obtain the values

$$
\begin{aligned}
L_3(u) &\approx -3 \cdot 10^{-5} &> \epsilon \\
L_4(u) &\approx -3 \cdot 10^{-5} &> \epsilon
\end{aligned}
$$

from which we conclude that u cannot be incident to v, since it is too far from each of the lines whose intersection is v. But we also obtain

$$
\begin{aligned}
L_1(v) &= 0 &< \epsilon \\
L_2(v) &\approx -7 \cdot 10^{-12} &< \epsilon
\end{aligned}
$$

from which we must conclude that v is incident to u, since it lies extremely close to both lines. Therefore, although they ask the same geometric question, the two computations yield contradictory results.

Graphically, the situation is summarized in Figure 4.1. The bound ϵ conceptually defines a narrow band around each line L_i such that every point inside that band is considered to lie on L_i. In consequence, there is a diamond-shaped region enclosing each vertex w, the intersection of the two bands, such that every point inside the diamond region is considered coincident with w. Depending on how the two diamonds intersect, the vertices are considered coincident or not.

How does this asymmetry affect a solid modeler? Recall the problem of intersecting two solids, A and B, in boundary representation, and consider the following conceptual approach:

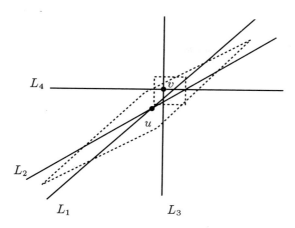

Figure 4.1   Vertex Incidence Regions

1. Mark on the surface of solid A the curves in which the surface of solid B intersects.

2. Reverse the roles of A and B and repeat step 1.

3. Construct the surface of $A \cap B$ by merging the relevant parts of the boundary of A and B.

This algorithm will decide every vertex/vertex incidence with two different computations that are the three-dimensional analogue of the preceding algorithms. Thus, a floating-point implementation will claim contradictory incidences on certain inputs A and B, and the curves marked on both solids will be incompatible in that case, causing the algorithm to fail.

Incidence Intransitivity

Consider introducing symmetry into the point-equality test by asking "is the distance between u and v smaller than a specific threshold?" using the following method:

1. Compute the coordinates of u and of v, by intersecting the respective lines.

2. If the Euclidian distance between u and v is smaller than ϵ, decide $u = v$; otherwise, decide $u \neq v$.

This method is symmetric, but it does not exhibit transitivity. Specifically, we choose the three points u, v, and w such that u is incident to v, v is

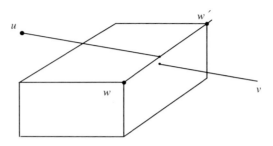

Figure 4.2   Topological Inconsistency When Intersecting Edges

incident to w, but u is *not* incident to w. We assume that epsilon is 10^{-10}.

$$u = (0,\, 0) \qquad v = (0,\, 0.8 \cdot 10^{-10}) \qquad w = (0,\, 1.6 \cdot 10^{-10})$$

Clearly, the distance between the adjacent pairs is less than ϵ, but the distance between u and w is greater than ϵ.

Assume we intersect two polyhedra, A and B, where one of the edges (u, w) of A is somewhat shorter than 2ϵ. Consider a position of B in which one of its vertices v is approximately in the middle of the edge. Having implemented the symmetric vertex incidence test, we are in the uncomfortable situation that v is incident to two different vertices of A.

Compensating for the intransitivity of point coincidence is difficult. A typical approach is to avoid the problem by requiring that no edge of a polyhedron is shorter than a specific tolerance δ. The magnitude of δ must be related to ϵ. In our example, $\delta > 2\epsilon$ is necessary. However, *every* pair of vertices, whether adjacent or not, must be separated by δ, and possible incidence computations among derived points — for example, edge/face intersections — may necessitate other such minimum-feature-size constraints. The resulting δ will depend on the details of the geometric operation, but the possibility of propagating errors makes it difficult to derive good values.

Topology Violations

The inaccuracy of numerical calculations has other implications for the validity of deduced geometric fact. In particular, when determining how the edges of two polyhedra intersect in three dimensions, we might deduce a configuration such as the one shown in Figure 4.2. When intersecting the edge (u, v) with the top face, we may well conclude that it is sufficiently

close to the edge (w, w'), due to large positional perturbations caused by
the shallow angle at which (u, v) intersects the top face. Now, when intersecting (u, v) with the side face, a more accurately determined point of
intersection can lead us to conclude that (u, v) does not intersect (w, w').
This inconsistency in incidence determination constitutes a violation of the
topology that is likely to cause trouble subsequently. Avoiding this problem
requires coordinating different incidence computations; for instance, as we
did in Chapter 3. As we will see later in this chapter, determining that all
decisions have been fully coordinated may be hard.

4.2.3 Line-Intersection Conditioning

As we have seen, the result of a floating-point computation may have considerable error, yet at other times it may be exact. It is not always possible
to quantify precisely how floating-point errors propagate in complex sequences of numerical calculations. However, a sensitivity analysis can be
performed that estimates the likely actual error. This analysis is based on
the following concept.

We assume that the result of a floating-point calculation is exact. But,
instead of being exact for the actual inputs to the computation, the results are exact for some other inputs that are a perturbation of the actual
ones. Intuitively, if a small input perturbation yields only a small change
in the result, it is reasonable to assume that such a calculation has only a
small error. If, on the other hand, small input perturbations — due, for
example, to roundoff — may result in large changes of the result, then the
computation is likely to have large errors in the result.

More precisely, if an input is changed by ϵ, the output changes by a
function $\delta(\epsilon)$. For small values of ϵ, there may exist a constant κ such that
$\delta(\epsilon) \approx \kappa\epsilon$. If κ is small, then $\delta(\epsilon)$ is small whenever ϵ is small, and we say
that the calculation is *stable* or *well conditioned*. If κ is large, then $\delta(\epsilon)$ is
large for small ϵ. In that case, we speak of an *unstable*, or *ill-conditioned*
calculation. The number κ is called the *condition number*.

Note that a calculation may be ill conditioned because of inherent sen-
sitivities of the problem to input perturbation, or because of the details of
the algorithm used. Although problem ill conditioning is unavoidable, we
may be able to circumvent ill-conditioned computations by redesigning the
algorithm.

Numerical analysis has developed many stable algorithms. Nevertheless,
the propagation of numerical errors cannot always be kept small, since the
sensitivity to input perturbations depends in part on the nature of the
problem. As an example, we analyze the condition number of the problem
of determining the intersection of two lines in the plane. Intuitively, we
expect that the intersection can be determined with good accuracy when
the lines intersect at nearly a right angle, and we expect poor accuracy for
lines that intersect at angles close to zero or 180°.

Finding the intersection of two lines involves matrix inversion. Given the lines

$$a_1 x + b_1 y + c_1 = 0$$
$$a_2 x + b_2 y + c_2 = 0$$

we invert the matrix

$$A = \begin{pmatrix} a_1 & b_1 \\ a_2 & b_2 \end{pmatrix}$$

Matrix inversion has been studied extensively in numerical analysis, and the *condition number* of a matrix A measures the sensitivity of the inverse A^{-1} to perturbations in the entries of A. So, the accuracy with which the matrix can be inverted can be estimated by the condition number of A.

The condition number of a matrix can be calculated from the norm of the matrix and its inverse. A *matrix norm* is a function f that maps the matrix A to a nonnegative real number with the following properties:

1. $f(A) = 0$ iff A contains all zeros.

2. If A and B have the same dimension, then $f(A + B) \leq f(A) + f(B)$.

3. For any real number u, $f(uA) = |u| f(A)$.

The *infinity norm* of the $n \times n$ matrix A is

$$\| A \|_\infty = \max_{1 \leq i \leq n} (\sum_{j=1}^{n} |a_{ij}|)$$

The condition number of A is given by

$$\kappa = \| A \|_\infty \| A^{-1} \|_\infty$$

We derive the condition number of the matrix A in terms of the angle between the two lines.

It is not hard to see that the matrices

$$\begin{pmatrix} a_1 & b_1 \\ a_2 & b_2 \end{pmatrix} \quad \text{and} \quad \begin{pmatrix} da_1 & db_1 \\ ea_2 & eb_2 \end{pmatrix}$$

have the same condition number, with $d, e \neq 0$. So, we may assume that the matrix is

$$A = \begin{pmatrix} \cos(\alpha) & -\sin(\alpha) \\ \cos(\alpha + \beta) & -\sin(\alpha + \beta) \end{pmatrix}$$

where α is the angle between the x axis and the first line, and β is the angle between the two lines. The inverse of A is

$$A^{-1} = -\frac{1}{\sin(\beta)} \begin{pmatrix} -\sin(\alpha + \beta) & \sin(\alpha) \\ -\cos(\alpha + \beta) & \cos(\alpha) \end{pmatrix}$$

So, we can estimate $\| A \|_\infty \leq 2$ and $\| A^{-1} \|_\infty \leq 2/\sin(\beta)$, assuming $\beta < 180°$. Therefore,

$$\kappa \leq \frac{4}{\sin(\beta)}$$

This estimate shows that the system is well conditioned for angles β close to 90°, and is ill conditioned for angles close to 0° or 180°.

Under extremely favorable circumstances, we expect a perturbation of the input coefficients of order 2^{-t}, where t is the mantissa length, due to roundoff in the last representable digit. For small angles β, we have $\sin(\beta) \approx \beta$. Hence, for an intersection angle of $1/2^m$, we expect to lose about $m + 2$ binary digits.

We demonstrate the loss of precision due to small perturbation; for example, due to roundoff. Assume that the line intersection (u_x, u_y) is computed as before:

$$\begin{aligned} D &= a_1 b_2 - a_2 b_1 \\ u_x &= (c_2 b_1 - c_1 b_2)/D \\ u_y &= (a_2 c_1 - a_1 c_2)/D \end{aligned}$$

We consider the pair of lines:

$$-x + y = 0$$
$$-(1 + q)x + (1 - q)y + 2q = 0$$

With $q = 1/2^m$ and $m > 5$, these lines intersect exactly in the point $(1, 1)$, at an angle q of less than 1°. Moreover, as long as m does not exceed the mantissa length, the coefficients are exact in floating-point representation. With these coefficients, the intersection point $(1, 1)$ is determined without error by floating-point arithmetic. We then perturb the coefficients by

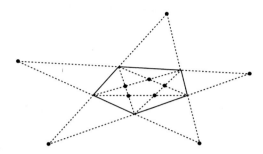

Figure 4.3   *going in* and *going out* Operations

$p = 1/2^t$, choosing t to machine precision. Specifically, we solve the following perturbed system, expected to lead to the largest deviations with a coefficient error no greater than machine precision:

$$-(1 + p)x + (1 - p)y = 0$$
$$-(1 + q - p)x + (1 - q + p)y + 2q = 0$$

With $q = 1/2^{18}$, the two lines intersect at approximately 1 arc second, resulting in a condition number of 2^{20}. So, we expect to lose about 20 significant binary digits when perturbing the system by machine precision, corresponding roughly to 6 decimals. Double-precision arithmetic carries approximately 16 decimals in a mantissa of 53 bits. The computation for the unperturbed system yields exactly $(1.0, 1.0)$. The perturbed system yields the point $(1 + 3 \cdot 10^{-11}, 1 + 3 \cdot 10^{-11})$ for $t = 53$, in good agreement with predictions.

It is important to remember that the conditioning of line intersection is inherent in the problem, not in the specific algorithm. Some algorithms will do consistently better than others by avoiding, where possible, computations that incur larger perturbations. However, only exact arithmetic will always handle ill-conditioned intersections accurately, provided the input data are not corrupted.

4.2.4 Compound Geometric Operations

A specific difficulty with geometric computation is that we want to subject a geometric object to several operations in sequence. That is, the output of one computation becomes the input to the next. In this situation, precision losses in one operation may accumulate, and may be magnified by subsequent operations. We consider a simple geometric problem that demonstrates this phenomenon.

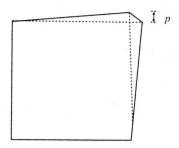

Figure 4.4   Example Pentagon

Consider a pentagon P in the plane. We draw the five diagonals of P; their intersections define a contained, smaller pentagon Q. Let us call the operation of passing from P to Q *going in*, and write symbolically $Q = in(P)$. Similarly, we extend the five sides of P to their intersections, thus obtaining a larger pentagon Q' that contains P. We call this operation *going out*, and write $Q' = out(P)$. Clearly, $P = out(in(P))$ and $P = in(out(P))$; see Figure 4.3. Beginning with P, let us iterate the *going in* operation m times, obtaining $Q = in^m(P)$, and then compute $P' = out^m(Q)$. Ideally, the coordinates of the vertices of P and of P' should be equal. In practice, they may differ by a large error, even for small values of m.

We take the pentagon with vertices at $(0,0)$, $(1,0)$, $(0,1)$, $(1+p,1)$, and $(1, 1+p)$, for small values of p; see also Figure 4.4. Table 4.1 shows the results, with all computations done in double precision. The table demonstrates dramatically that the numerical results from this simple geometric operation can be quite inaccurate.

To understand the reason for the poor accuracy, we must analyze the angles between intersecting lines as a function of p. In the first *going in*

p	$out^2(in^2())$	$out^3(in^3())$	$in^2(out^2())$	$in^3(out^3())$
0.1	$9 \cdot 10^{-14}$	$2 \cdot 10^{-12}$	$1 \cdot 10^{-14}$	$1 \cdot 10^{-13}$
0.01	$8 \cdot 10^{-12}$	$2 \cdot 10^{-9}$	$6 \cdot 10^{-13}$	$7 \cdot 10^{-11}$
0.001	$5 \cdot 10^{-10}$	$2 \cdot 10^{-6}$	$5 \cdot 10^{-8}$	$9 \cdot 10^{-8}$
0.0001	$5 \cdot 10^{-8}$	$1 \cdot 10^{-3}$	$5 \cdot 10^{-5}$	$2 \cdot 10^{-4}$
0.00001	$4 \cdot 10^{-7}$	$7 \cdot 10^{-1}$	$1 \cdot 10^{-1}$	$2 \cdot 10^{-1}$
0.000001	$2 \cdot 10^{-4}$	$7 \cdot 10^{-1}$	$1 \cdot 10^{+2}$	$5 \cdot 10^{+2}$

Table 4.1   Absolute Error for Iterating *going in* and *going out* Operations

operation, no angle is smaller than 45°. In the next *going in* operation, angles as small as $\tan(p)$ arise; in the third operation, angles diminish to approximately $\tan(p^2)$. So, with small values for p, the composite condition number for computing $out^2 in^2(P)$ is proportional to $1/p^3$. Hence, in the column labeled $in^2(out^2())$, we expect the error to grow at least with 10^3, and this is confirmed by the experiments.

4.3 Exact Rational Arithmetic

Given the accuracy problems of floating-point arithmetic, it is tempting to use exact numbers throughout. For geometric objects with linear elements, the most natural choice is to use rational numbers. As we saw in the case of the pentagon problem, however, the iteration of geometric operations can result in an unbounded growth of the digits we need to represent. For this reason, we must limit the numerical precision by defining a grid of representable planes beforehand.

We now study an exact approach to polyhedral intersection based on limited precision rationals. After discussing the grid of representable points, lines, and planes, we explain the details of polyhedral intersection in this framework. To maintain correctness, however, simple operations such as translation and rotation must be considered carefully, since they require approximating points and planes that are not necessarily directly representable. We conclude with a discussion of some of the strengths and weaknesses of this approach.

4.3.1 The Grid of Representable Elements

Consider polyhedra in which the face equations are given numerically, and all other information is symbolic. Thus, vertices are defined as the intersection of three distinct planes, and lines containing edges as the intersection of two distinct planes. A plane equation has the form

$$ax + by + cz + d = 0$$

where a, b, c, and d are integers. We bound the magnitude of the coefficients by requiring that $-L \le a, b, c \le +L$, where L might be $2^{48} - 1$. Moreover, d is bounded by the square of L, as $-L^2 \le d \le L^2$.

The rationale for bounding the constant coefficient d differently is shown in Figures 4.5 and 4.6, for two dimensions. In Figure 4.5, all coefficients are bounded uniformly. We see that the resulting grid is less uniform than is the grid of Figure 4.6, obtained by bounding d as explained previously. When computing with projective point coordinates (x, y, z, w),[1] then these bounds become uniform.

---

[1] See Section 5.2 in Chapter 5.

Figure 4.5   Grid of Lines $ax + by + c = 0$, Where $|a|, |b|, |c| < 3$

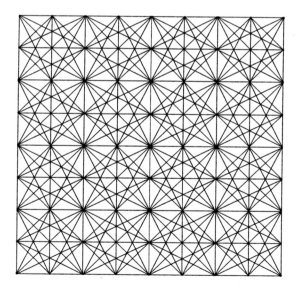

Figure 4.6   Grid of Lines $ax + by + c = 0$, Where $|a|, |b| < 3$, and $|c| < 9$

Since the projective point (x, y, z, w) corresponds to the affine point $(x/w, y/w.z/w)$, when $w \neq 0$, each point coordinate and each plane coefficient is then an integer of magnitude at most L.

4.3.2 Boolean Operations

We are given two polyhedra with exact plane equations. When we perform regularized Boolean operations on them, the faces bounding the result will be contained in the faces of the input polyhedra. It follows that the set of equations needed to specify the geometric position of the result polyhedron is a subset of the equations of the input polyhedra. Thus, it is always possible to represent the result of Boolean operations provided the input polyhedra are representable, and there will be no growth in the precision of the numerical data.

When examining the algorithm in Chapter 3, we see that the numerical calculations needed to construct the result polyhedron are all reducible to testing whether a point u, given as the intersection of the planes P_1, P_2, and P_3, is above, on, or below a plane P_4. This test can be implemented as follows. Let $P_i = a_i x + b_i y + c_i z + d_i = 0$, and $i = 1, 2, 3, 4$. The coordinates of the intersection $u = (u_x, u_y, u_z)$ can be computed from the following expressions:

$$D = \begin{vmatrix} a_1 & b_1 & c_1 \\ a_2 & b_2 & c_2 \\ a_3 & b_3 & c_3 \end{vmatrix}$$

$$U_x = - \begin{vmatrix} d_1 & b_1 & c_1 \\ d_2 & b_2 & c_2 \\ d_3 & b_3 & c_3 \end{vmatrix}$$

$$U_y = - \begin{vmatrix} a_1 & d_1 & c_1 \\ a_2 & d_2 & c_2 \\ a_3 & d_3 & c_3 \end{vmatrix}$$

$$U_z = - \begin{vmatrix} a_1 & b_1 & d_1 \\ a_2 & b_2 & d_2 \\ a_3 & b_3 & d_3 \end{vmatrix}$$

as

$$u_x = U_x/D$$
$$u_y = U_y/D$$
$$u_z = U_z/D$$

Thus, the point u will be above, on, or below the plane P_4 iff the expression

$$a_4 u_x + b_4 u_y + c_4 u_z + d_4$$

is greater than, equal to, or less than zero, respectively. Multiplying by D, this expression becomes

$$a_4 U_x + b_4 U_y + c_4 U_z + d_4 D$$

which is the development of the determinant

$$J = \begin{vmatrix} a_1 & b_1 & c_1 & d_1 \\ a_2 & b_2 & c_2 & d_2 \\ a_3 & b_3 & c_3 & d_3 \\ a_4 & b_4 & c_4 & d_4 \end{vmatrix}$$

However, since D may be negative, we must correlate the signs of J and of D. Thus, u is above P_4 iff J and D both have the same sign; it is below P_4 iff J and D have opposite signs. The point u is on P_4 iff $J = 0$.

Example 4.1: Consider the intersection $u = (1, 1, 1)$ of the three planes $P_1 : x - 1 = 0$, $P_2 : y - 1 = 0$, and $P_3 : 1 - z = 0$. Given the plane $P_4 : x + y - z = 0$, we test whether u is above, on, or below P_4. The determinant J evaluates to -1, so u is not on P_4. Moreover, the determinant D is -1, so u is above P_4. $\diamond$

The evaluation of J requires summing products of the form $a_i b_j c_k d_l$. Each product is bounded by L^5, and there are at most 24 such products; hence, the magnitude of J can be bounded by $24L^5$. If the precision bound L is expressed in terms of l binary digits, then this means that performing Boolean operations requires $5l + 5$ binary digits for all intermediate computations.

4.3.3 Rigid Motions

If a grid plane is rotated or translated, it is clear that the resulting plane may not be representable. For example, when rotating the plane $z = 0$ about the x axis by $30°$, we obtain the plane $ay + bz = 0$ with a coefficient ratio $a : b$ of $1 : \sqrt{3}$. Thus, this plane cannot be represented with integer coefficients. In consequence, we must investigate ways in which to perform these operations approximately, without violating the integrity of objects. In particular, a plane P that should be moved to a position Q' that is not representable must be moved instead to a nearby plane Q that is representable. We call this process *element rounding*. Throughout, we assume that every plane equation $ax + by + cz + d = 0$ is *reduced*; that is, there is no common factor dividing all four coefficients.

Translation

Consider the translation

$$
\begin{aligned}
x_1 &= x - t_x \\
y_1 &= y - t_y \\
z_1 &= z - t_z
\end{aligned}
$$

It maps the plane
$$P: ax + by + cz + d = 0$$
to the plane
$$P': ax_1 + by_1 + cz_1 + e = 0$$

where $e = d + at_x + bt_y + ct_z$. Since P is reduced, P' must also be reduced. Hence, P' is representable iff $|e| \leq L^2$. In that case, the translation is exact. Otherwise, the plane is not representable and must be rounded, as described later.

Rotation

Every rotation can be expressed as a sequence of rotations about the coordinate axes. We therefore restrict the discussion to a single rotation about the z axis. Rotations about the other coordinate axes are analogous. Such a rotation corresponds to a coordinate transformation of the form

$$
\begin{aligned}
x_1 &= ux - vy \\
y_1 &= vx + uy
\end{aligned}
$$

where $u^2 + v^2 = 1$; that is, $u = \cos(\alpha)$ and $v = \sin(\alpha)$. Without loss of generality, we assume that $-90° \leq \alpha \leq 90°$.

Given an angle α, u and v could be irrational. Therefore, we locate a nearby angle α' such that u and v are rational; that is, we seek a rational point (u', v') on the unit circle close to the point (u, v). A simple method for finding rational points on the circle is to use the rational parametric form of the circle, given by

$$
u' = \frac{1 - t^2}{1 + t^2}
$$

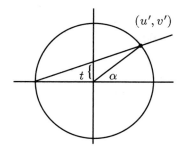

Figure 4.7   Parameter Interpretation of t

$$v' \;=\; \frac{2t}{1+t^2}$$

where we substitute a rational number for t. The parameter t has a geo-metric meaning, shown in Figure 4.7, and can be expressed in terms of α as $t = \tan(\alpha/2)$. From the rational approximation m/n of t, we obtain the rational point (u', v'), where

$$u' \;=\; \frac{n^2 - m^2}{n^2 + m^2}$$
$$v' \;=\; \frac{2nm}{n^2 + m^2}$$

on the unit circle. Using this point, the plane

$$P = ax + by + cz + d = 0$$

is thus transformed into the plane

$$P' = a'x_1 + b'y_1 + cz + d = 0$$

where $a' = au' - bv'$ and $b' = av' + bu'$. After clearing the denominator and reducing the equation, the resulting coefficients might exceed L in magnitude, and, if so, the plane must be rounded.

4.3.4 Rational Approximations

The operations of the previous section necessitate two types of approximations:

1. Given a positive real number w, find a rational number p/q approximating w such that q does not exceed a bound Q.

2. Given a plane equation $ax + by + cz + d = 0$, find a nearby plane equation that is representable; that is, find a plane $a'x + b'y + c'z + d' = 0$ with integer coefficients such that $|a'|, |b'|, |c'| \leq L$, and $|d'| \leq L^2$.

As we shall see, the techniques for approximating a real number can be used for the second problem also.

Rational Approximations of a Real Number

Let w be a positive real number. We wish to approximate w by a rational number p/q such that $q \leq Q$. We exclude exhaustive search, since it takes time proportional to Q, and hence is too slow in practice.

The first method will simply use $q = Q$. Let $p = [wQ]$ be the closest integer to wQ. Then the rational p/Q is an approximation of w. Moreover, since $|wQ - [wq]| \leq 0.5$, the error in this approximation is bounded by $1/(2Q)$. We call this the *naive* approximation method. For example, with $w = 0.123$ and $Q = 100$, we obtain the approximation $12/100 = 3/25$, with a total error of 0.003. Note that the approximation can be constructed in constant time.

The second method uses continued fractions to approximate w. The *continued-fraction representation* of a positive real w is an infinite sequence of integers $(k_0, k_1, k_2, ...)$ such that w is the limit of *convergents* u_i of the form

$$u_0 = k_0, \qquad u_1 = k_0 + \frac{1}{k_1}, \qquad u_2 = k_0 + \cfrac{1}{k_1 + \cfrac{1}{k_2}},$$

$$u_3 = k_0 + \cfrac{1}{k_1 + \cfrac{1}{k_2 + \cfrac{1}{k_3}}}, \qquad \cdots$$

Given a positive real number w, the following algorithm constructs the continued-fraction expansion of w:

1. Set $r_0 = w$ and $k_0 = \lfloor w \rfloor$.

2. Repeat the following for $i = 1, 2, ...$, until $r_i = k_i$: Set

$$r_i = \frac{1}{r_{i-1} - k_{i-1}} \qquad k_i = \lfloor r_i \rfloor$$

If w is a rational number, then the algorithm terminates eventually with $r_n = k_n$. In this case, we define $k_{n+1} = k_{n+2} = \ldots = 0$. Otherwise, the algorithm determines an infinite sequence of integers k_i.

The computation of the ith convergent

$$u_i = k_0 + \cfrac{1}{k_1 + \cfrac{1}{k_2 + \cdots \cfrac{1}{k_{i-1} + \cfrac{1}{k_i}}}}$$

is facilitated by the following recurrence. For $i = 0, 1, 2, \ldots$, let $u_i = p_i/q_i$, and define $p_0 = k_0$, $q_0 = 1$, $p_{-1} = 1$, $q_{-1} = 0$. Then

$$u_i = \frac{k_i p_{i-1} + p_{i-2}}{k_i q_{i-1} + q_{i-2}}$$

for $i \geq 1$. The convergents $u_i = p_i/q_i$ are rational approximations of w whose precision is

$$|w - u_i| \leq \frac{1}{q_i^2}$$

Since we bound the denominator of the approximation, it makes sense to speak of the *best* approximant of w. If Q is the bound on the denominator, then p/q is the best approximant if

$$|w - \frac{p}{q}| \leq |w - \frac{r}{s}|$$

for all integers r and s such that $0 < s < Q$. It is known from number theory that the best approximant of w either is a convergent u_i of the continued-fraction expansion of w, or else has the form

$$\frac{k p_{i-1} + p_{i-2}}{k q_{i-1} + q_{i-2}}$$

where $k_i/2 \leq k < k_i$. The latter fraction is called a *quasi-convergent*.

Using these facts, we therefore determine an approximation for w as follows:

1. Compute the continued-fraction expansion, as specified previously.

2. On determination of the next k_i, test whether $q_i = k_i q_{i-1} + q_{i-2}$ is greater than Q. If so, set $n = i - 1$ and stop; otherwise, continue the expansion.

3. Determine the largest k between $k_{n+1}/2$ and k_{n+1} such that $kq_n + q_{n-1} \leq Q$. Choose either u_n or the quasi-convergent using k, depending on which rational is closer to w.

Thus, we obtain a rational approximant p/q satisfying $q \leq Q$. It can be shown that the error of this approximation is bounded by $1/(qQ)$. We call this the *continued-fraction* approximation method.

To analyze the complexity of the continued-fraction method, we consider the number of iterations needed to construct the approximant. Clearly, the slowest growth of the denominator sequence $(q_1, q_2, ...)$ happens when all k_i are 1. In this case, the q_i form the Fibonacci sequence,

$$1, 1, 2, 3, 5, 8, 13, ...$$

Let $\Phi = (1 + \sqrt{5})/2$. From number theory we know that the ith Fibonnaci number is larger than Φ^{i-2}. Hence, the method requires $O(\log(Q))$ steps and determines the best approximant p/q with $q < Q$.

The continued-fraction method is easy to implement. However, the repeated divisions can introduce errors in the approximation. For example, when approximating 0.123, the following sequence of pairs (r_i, k_i) is determined, using double-precision floating-point arithmetic:

$$
\begin{aligned}
k_0 &= 0 & r_0 &= 0.123 \\
k_1 &= 8 & r_1 &= 0.13008107624663445 \\
k_2 &= 7 & r_2 &= 0.687513271369275 \\
k_3 &= 1 & r_3 &= 0.45451737681859816 \\
k_4 &= 2 & r_4 &= 0.20013590459294717 \\
k_5 &= 4 & r_5 &= 0.9966046923658309 \\
k_6 &= 1 & r_6 &= 0.00340687500229432343 \\
k_7 &= 293 & r_7 &= 0.5241220372356565 \\
&\vdots & &\vdots
\end{aligned}
$$

Here, r_7 should be 1, since the correct expansion of 0.123 is

$$(0, 8, 7, 1, 2, 4, 1, 0, 0, 0, ...)$$

Thus, it is important to compare the accuracy of the convergents with the original number at each step in the expansion iteration.

Element Rounding

Now consider approximating an arbitrary plane equation by one whose coefficients are bounded by L and L^2, respectively. For notational simplicity, we broaden the problem and approximate

$$a_1 x + a_2 y + a_3 z + a_4 = 0$$

where the a_i are reals and should be approximated with integers bounded separately by $|a_i| \le L_i$. It is our intention to reduce this problem to separate approximation problems for the coefficients.

The ratio $|a_i|/L_i$ measures by how much the coefficient a_i exceeds its bound. Dividing by the maximum ratio, we obtain a plane equation $b_1 x + b_2 y + b_3 z + b_4 = 0$, in which one coefficient is $|b_k| = L_k$ and the others obey $|b_i| \le L_i$. Next, we divide by b_k and obtain an equation in which the kth coefficient is 1.

$$w_1 x + w_2 y + w_3 z + w_4 = 0, \qquad w_k = 1$$

By approximating the w_i with rationals $|p_i/q| \le |w_i|$, where $q \le L_k$, we obtain the approximate equation

$$r_1 x + r_2 y + r_3 z + r_4 = 0, \qquad r_k = 1$$

After multiplying with q, all coefficients satisfy the required bounds. Thus, we have reduced the problem of approximating the coefficients simultaneously to a problem of approximating each coefficient separately, albeit with a uniform bound on the denominator.

Example 4.2: Consider the plane equation

$$3.2x + 4.5y + 12.3z + 30 = 0 \qquad (4.1)$$

where the coefficients of x, y, and z should be bounded by 3, and the constant term by 9. The maximum ratio is $12.3/3 = 4.1$; hence, we divide by 4.1 and obtain

$$0.7804878x + 1.0975610y + 3z + 7.3170732 = 0$$

Subsequent division by 3 yields the equation

$$0.2601626x + 0.3658537y + z + 2.4390244 = 0$$

So, with a bound $q = 3$, the approximation to equation (4.1) is therefore

$$\frac{1}{3}x + \frac{1}{3}y + z + \frac{7}{3} = 0$$

which is equivalent to

$$x + y + 3z + 7 = 0$$

The naive method for constructing a rational approximant to a real lends itself naturally to the problem of element rounding, since the rational approximations will have uniform denominators.

The continued-fraction method, in contrast, often gives better approximants, but it does not result in uniform denominators. By using the denominator bound $\sqrt[4]{L_k}$, we can circumvent this difficulty, and we can also construct plane-equation approximants.

4.3.5 Object Reconstruction

If a polyhedron has been subjected to a translation or a rotation, some of its elements may have been rounded. In consequence, the integrity of the object may have been violated. To appreciate this problem, consider Figures 4.8 through 4.10, where we have restricted the modeling domain to two dimensions.

Figure 4.8 shows the union of 150 triangles, randomly generated with one vertex on a circle of radius 10^{-4}, and the other two vertices on the unit circle. We observe that the boundary of the resulting object contains many small features, such as the narrow crack shown in magnification in Figure 4.10. When translating or rotating the object, we have no guarantee that in the new position there exist representable grid lines that can bound such a feature. Possibly, then, element rounding may have altered the feature to look as shown in Figure 4.11, so a simple polygon might be changed to one whose edges intersect.

To sidestep this problem, we reduce it to the primitive objects from which all complex polyhedra are built using Boolean operations. That is, when translating or rotating a complex polyhedron P, we *separately* translate or rotate the primitives from which P has been built, and then reconstruct P from the resulting primitive objects. If the primitives can be translated or rotated without violating their integrity, then this reconstruction approach eliminates the problem for complex polyhedra, albeit with a penalty in efficiency. Moreover, the topology may change slightly, since element rounding may alter somewhat the shape of each primitive.

We now consider the problem of maintaining the topological integrity of primitive objects. Presumably, this problem is simpler, since the topology of primitive objects can be kept very simple. That is, we could restrict

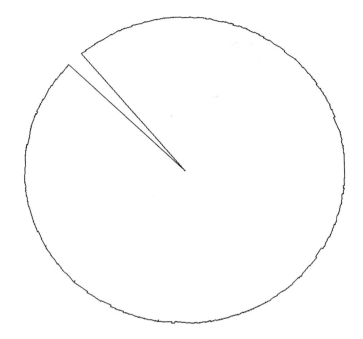

Figure 4.8   Union of 150 Random Triangles

the primitives to be parallelepipeds, from which all polyhedra could be constructed in principle by a suitable sequence of regularized Boolean operations. More generally, we postulate that all primitive polyhedra are *trihedral*; that is, exactly three faces are incident at each vertex. Trihedral polyhedra are also called *simple* in the literature. So, when slightly altering the plane equation, trihedral vertices remain trihedral, unless an incident edge of the primitive object is small compared to the positional perturbation of the plane.

Assume that the primitive object is a parallelepiped, with the six plane equations

$$
\begin{array}{llll}
P_{x0}: & -x = 0 \qquad & P_{x1}: & x = a \\
P_{y0}: & -y = 0 \qquad & P_{y1}: & y = b \\
P_{z0}: & -z = 0 \qquad & P_{z1}: & z = c
\end{array}
$$

Here a, b, and c are the side lengths of the parallelepiped and are positive. They are rational, with a numerator that is less than L^2 and a denominator that is less than L. We note that the vertices on the plane P_{x0} lie below the plane P_{x1}, and that the vertices on the plane P_{x1} lie below the plane P_{x0}.

Figure 4.9   Border, Magnified Three Times

Similarly, the vertices on the plane P_{y0} lie below the plane P_{y1}, and so on. Thus, we have 24 consistency conditions specifying that a certain vertex lies below a certain plane. It is clear that these can be evaluated for the translated or rotated primitive, after element rounding. When satisfied, the new primitive is topologically valid. If one or more condition is violated, then the motion destroys the integrity of the primitive.

4.3.6 Remarks on Using Rational Arithmetic

When using rational arithmetic, it is crucial to control the growth of digits in repeated geometric operations. This is accomplished by requiring that

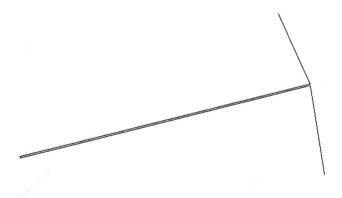

Figure 4.10   Border, Magnified 500 Times

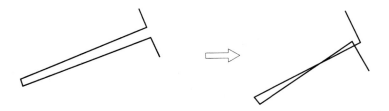

Figure 4.11   Possible Feature Alteration Through Translation or Rotation

all shape elements be derived from a fixed grid of representable planes. Because translation and rotation may require element rounding, object reconstruction from separately translated or rotated trihedral primitives may be necessary. Moreover, the primitives must satisfy a minimum-feature-separation criterion, so we can be assured that the shape alterations due to element rounding do not invalidate the topology.

Although rational approximation to real numbers is fairly well understood, the process of approximating planes in this context is not fully explored. For example, the quality of the plane approximation depends on which part of it is the final face area. If this area is in the vicinity of the origin, small rotations of the plane can be tolerated, provided the center of rotation is nearby. If the face area is distant, small rotations about the origin can lead to large positional perturbations of the face.

The method has been based on representing the plane equations numerically. Alternatively, we could represent vertex coordinates, placing a bound on the precision. When we do so, a plane on which a set of points lies has coefficients that must be of bounded length. Again, translations and rotations may necessitate element rounding and object reconstruction. Rather than being trihedral, the primitives now must have triangular faces so that positional perturbations of the vertices, due to element rounding, can be accommodated. In this style of representation, element rounding seems easier and better behaved, since rounding vertex coordinates does not cause large perturbations elsewhere.

As mentioned earlier, element rounding may introduce slight shape alterations. When reconstructing an object, there is no guarantee that two primitives that intersect prior to a rigid motion will also intersect afterwards. In consequence, the reconstructed object may differ in detail from the original object. It is unclear whether the approach can be modified in such a way that the object topology is preserved.

4.4 Representation and Model

When working with floating-point numbers, imprecise numerical results are inevitable. In consequence, internal inconsistencies of the representation of a geometric object are possible. So, we need to elucidate *what* is described by such a representation. Only after we are in possession of a precise geometric meaning of such representations can we address the question whether a geometric algorithm has been correctly implemented. Thus, we introduce the concepts of *representation* and *model*. After these concepts have been explained and a definition of correctness has been given, we discuss several approaches to robust geometric computations and related results that illustrate some of the technical difficulties.

A *representation* is a data structure intended to describe a geometric object, possibly using imprecise arithmetic data. It contains symbolic data describing adjacencies and incidences, and, usually, arithmetic data, such as the plane coefficients for each face. A representation has a *model*, if there exists an object in Euclidian space satisfying the symbolic part of the description precisely. To the numerical data of the representation, there corresponds numerical data of the model. The numerical model data might require infinite-precision numbers.

As an example, consider the representation of a cube, whose symbolic data specifies only the topology of vertices, edges, and faces, but makes no mention of the fact that the faces are square and that opposite faces are parallel. Then any six-sided trihedral polyhedron with quadrilateral faces will be a model, irrespective of the approximate numerical data of the representation that might have been given as vertex coordinates. It is clear that this definition of model is too broad to be useful, so we attempt to capture more accurately the intent of the representation.

Clearly, the intuition of a representation is that the numerical data given are close to the exact data intended. Therefore, it makes sense to compare the exact numerical data of the model with the approximate numerical data of the representation: A model M of a given representation R is ϵ-*close*, if the largest deviation of the numerical data of the representation from the exact model data is not greater than ϵ. This is an absolute error notion that suffices for our purposes, but it could clearly be replaced by a relative error definition.

A given representation may have exact numerical data. In this case, the representation is its own model, and such a model is called the *natural* model of the representation. To determine whether a given representation possesses a natural model, we verify whether the numerical data, considered to be exact as written, are consistent with the topological data. Of course, this requires sufficient precision in the calculation so as not to lose information. In some cases it is clear that the representation has a natural model. For example, a point set in the plane always has a natural model, since there are no symbolic data to be satisfied. On the other hand, the representation of a polyhedron need not have a natural model.

We can now clarify when a k-ary geometric operation op is correctly implemented: The implementation of op is *correct*, if for every legitimate input representation R_i there exists a model M_i such that the following are true:

1. The algorithm constructs an output representation R without failing.

2. There is a model M of R such that $M = op(M_1, ..., M_k)$.

The definition is further refined to capture the precision of the algorithm as follows: Given that each model M_i is ϵ-close to its representation, the model M is $\delta(\epsilon)$-close to R. Here, one wants a function δ such that $\delta(\epsilon)$ is not excessively large compared to ϵ.

In the case of polyhedra, it is common to assume that the representation describes a model that is ϵ-close to a given representation. This is often expressed by saying that there is a "fuzz region" enveloping the surface, and that the intended exact polyhedron lies within this fuzz region. As we shall demonstrate next with an example, from a mathematical point of view, this appealing intuitive concept is defective.

4.4.1 Models of Purely Symbolic Representations

We consider whether a purely symbolic representation of a geometric object possesses a model. No numerical data are given in the representation; hence, a model exists iff we can assign real numbers to the symbolic coordinates such that the constraint equations implied by the symbolic representation are satisfied. We wish to show that this existence question is nontrivial.

As an example, we consider geometric objects consisting of *lines*, given as $[a, b, c]$, and *points*, given as (u, v, w), where a, b, c, u, v, and w are symbols. We consider points and lines in projective 2-space. See also Section 5.2 of Chapter 5.

The triple $[a, b, c]$ symbolizes the line equation $ax + by + cz = 0$, where z is the homogenizing variable. The triple (u, v, w) are the projective point coordinates. Specifying that the point $P = (u, v, w)$ is *incident* to the line $L = [a, b, c]$ means that the equation $au + bv + cw = 0$ can be satisfied, and we write this fact as $L(P)$.

We specify an arrangement of points and lines by the following rules:

(D1) All lines and points must be declared in advance, as triples of symbols. No two lines and no two points so declared are equal.

(D2) If a point P is incident to a line L, then this fact is explicitly stated as $L(P)$. If two lines L_1 and L_2 intersect in the declared point P, then this fact is expressed explicitly by the two incidence statements $L_1(P)$ and $L_2(P)$.

(D3) No other incidences exist among declared points and lines except those explicitly stated.

These rules mirror the common requirement of boundary representation schemata that vertices, edges, and faces be distinct, and that they do not intersect except in explicitly specified adjacencies.

Given a symbolic object specification in the preceding methodology, we investigate whether it can be realized as a point/line configuration in real two-dimensional projective space $\mathbf{P}^2$. That is, we ask whether there exists an assignment of real numbers to the symbols such that

1. The equations entailed by (D2) are satisfied.

2. All points and lines are distinct and satisfy (D3).

Consider the following configuration, consisting of nine distinct points,

$$P_1 = (u_1, v_1, w_1), \ldots, P_9 = (u_9, v_9, w_9)$$

and of nine distinct lines

$$L_1 = [a_1, b_1, c_1], \ldots, L_9 = [a_9, b_9, c_9]$$

The required incidences are as follows:

$$
\begin{array}{cccccc}
L_1(P_1), & L_1(P_3), & L_1(P_5), & L_2(P_2), & L_2(P_4), & L_2(P_6), \\
L_3(P_1), & L_3(P_2), & L_3(P_7), & L_4(P_2), & L_4(P_3), & L_4(P_9), \\
L_5(P_3), & L_5(P_4), & L_5(P_8), & L_6(P_4), & L_6(P_5), & L_6(P_7), \\
L_7(P_5), & L_7(P_6), & L_7(P_9), & L_8(P_1), & L_8(P_6), & L_8(P_8), \\
L_9(P_7), & L_9(P_8), & L_9(P_9) & & &
\end{array}
$$

This configuration exists in $\mathbf{P}^2$ and is shown in Figure 4.12. However, if the last incidence constraint, $L_9(P_9)$, is removed, then there is no such configuration in $\mathbf{P}^2$, since that would contradict Pascal's theorem, a fact not easily recognized mechanically.

Consider a conic in which a hexagon has been inscribed. Pascal's theorem states that opposite sides of the hexagon intersect in three points that must be collinear. In Figure 4.12, the conic is degenerate in that it consists of the two lines L_1 and L_2. The hexagon has the vertices P_1 through P_6. The opposite sides $\overline{P_1, P_2}$ and $\overline{P_4, P_5}$ intersect in the point P_7. The other two pairs of opposite hexagon sides intersect in the points P_8 and P_9. By Pascal's theorem, therefore, P_7, P_8, and P_9 must lie on the line L_9.

This example demonstrates that a purely symbolic representation raises existence problems. Were we to base geometric operations on this representation, we would have to verify, for each object, whether it has a model

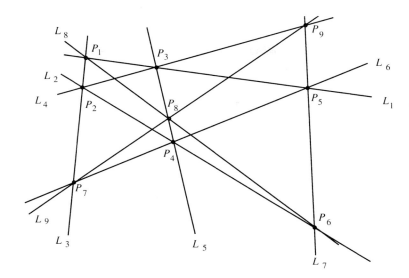

Figure 4.12   Realizable Point/Line Configuration

— that is, whether the object exists. There are algorithmic techniques
for deciding such questions, but they require potentially excessive symbolic
computations and an elaborate theoretical machinery to justify their correctness. Some citations are given at the end of the chapter.

A further difficulty with the purely symbolic representation is that an
actual embedding may require irrational coordinates. We demonstrate this
fact with the following example. Consider the configuration shown in Figure 4.13, consisting of the nine points $P_1, ..., P_9$ and the nine lines $L_1, ..., L_9$.
All incidence constraints are easily satisfied, except the incidence of point
P_9 with each of the four lines (P_1, P_5), (P_2, P_6), (P_3, P_7), and (P_4, P_8). The
configuration is realized by the pentagram some of whose points have irrational coordinates. We assume that it can also be realized with rational
point coordinates, and derive a contradiction from this assumption.

If the configuration can be realized with rational coordinates, then every
rational projective transformation of it must preserve both the incidences
and the rationality of the coordinates. From projective geometry, we know
that there exists a nonsingular projective transformation mapping two given
quadruples of points into each other, provided that no three points in a
quadruple are collinear.[2] So, we may assume without loss of generality
that the projective (x, y, w) coordinates of P_1, P_2, P_3, and P_4 are $(0, 0, 1)$,
$(1, 0, 1)$, $(1, 1, 1)$, and $(0, 1, 1)$, respectively.

---

[2]In Section 5.5.5 of Chapter 5, such transformations are explicitly constructed.

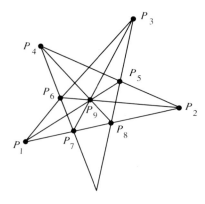

Figure 4.13   Incidence Configuration Requiring Irrational Points

Assume first that neither P_7 nor P_8 is at infinity. Then P_7 may be assigned the coordinates $(a, 0, 1)$ and P_8 the coordinates $(b, 0, 1)$. Note that $a \neq 0$ and $b \neq 0$, since all points must be distinct. So, $P_6 = (a, a, 1 + a)$, and $P_5 = (1, 1 - b, 2 - b)$. The coordinates of P_9 are $(b, b - a, 1 + b - a)$, because P_9 is the intersection of the lines (P_4, P_8) and (P_3, P_7). The point P_9 is also incident to the lines (P_1, P_5) and (P_2, P_6); hence,

$$
\begin{aligned}
b + a^2 - 2a &= 0 \\
b^2 - a &= 0
\end{aligned}
$$

Elimination of a yields the polynomial $b^4 - 2b^2 + b = 0$ with the roots $b_1 = 0$, $b_2 = 1$, $b_3 = -\frac{1}{2}(\sqrt{5} + 1)$, $b_4 = \frac{1}{2}(\sqrt{5} - 1)$. The rational roots b_1 and b_2 yield degenerate configurations. Hence, the realization of the nondegenerate configuration requires irrational coordinates, assuming all points are at a finite distance from the origin.

Since the configuration is symmetric, it suffices to consider that P_7 is at infinity. Since P_8 is on the line (P_1, P_7, P_2) and is not equal to P_7, we have therefore the coordinate assignments $P_7 = (1, 0, 0)$ and $P_8 = (b, 0, 1)$. A simple computation shows that now P_3 and P_6 must coincide, as must P_4 and P_9. But then P_9 cannot lie on $(P_2, P_6) = (P_2, P_3)$. In summary, the point coordinates in this configuration cannot all be rational, no matter how the configuration is realized in the plane.

4.4.2 The Role of Decision Making

Assume we implement a geometric algorithm using floating-point arithmetic. We know that we must deal with imprecise numerical data, and that we cannot always be certain that the outcome of some numerical computation allows us to draw correct conclusions. By carefully analyzing the condition number of each calculation, we can establish the following paradigm:

> A numerical computation C is carried out. Subsequent processing depends on making a logical decision based on whether the outcome of the computation is positive, zero, or negative. As long as the magnitude of the result r exceeds a certain threshold $t(C)$, we can make a correct decision based on r. If the magnitude of r is smaller than $t(C)$, then a decision based on r alone is uncertain.

When the decision is uncertain, we could make it arbitrarily; for instance, we could require that a result r of magnitude $|r| < t(C)$ is understood to mean $r = 0$. But such a decision could have consequences for other, later decisions, so we must make each decision in a logically consistent manner.

The paradigm allows us to identify three basic approaches to devising robust geometric algorithms:

1. Restructure all computations such that the logical decisions are independent.

2. Establish consistency of the decisions by symbolic reasoning. The reasoning steps analyze the logical dependencies and assume that the symbolic data are exact as written.

3. Establish consistency, altering the symbolic data as necessary.

4.4.3 Irredundant Decision Making

Inconsistencies among geometrically related logical decisions arise when different numerical computations are performed independently, even though their results are not independent. Therefore, we attempt to restructure the algorithm such that different computations that determine geometrically dependent questions are eliminated. This practical idea is illustrated by the algorithm for regularized intersection of Chapter 3. It requires a careful examination of the possible dependencies present among the numerical steps.

It seems unlikely that the approach is capable of eliminating *all* possibilities for failure. However, since the robustness of an algorithm increases perceptibly even when interdependencies are eliminated only partially, this approach is very attractive in practice.

4.4.4 Preserving Symbolic Data

Dependencies of logical decisions are not always simple to recognize. So, we add symbolic computations to determine logical consequences. How difficult is such symbolic reasoning in specific situations? In the case of intersecting two simple polygons in the plane, it is not at all difficult. However, when intersecting three polygons *simultaneously*, or when intersecting polyhedra, it could be quite hard.

Intersecting Polygons

Consider the problem of intersecting two polygons in the plane. This problem is sufficiently simple that all uncertain numerical results can be decided independently and no symbolic reasoning will be needed to maintain consistency. Nevertheless, the problem is not trivial and, by altering it slightly, we increase its difficulty.

Polygon intersection requires as subroutine numerical calculations to decide whether two edges intersect and whether, in particular, a vertex of one polygon is incident to an edge of the other polygon. The specific logical difficulty in an implementation is that the incidences, as determined by the algorithm, may not be satisfiable in Euclidian geometry; that is, that there need not be models of the input polygons that satisfy the incidences determined in the course of intersection. In view of this, we say that an edge e of polygon A is *overconstrained* if it contains one or more vertices of the polygon B in its interior.[3] For overconstrained edges we need to prove that these additional incidences can be satisfied in Euclidian geometry without sacrificing the fact that the edge is a line segment. Note that vertex/vertex incidences do not create such problems.

As an example, consider the two n-gons shown in Figure 4.14. If the intersection algorithm determines that every vertex of the first n-gon is incident to an edge of the second n-gon, and vice versa, then no two polygons exist in Euclidian geometry that satisfy every one of these incidences:

Proposition
Given two polygons A and B in the Euclidian plane, there is at least one edge that is not overconstrained.

Proof
Assume that the two polygons have m and n vertices, respectively. A vertex of polygon A cannot overconstrain two or more edges of B; hence, if every edge is overconstrained, then $m = n$. Consider the convex hull of the vertices of the two polygons. Then at least one vertex, say of A, must be a vertex of the convex hull, and this vertex cannot constrain any edge of B. Hence, there is at least one edge in B that is not overconstrained. $\square$

---

[3]We refer here to the *relative interior* of the edge; that is, to the edge without its end points.

Figure 4.14   Intersecting Two n-Gons

Now, if at least one edge is not overconstrained, then we can construct two model polygons[4] that satisfy all incidences that may have been postulated by the implementation. This is done by a placement strategy that constructs the model polygons in a specific sequence. The intuition is as follows: If an edge is not overconstrained, then it can be placed last. Thus, we remove all such edges, with their vertices, obtaining a set of polygonal arcs. Some of the removed edges have constrained other edges, so now there will be new unconstrained edges, since we removed edges along with their endpoints. These edges are removed next, and the procedure is repeated until no edges remain. Thereafter, the edges are reconstructed in Euclidian space and are placed such that the required incidences are satisfied. Since, at the time of placing, an edge is not overconstrained, there is no difficulty preserving the linearity of all edges. Thus, we can construct model polygons that satisfy all required incidences, and therefore can also obtain a model that is the intersection of these input models.

With these observations in mind, we implement polygon intersection in the expected manner, but require that any two vertices of a given polygon are no closer than 3ϵ to each other, and that the minimum distance from any vertex to another edge is also at least 3ϵ. If any vertex of A is closer than ϵ to an edge or vertex of B, then we decide that the distance is zero. If every edge is overconstrained, then we arbitrarily undo one such incidence. This must create an unconstrained edge somewhere, and hence permits the construction of suitable models establishing correctness.

After two polygon representations have been so intersected, the resulting representation need not satisfy the minimum separation bound on vertices and edges. Thus, a postprocessor may be needed that restores the minimum-feature-separation condition. Postprocessing may require obliterating short edges; that is, it affects the symbolic data as well.

---

[4]Polygons need not be simple; that is, the boundary is allowed to self-intersect.

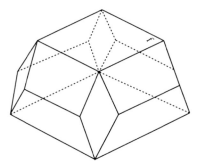

Figure 4.15   Repositioning the Face f Requires Changing Adjacent Faces

A key factor in the correctness of this procedure is that we do not consider additional constraints such as the possible collinearity of different polygon edges. Were we to do so, then the approach would fail because now a single vertex of B could overconstrain two or more edges of A.

A similar difficulty arises when intersecting three polygons *simultaneously*, for a single vertex of one polygon may simultaneously overconstrain an edge in each of the other two polygons. In particular, we can obtain configurations such as the one shown in Figure 4.12 from superimposing three polygons. We conclude that the simultaneous intersection of three or more polygons is more difficult, since it allows us to create configurations that are the subject of theorems in projective geometry. That is, in such problems, different incidence decisions are logically interdependent in possibly complex ways.

Remarks on Preserving Symbolic Data

Incidence requirements can lead to difficult reasoning problems. Polygonal intersection is free of these difficulties as long as we do not require satisfaction of additional positional properties, such as the collinearity of different edges. These constraints can be introduced, for example, by considering the *simultaneous* intersection of three or more polygons.

Polyhedral intersection in three dimensions is considerably more difficult, since it no longer is evident how to reposition a face consistently to satisfy incidence decisions. As an example, consider the polyhedron A shown in Figure 4.15. Assume we need to adjust the plane containing the face f to accommodate some incidence decisions we made when analyzing the position of A with respect to some other polyhedron B. Since we must preserve the planarity of f, at most two vertices can remain in the original position. At the other vertices, therefore, the shape and, possibly, the

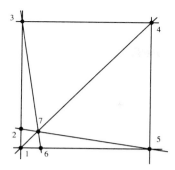

Figure 4.16   Sequence Dependence of Positional Perturbation

position of adjacent faces must also be changed to preserve the topological structure. In consequence, the operation of repositioning a face requires a global alteration of the polyhedron. Whether such an alteration can be carried out — that is, whether there exists a model of the altered polyhedron representation — is not immediately clear.

The stringent requirement that the topological data agree between representation and model also affects what bounds can be established on the closeness δ of the output model M, as a function of the closeness ϵ of the input models M_1 and M_2. The reason for this is foremost a technical one: As stated, when proving correctness of an implementation in this framework, we have to show that we can satisfy the incidence constraints introduced during the course of the computation, by consistently repositioning the elements of the input models. In all likelihood, this repositioning is sequential, for proof purposes; for instance, as in the polygon intersection algorithm. But the repositioning sequence affects the final position of the vertices, edges, and faces. For example, consider the configuration shown in Figure 4.16. Here, positioning vertices in the order 1, 3, 4, 5, 2, 7, 6 is much more favorable than is positioning them in the order 1, 2, 7, 6, 3, 4, 5, since a small position perturbation of the vertices 2, 6, and 7 leads to a large perturbation of the vertices 3 and 5. Thus, not only would we like to show that a consistent sequence of repositioning operations exists, for all inputs and all incidence decisions based on the inputs, but also that the specific sequence leads to small positional perturbations.

4.4.5 Altering the Symbolic Data

So far, we have required that the symbolic data of the representation be satisfied by the model. Thus, the symbolic data are considered more trustworthy than are the numerical data, when deducing the intended meaning

Figure 4.17   Vertex Shifting

of a given representation. The rationale for giving priority to the symbolic data is that they can be represented easily without error. Assuming that there exists a reliable method for defining geometric objects, the symbolic data in the representation ought to be correct as given. However, objects are often constructed from other objects by geometric operations, so there is the chance that the implementation has introduced some unintended alterations into the symbolic data. Especially if some elements of an input object have been repositioned over large distances, the topology of the output object could well differ from what was intended. Therefore, if altering the symbolic data slightly would result in smaller positional perturbations, we could also take the view that the numerical data are more accurate than are the symbolic data. This motivates exploring the consequences of changing the symbolic data; for example, by subdividing edges and faces, followed by slight positional perturbations of the subdivided elements.

For polygonal regions in the plane, we can base such an approach on the concept of normalizing the input data. We postulate that no two vertices are closer than some tolerance ϵ, and that, likewise, no vertex is closer to an edge than ϵ. The algorithm alters the input data to satisfy these two requirements. Two operations are needed, *vertex shifting* and *edge cracking*, illustrated in Figures 4.17 and 4.18.

Vertex shifting merges two vertices that are closer than ϵ into a single one. There is no difficulty doing this if we base the representation on vertex

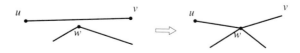

Figure 4.18   Edge Cracking

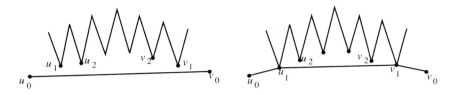

Figure 4.19 Additive Positional Perturbation in Edge Cracking

coordinates. Having so identified all vertices that lie close, we next apply edge cracking and subdivide any edge provided that there is a vertex that lies close to it. If the edge is (u, v), and w lies close to it, then (u, v) is replaced by the two edges (u, w) and (w, v). Thus, new edges and vertices are introduced, thereby modifying the symbolic, topological data.

The sequential nature of eliminating near coincidence of vertices and edges in the subdivision method can introduce positional perturbations that are much larger than ϵ. An example for edge cracking is shown in Figure 4.19. Here, the initial cracking of (u_0, v_0) by the vertices u_1 and v_1 brings the vertices u_2 and v_2 close to the middle segment (u_1, v_1), which is cracked next. This, in turn, introduces further subdivision, so the largest vertex displacement, in this case, is proportional to $n\epsilon$, where n is the number of vertices.

4.5 Discussion

We have discussed several competing approaches for dealing with the accuracy and robustness problems in geometric computation. Roughly speaking, they fall into one of four categories:

1. Guarantee exact data by using bounded rational arithmetic, or exact algebraic numbers.

2. Ameliorate the problem by restructuring the algorithm to limit the redundancies among the numerical computations performed.

3. Include reasoning steps in the computation, but try to satisfy the symbolic input data exactly.

4. Alter the meaning of the geometric elements; that is, modify the symbolic data in an attempt to minimize positional perturbations.

So far, exact approaches have not had a significant impact on geometric modeling systems in practice, due to the perceived inefficiency of implementing exact arithmetic computations. It may well turn out, however, that the tradeoff between robustness and efficiency is so exacting that we may have to reevaluate our demands for efficiency.

For linear geometric objects, the bounded-precision-rational arithmetic approach offers both accuracy and a measure of efficiency. However, the need to reconstruct P for a rigid motion and the fact that this may alter the topology of P are limitations. It is not clear how conveniently the approach can generalize to geometric objects with nonlinear elements. Specifically, the intersection of planes with integer coefficients is a rational point, but the intersection of quadric surfaces with integer coefficients need not be rational. Already in two dimensions, the intersection of the circle $x^2 + y^2 - 1 = 0$ with the line $x - y = 0$ is irrational. Once the range of coefficients is fixed, it is clear that there must be a fixed minimum distance between any two representable distinct points. However, estimates of the needed precision to separate them are unfavorable.

In Section 4.4.1, we showed that the topology of certain objects may lead to existential problems, since not all object descriptions make sense. We concentrated on purely symbolic descriptions to show that this problem is independent of whether or not we have numerical data. An important conclusion to draw from the example is that the familiar description of geometric objects using inexact numerical data may contain subtle errors.

The existence problem is the main motivation for drawing a distinction between representation and model. It is clear that we cannot simultaneously represent all geometric models; a simple counting argument shows that. More important, we cannot naively assume that a given representation makes sense, even though, based on approximate metric data, the computer is able to give, for instance, a graphical rendering of it that appears to be meaningful.

In practice, heuristics are employed that ameliorate but do not eliminate the robustness problem. Conceptually, we view these heuristics as attempts to reduce the logical interdependence of decisions that are based on numerical computations. For example, when intersecting polyhedra, the asymmetry of the algorithm presented in Chapter 3 ensures that many incidence questions are not asked in two different ways. Rather, once incidence or nonincidence has been decided on, this fact is used to subdivide the faces of polyhedron A and of polyhedron B simultaneously. Other heuristics include structuring the computations such that numerical *input* data are used where possible, rather than *derived* numerical data being used. For example, when testing edge/edge intersection, the computations are expressed in terms of the plane equations involved, and do not use a derived parametric representation of the two edges.

A strict adherence to the topological data seems to necessitate symbolic reasoning. In general, such reasoning can be expensive; see also the next section. It is possible that some geometric operations of interest to solid modeling do not require expensive reasoning, but this topic is relatively unexplored.

4.6 Notes and References

Condition numbers and related concepts for analyzing the sensitivity of floating-point algorithms are standard techniques in numerical analysis. When we are dealing with linear geometric objects, as we have done so far, books on matrix techniques, such as Golub and van Loan (1983), are useful. The pentagon example discussed in Section 4.2.4 was proposed by Dobkin and Silver (1988), who advocate extending the precision of the mantissas dynamically during the computations as required. Similar numerical examples can be generated with matrices. First, multiply A and its inverse each m times with itself. Then, multiply the resulting matrices with each other, and compare the product to the identity matrix.

The material on exact rational arithmetic is from a lecture K. Sugihara gave in 1987 at the IMA Summer Program on Robotics at the University of Minnesota. This material is appearing now; see Sugihara and Iri (1988 and 1989). Several element-rounding techniques are discussed in Sugihara (1987). For plane rounding, Sugihara also considers the *basis-reduction method* — see, for example, Lovász (1986) — which usually gives better results than does the continued-fraction method. However, both methods ignore the interaction between coefficient perturbation and the locality of the final face on the plane.

Karasick, Lieber, and Nackman (1989) experiment with adaptive techniques for reducing the cost of rational arithmetic without bounding the precision of the rationals involved. Given a determinant $|A|$ with rational entries whose sign must be determined, they try to transform $|A|$ to another determinant $|A'|$ whose entries are also rationals but have numerators and denominators of smaller precision. Under certain conditions, the determinant $|A'|$ has the same sign as $|A|$ and can be found quickly. In that case, the evaluation of $|A'|$ is cheaper. If the conditions are not met, then $|A|$ must be evaluated and no savings are realized. Karasick, Lieber, and Nackman report that a Delaunay triangulation algorithm with rational arithmetic can be sped up by several orders of magnitude using this approach.

The notion of representation and model, and the approach to designing robust implementations that preserve the symbolic data, were developed in Hoffmann, Hopcroft, and Karasick (1988). The paper notes the connection between Pascal's theorem and the simultaneous intersection of three polygons, and an expanded version discusses the line configuration requiring irrational coordinates. The idea of limiting the interdependence of numerical computation is from Hoffmann, Hopcroft, and Karasick (1987).

The problem of whether a specific point/line configuration can be realized in Euclidian geometry can be investigated using oriented matroid theory. Bokowski and Sturmfels (1986) and Bokowski, Richter, and Sturmfels (1989) give an algorithm solving the problem. See also Bokowski and Sturmfels (1989).

A variation of the embedding problem arises in geometric theorem proving: Given an embedded configuration, we typically ask whether certain additional incidences are satisfied. Different techniques for solving such problems can be found in Chou (1988), in Kapur (1986), and in Kutzler (1988). All algorithms for geometric theorem proving may require exponential running times on planar configurations composed from circles and lines. As Hong (1986) shows, the symbolic computations arising in this context can be replaced by equivalent numerical computations carried out at sufficiently high precision. However, in the case of configurations consisting of circles and lines, exponentially many digits may be needed. See also Section 7.6 in Chapter 7 for a Gröbner basis approach to geometric theorem proving.

The method of Section 4.4.5 is the *data-normalization* technique of Milenkovic (1988). Milenkovic proposes a second paradigm for altering the symbolic data, called the *hidden-variable* method. In it, each line is replaced by an *x, y-monotonic curve* having the property that the curve does not intersect a line parallel to the coordinate axes more than once and is close to the line within some global bound. The method is based on careful computations of line-intersection points. Whenever a new intersection point is determined, consistency calculations are performed that may refine other line-intersection points, so that a topologically consistent function can be constructed that assigns to each point/line pair one of the labels **on**, **above**, or **below**, with the obvious meaning.

A related approach to finite-precision geometric computation is presented in Greene and Yao (1986). Considering an integer grid of representable points and a set of line segments whose endpoints are representable, they break line segments to reposition intersections on representable points. Theorems are given that prove termination and consistency of the procedure.

Recall that the result of certain numerical computations must be compared with zero, and that conclusions are drawn depending on whether the result is positive, zero, or negative. For instance, the computation might determine the Euclidian distance of a point from a plane, and the result would then indicate whether the point is on the positive or negative side of the plane, or that it lies on the plane. Let us call the zero case a *positional degeneracy*. Positional degeneracies can be eliminated by perturbing the coordinates of the elements relative to each other, after which we would need to consider only two possible outcomes; namely, whether the result is positive or negative.

Most geometric algorithms simplify substantially when positional degeneracies are eliminated from consideration, and this is a major motivation of research on this subject. Edelsbrunner and Mücke (1988) propose the

"SOS method," and prove that the final perturbations eliminate all existing degeneracies while not creating new ones. Yap (1988) presents a similar technique. Both schemes require fairly simple geometric input objects and exact arithmetic. Edelsbrunner and Mücke (1988) consider points and eliminate collinearity of three and coplanarity of four or more points. Yap (1988) takes a more abstract approach. Under the assumption that all numerical computations can be expressed as fixed polynomials in the input parameters, he shows that consistent perturbations exist that eliminate the possibility of any polynomial evaluating to zero.

It would seem that perturbation schemes not only pay off in that geometric algorithms become simpler, but that they also could increase robustness. However, two difficulties must be addressed:

1. We must ascertain that a perturbation is permissible. In the context of solid modeling, a positional degeneracy such as the coincidence of two face planes may be intentional. A perturbation of the relative position of the planes could be contrary to the designer's intentions, and hence would be inappropriate.

2. The challenge in designing a perturbation scheme is to maintain the integrity of the geometric objects whose elements have been so perturbed. As we saw in the example of point/line incidences, this can be a difficult problem.

The first difficulty is problem-dependent, and there are applications in which perturbation makes sense. For instance, perturbations seem to be appropriate when eliminating hidden lines during graphic display operations; see Sugihara (1989).

The second difficulty is technical in nature. For example, Yap's method would need to be extended such that the zeros of a certain subset of the polynomials are preserved. This subset would contain polynomials that express constraints of incidence, coplanarity, and so on. Such extensions have not been incorporated thus far. However, geometric theorem proving could provide the necessary tools fairly conveniently.

CHAPTER 5

Representation of Curved Edges and Faces

The focus of this chapter is the question of how to represent curved surface elements in boundary representation. Simple conventions suffice for the planar situation. For example, the geometric locus of an edge can be specified by the coordinates of its two bounding vertices. Curved boundary elements are not that simple, and we have to give a two-part description, consisting of a surface or space curve, the *carrier* of the face or edge, and a *boundary description* that delimits a subarea or segment. In the case of planar faces, the carrier is the plane containing the face and the boundary description is an edge graph. The carrier for an edge of a polyhedron is a line and can be inferred from the vertices.

In this chapter, we explore some of the issues arising when specific conventions are chosen for the two parts. In the case of the carrier specification, we discuss ways in which the surface can be given, and explain techniques for converting between them. When specifying the bounding structure of edges and faces, some geometric problems must be considered to avoid ambiguities. These are also discussed.

We restrict attention to algebraic surfaces and curves. This restriction is reasonable in the sense that the class is very rich and includes most of the curves and surfaces used in, for instance, engineering design. In particular, this class includes all the major parametric surfaces used in geometric modeling, including Bezier surfaces, nonuniform rational B-splines, and so on. It does not include all surfaces and space curves, however. For example, the helix is not an algebraic space curve.

5.1 Chapter Overview

We begin with a brief review of affine versus projective space. Although one ordinarily considers geometric objects in affine spaces only, there is a technical advantage to considering them also in projective space. For example, the question whether a curve has a rational parametric form cannot be decided unless curve properties "at infinity" are taken into account, and these properties are revealed when the curve is considered in projective space.

We then explain basic properties of implicit and parametric curve and surface representations. Both methods have distinct and complementary advantages. In the case of implicit surfaces, it is straightforward to decide whether a given point in space is or is not on the surface. For a parametric surface, on the other hand, it is easy to generate points that lie on the surface.

Because of such complementary strengths, the problem of how to convert from one form to the other is of great practical interest. General techniques exist for converting from parametric to implicit form, at least in principle, and we review here a simple version based on the Sylvester resultant. In Chapter 7, we show how to use Gröbner bases techniques for this purpose.

Whereas the conversion from parametric to implicit form is always possible, the conversion from an implicit to a parametric form depends on specific properties not shared by all algebraic curves and surfaces. These properties are fairly technical in nature and determining them algorithmically is difficult, so we omit this characterization. Instead, we give several methods for parameterization that are applicable to restricted classes of curves and surfaces.

Parameterization of quadratic curves and surfaces is a classical problem, and we give two different methods. We then discuss in detail the parameterization of cubic curves. Some higher-degree curves and surfaces are easy to parameterize, including the class of *monoids*. For this reason, monoids have been proposed by some authors as a basic shape element in geometric modeling. We discuss monoid parameterization also.

Up to this point, the material deals with representations of the carrier of edges and faces. The identification of edges and faces on curved carriers raises problems not encountered in the polyhedral domain, as discussed toward the end of the chapter. The problem here is that the geometric and topological structure of the carrier creates opportunities for ambiguities in that, for example, the specification of an edge as a segment bounded by two points on a space curve could be interpretable in different ways. In consequence, additional data are needed to disambiguate the representation.

5.2 Affine and Projective Spaces

We will use both affine and projective spaces. *Affine* n-dimensional space is the familiar n-space.[1] Using Cartesian coordinates, a point in this space has coordinates

$$(x_1, x_2, ..., x_n)$$

where the x_i are always finite. Ordinarily, the coordinate values of the x_i are real numbers, but for some results from algebraic geometry we must also consider points with complex coordinates. When this fact is critical, we will mention it explicitly.

Projective n-dimensional space consists of points with $n + 1$ coordinates $(x_0, x_1, x_2, ..., x_n)$, where not all x_k are zero. Again, each coordinate value is finite. Moreover, for nonzero numbers t, both $(x_0, x_1, ..., x_n)$ and $(tx_0, tx_1, ..., tx_n)$ describe the same point. The variable x_0 is sometimes called the *homogenizing* variable. We will usually write it as the first coordinate. However, any one of the other variables could be considered to be the homogenizing variable, a fact we will illustrate further.

As before, we may have to consider complex coordinates. In projective space, the points $(0, x_1, ..., x_n)$ are said to be *points at infinity*. These points form the hyperplane $x_0 = 0$. In particular, for $n = 2$, the points at infinity comprise the *line* at infinity.

Affine n-space can be considered a restriction of projective n-space by requiring $x_0 \neq 0$. In this sense, we might say that affine space is the finite part of projective space. In turn, projective n-space can be embedded into affine $n + 1$ space as follows: Consider each point $(a_0, a_1, a_2, ..., a_n)$ of projective space as the line

$$
\begin{aligned}
x_1 &= a_1 t \\
x_2 &= a_2 t \\
&\vdots \\
x_n &= a_n t \\
x_{n+1} &= a_0 t
\end{aligned}
$$

In consequence, projective n-space is the space of all lines in affine $(n + 1)$-space that contain the origin. The restriction of projective n-space to affine n-space may now be considered to be all points in which the embedded line space intersects the plane $x_{n+1} = 1$. Figure 5.1 illustrates the embedding of two-dimensional projective space into three-dimensional affine space. In the figure, the point $P = (a_0, a_1, a_2)$ of projective 2-space corresponds to the line l through the origin of affine 3-space. The point $p = (a_1/a_0, a_2/a_0)$

---

[1]Euclidian space, considered in Chapter 2, Section 2.4, is affine space endowed with the Euclidian distance metric.

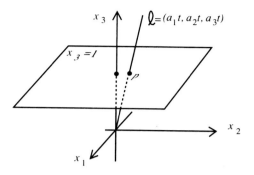

Figure 5.1   Embedding Projective Space into Affine Space

corresponding to P in affine 2-space is embedded into affine 3-space as the intersection of the line l with the plane $x_3 = 1$.

In affine spaces, the *origin* $(0, 0, ..., 0)$ is a distinguished point. In projective n-space, we distinguish $n + 1$ *fundamental* points with the coordinates

$$(1, 0, ..., 0, 0)$$
$$(0, 1, ..., 0, 0)$$
$$\vdots$$
$$(0, 0, ..., 1, 0)$$
$$(0, 0, ..., 0, 1)$$

For example, in the projective plane, the point $(1, 0, 0)$ is the affine origin, the point $(0, 1, 0)$ is the intersection of the x axis with the line at infinity, and the point $(0, 0, 1)$ is the intersection of the y axis with the line at infinity. The fundamental points span the *tetrahedron of reference*.

An *affine transformation* is a linear transformation of the form

$$
\begin{aligned}
y_1 &= a_{11}x_1 + a_{12}x_2 + ... + a_{1n}x_n + b_1 \\
y_2 &= a_{21}x_1 + a_{22}x_2 + ... + a_{2n}x_n + b_2 \\
&\vdots \\
y_n &= a_{n1}x_1 + a_{n2}x_2 + ... + a_{nn}x_n + b_n
\end{aligned}
$$

Intuitively, an affine transformation may shear or stretch a geometric shape.

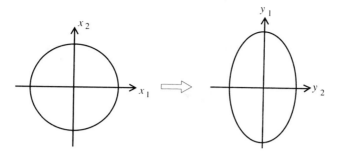

Figure 5.2   Affine Transformation of a Circle

Simple examples include rotations and reflections. Note that the matrix

$$\begin{pmatrix} a_{11} & a_{12} & \cdots & a_{1n} \\ a_{21} & a_{22} & \cdots & a_{2n} \\ \vdots & \vdots & & \vdots \\ a_{n1} & a_{n2} & \cdots & a_{nn} \end{pmatrix}$$

can be singular, in which case the transformation achieves a parallel projection.

Example 5.1:   The affine transformation

$$\begin{aligned} y_1 &= x_1 \\ y_2 &= x_1 + x_2 \end{aligned}$$

changes the circle $x_1^2 + x_2^2 - 1$ into the ellipse $2y_1^2 - 2y_1y_2 + y_2^2 - 1$. See also Figure 5.2. $\diamond$

A *projective transformation* is a linear transformation of the form

$$\begin{aligned} y_0 &= a_{00}x_0 + a_{01}x_1 + a_{02}x_2 + \ldots + a_{0n}x_n \\ y_1 &= a_{10}x_0 + a_{11}x_1 + a_{12}x_2 + \ldots + a_{1n}x_n \\ y_2 &= a_{20}x_0 + a_{21}x_1 + a_{22}x_2 + \ldots + a_{2n}x_n \\ &\vdots \\ y_n &= a_{n0}x_0 + a_{n1}x_1 + a_{n2}x_2 + \ldots + a_{nn}x_n \end{aligned}$$

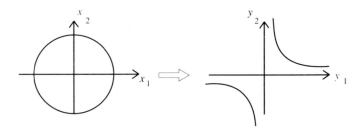

Figure 5.3   Projective Transformation of a Circle

It is well known that a projective transformation can change a circle into any conic section. Singular projective transformations are routinely used in computer graphics for computing perspective images.

Example 5.2:   The projective transformation

$$y_0 = x_2$$
$$y_1 = (x_0 + x_1)/2$$
$$y_2 = (x_0 - x_1)/2$$

changes the circle $x_1^2 + x_2^2 - x_0^2$ into the hyperbola $y_0^2 - 4y_1y_2$, shown in Figure 5.3. ◇

5.3 Implicit Representations

5.3.1 Implicit Surfaces

Every algebraic surface in affine 3-space is determined by an implicit equation

$$f(x, y, z) = 0$$

where $f(x, y, z)$ is a polynomial in the unknowns x, y, and z. The surface consists of all points (x, y, z) that satisfy this equation. In solid modeling, real coordinates are considered. However, to apply results from algebraic geometry, we must allow complex coordinates; see also Section 7.2.1 in Chapter 7.

The surface is *irreducible* if f does not factor over the field of complex numbers; that is, if there do not exist two nonconstant polynomials $h(x, y, z)$ and $k(x, y, z)$, possibly with complex coefficients, such that $f(x, y, z) = h(x, y, z)k(x, y, z)$. A surface that is not irreducible is *reducible*. For example, the cylinder $x^2 + y^2 - 1 = 0$ is an irreducible surface, but $x^2 + y^2 = 0$ is a pair of planes, for $x^2 + y^2 = (x + iy)(x - iy)$. The planes have points with complex coordinates and intersect in the real line $x = y = 0$. Note that, over the field of real numbers, $x^2 + y^2$ does not factor. Determining algorithmically whether a given polynomial $f(x, y, z)$ factors over the field of complex numbers is difficult.

Reducibility of a surface $f = 0$ means geometrically that the surface can be decomposed into two separate surfaces, each of which can be described separately by an implicit equation. This requires examining the surface in complex space, since we can find examples of surfaces in real three-dimensional space that appear to consist of two disjoint components that are, in fact, connected when complex surface points are considered.

The *gradient* or *normal* vector of the surface $f(x, y, z) = 0$ is the vector (f_x, f_y, f_z), where f_x, f_y, and f_z are the partial derivatives of f by x, y, and z, respectively. For example, the gradient of the sphere $f = x^2 + y^2 + z^2 - 1 = 0$ at the point (x, y, z) is $(2x, 2y, 2z)$. So, at $(1, 0, 0)$, the gradient is $(2, 0, 0)$. Sometimes, the gradient vector is *normed* to length 1. A point (x_0, y_0, z_0) on an irreducible surface $f = 0$ is *regular* if the gradient at the point is not the zero vector. Otherwise, the point is *singular*.

For every surface point, there exists a *tangent space* to the surface, consisting of all tangent lines to the surface at that point. It can be proved that, at a regular point, the tangent space is a plane, called the *tangent plane*. At a singular point, the tangent space is a *cone*; that is, it is a surface generated by lines each containing the singular point.

Assume that the surface $f = 0$ contains the origin. It is not difficult to show that, at the origin, the equation of the tangent space is given by the terms of lowest degree in f. For example, the sphere $x^2 + y^2 + z^2 - 2x = 0$ contains the origin and has at that point the tangent plane $2x = 0$.

The terms of lowest order are called the *initial form* of f. If the origin is a regular point of $f = 0$, then the initial form is linear; that is, the tangent space equation is that of a plane. If the origin is singular, then the initial form of f is nonlinear and describes the tangent cone.

Consider the initial form $h(x, y, z)$ of $f(x, y, z)$, and assume that the origin is a singular surface point. All terms in h have equal degree $d > 1$. Consider any point $p = (a, b, c)$ on the surface $h = 0$, where p is not the origin. Then the point $q = (ta, tb, tc)$ is also on $h = 0$ for all values of t, since $h(q) = t^d h(p)$. It follows that h contains the line

$$
\begin{aligned}
x &= ta \\
y &= tb \\
z &= tc
\end{aligned}
$$

Note that this line contains the origin. Since the line is constructed with an arbitrary point $p \neq (0, 0, 0)$ on $h = 0$, we have shown that the initial form defines a cone whose vertex is the origin.

The initial form gives information about the surface geometry at the origin. Similarly, the *degree form* of f, consisting of all terms of highest degree in f, yields information about the surface behavior at infinity.

The polynomial f describing a surface $f = 0$ is not a unique description of the surface, since $cf(x, y, z) = 0$ also describes the surface, provided that c is not zero. For this reason, a surface of degree n can be considered as a point in projective m-space, where $m + 1$ is the number of possible coefficients; that is,

$$m = \binom{n+3}{3} - 1 = \frac{n(n^2 + 6n + 11)}{6}$$

For example, to each quadric in 3-space there corresponds a point in projective 9-space, since a quadric is specified by the ratio of 10 coefficients.

The formula for m is derived as follows. Let $T(n, k)$ be the number of terms of degree up to n that can be formed with k variables. Clearly, $T(n, 1) = n + 1$. When forming all terms with $k + 1$ variables, we can group them by x^j, where x is one of the variables. Then the group for x^j consists of all terms $x^j u$, where u is formed with k variables and has degree $0, 1, ..., n - j$. The possible terms u are, therefore, all terms of degree up to $n - j$ that are formed with k variables, so

$$T(n, k+1) = \sum_{j=0}^{n} T(j, k)$$

By induction, one shows easily that

$$T(n, k) = \binom{n+k}{k}$$

Note that $m = T(n, 3) - 1$.

If f is multiplied with a polynomial g, then the zeros of the product $g(x, y, z)f(x, y, z) = 0$ are of the union of the zeros of $f = 0$ and of the zeros of $g = 0$. When g is varied, only the zeros of f are in every zero set. This motivates defining the surface $f = 0$ as the set of *common* zeros of all polynomials of the form $g(x, y, z)f(x, y, z)$, where g is any polynomial, including the trivial polynomial c, where c is a constant. The set of all such polynomials is an *ideal* — more precisely, a *principal ideal* — and f is a *generator* of the ideal. Ideals will be discussed in Chapter 7.

The polynomial $f(x, y, z) = 0$ describes a surface in affine 3-space. The corresponding surface in projective 3-space is obtained through *homogenizing* the polynomial f; that is, by substituting x/w for x, y/w for y, and z/w for z in f, followed by clearing the denominators.[2] The resulting polynomial $F(x, y, z, w)$ is the *homogeneous form* of f. All of its terms are of equal order. Similarly, the affine form can be obtained from F by substituting 1 for w in F. For example, the affine quadric

$$x^2 + 2x + y^2 + z^2 - 1 = 0$$

is homogenized as
$$x^2 + 2xw + y^2 + z^2 - w^2 = 0$$

We have used w as the additional, *homogenizing* variable. However, by a simple homogeneous transformation, we can rename variables. In effect, the embedding of affine space into projective space is changed by such a transformation. For example, consider $x = 0$ to be the plane at infinity. Then the affine part of projective space consists of the points

$$\left\{ \left(\frac{y}{x}, \frac{z}{x}, \frac{w}{x} \right) \;\middle|\; x \neq 0 \right\}$$

so the finite part of the surface $x^2 + 2xw + y^2 + z^2 - w^2 = 0$ is the surface

$$1 + 2w + y^2 + z^2 - w^2 = 0$$

in affine (y, z, w)-space. This may change the shape of the surface since now, as it were, we "see" a different finite part of it. In our example, the sphere $x^2 + 2x + y^2 + z^2 - 1 = 0$, in (x, y, z)-space, has been changed to the hyperboloid $1 + 2w + y^2 + z^2 - w^2 = 0$, in (y, z, w)-space.

5.3.2 Implicit Curves

An algebraic space curve is the common intersection of two or more surfaces. Although solid modeling usually restricts attention to those space curves that are the intersection of just two surfaces, one should remember that certain space curves cannot be defined algebraically as the intersection of only two surfaces.[3]

---

[2] Note that we use the same coordinate variables for the affine and the projective spaces.

[3] There are subtleties in this statement that are discussed in Chapter 7, Sections 7.2.5 and 7.2.6.

As in the case of surfaces, a space curve can be understood as the set of common zeros of all polynomials of the form $u_1 f_1 + u_2 f_2 + \cdots + u_k f_k$, where the u_i are arbitrary polynomials in x, y, and z, and the f_i are fixed polynomials defining the intersecting surfaces. The polynomials of this form constitute the ideal generated by the f_i.

A *rational map* between two projective spaces of the same dimension is a map

$$
\begin{aligned}
y_0 &= F_0(x_0, ..., x_n) \\
y_1 &= F_1(x_0, ..., x_n) \\
&\vdots \\
y_n &= F_n(x_0, ..., x_n)
\end{aligned}
$$

where the F_i are homogeneous polynomials of the same degree. It induces the rational map

$$
y_i = \frac{F_i(1, x_1, ..., x_n)}{F_0(1, x_1, ..., x_n)}
$$

between the embedded affine spaces. A rational map is *birational* if it is invertible; that is, if there exists an inverse rational map. Simple examples of birational maps are provided by the (rational) parametric representation of certain curves and surfaces. Here, a parametric curve is in birational correspondence with a line, and a parametric surface is in birational correspondence with the plane. From algebraic geometry, we know that every algebraic space curve is in birational correspondence with some plane algebraic curve. As we shall see, this fact plays a role in some surface-intersection algorithms.

5.3.3 Bezout's Theorem

Algebraic geometry has studied the relationship between the degree of an algebraic curve and the number of points in which that curve intersects another algebraic curve. The first theorem of this kind is due to Bezout and is as follows.

Theorem
Let f and g be two algebraic curves of degree m and n, respectively. If f and g intersect in more than mn points, then they have a common component.

In consequence, two curves that do not share a common component have at most mn intersection points. By assigning multiplicities to some of these intersections, we can put the theorem into a stronger form.

Theorem
Let f and g be two algebraic curves of degree m and n, respectively. Then f and g intersect in exactly mn points, or they have a common component.

In this form, Bezout's theorem is valid only if we consider the complex curve points, as well as curve points at infinity. In the parlance of Chapter 7, we must consider the curves in projective space over an algebraically closed ground field.

We can use Bezout's theorem to explain when a curve point is a multiple point. Take a point u on the plane algebraic curve f of degree n and consider a set of lines through u. By Bezout's theorem, most of these lines intersect f in n points. If a line intersects f in $n - 1$ additional points, then u is a *simple* or a *regular* point. A point that is not simple is a *multiple* or *singular* point. Note that it is not appropriate to infer multiplicities from the graphs of the curves in real affine space.

It is known that an algebraic curve has only a finite number of points that are not simple, and that a line has no multiple points. So, if all lines through u intersect f in less than $n-1$ additional points, then u is a multiple point. This definition of a multiple point is useless, however, because of the following.

Consider turning a line l through the curve point u. As the line rotates, centered at u, it intersects f in a fixed number of additional points, say $n - m$, where m is the multiplicity of u, except for finitely many positions at which l intersects f in less than $n - m$ additional points. Each such exceptional position defines a *tangent* to f at u.[4] If u is a regular point, there is only one such exceptional position. If u is a multiple point, then there could be up to m different exceptional positions, where m is the multiplicity of the point. Therefore, we define *point multiplicity* as follows.

The point u on the curve f has *multiplicity* m if an infinite number of lines through u intersect f in $n - m$ additional points. In particular, if infinitely many lines intersect f in $n - 2$ additional points, then u is a *double point*. Again, this procedure makes sense only if complex as well as real curve points are considered, and when intersections at infinity are considered.

Bezout's theorem can be generalized to surfaces and space curves as follows.

Theorem

An algebraic space curve of degree m intersects an algebraic surface of degree n in mn points unless a curve component is contained in the surface. Two algebraic surfaces of degree m and n, respectively, intersect in an algebraic curve of degree mn unless they have a common component.

As before, we must consider the curves and surfaces in complex projective space.

---

[4]Let f be a curve that contains the origin. Then we can show that the exceptional line positions are given by the roots of the initial form of f.

5.4 Parametric Representations

5.4.1 Parametric Surfaces

Some, but not all, algebraic surfaces possess a parametric representation. Such a representation consists of three functions:

$$
\begin{aligned}
x &= h_1(s,t) \\
y &= h_2(s,t) \\
z &= h_3(s,t)
\end{aligned}
$$

For specific values of s and t, these functions assign the coordinates of a surface point in (x,y,z)-space. For example, the unit sphere can be parameterized by

$$
\begin{aligned}
x &= \frac{1 - s^2 - t^2}{1 + s^2 + t^2} \\
y &= \frac{2s}{1 + s^2 + t^2} \\
z &= \frac{2t}{1 + s^2 + t^2}
\end{aligned}
$$

From the parameter values $s = t = 1$, we obtain, for instance, the point $(-\frac{1}{3}, \frac{2}{3}, \frac{2}{3})$ on the sphere.

In the example of the sphere, the parameterization does not "reach" the point $(-1, 0, 0)$, unless infinite values of s and t are permitted. We refer to such points as *singularities* of the parameterization. Infinite parameter values raise computational problems. Later, we give a projective parameterization of the sphere that avoids such singularities.

We view a parametric representation as a map from the (s,t)-plane to the surface in (x,y,z)-space. Most of the time, this map will be *rational*; that is, the functions h_1, h_2, and h_3 will be ratios of polynomials in s and t. In special situations, they can be polynomial. A mathematical characterization of when a rationally parameterizable surface has, in fact, a polynomial parameterization is a nontrivial problem. Note, however, that a rational parameterization of a surface in affine (x,y,z)-space corresponds to a polynomial parameterization of the same surface in projective (w,x,y,z)-space. The projective unit sphere is defined parametrically as

$$
\begin{aligned}
x &= 1 - s^2 - t^2 \\
y &= 2s \\
z &= 2t \\
w &= 1 + s^2 + t^2
\end{aligned}
$$

We typically view (s, t)-space as an affine plane, expecting that distinct pairs (s, t) correspond to distinct surface points. We call such a parameterization an *affine* parameterization. On occasion, we will want a *projective* parameterization. Then the map is between a projective plane with, say, (r, s, t) coordinates and the surface in (x, y, z)-space. For $u \neq 0$, (r, s, t) and (ur, us, ut) yield the same surface point, since both coordinate triples refer to the same point in the projective plane. A projective parameterization of the affine unit sphere is

$$
\begin{aligned}
x &= \frac{r^2 - s^2 - t^2}{r^2 + s^2 + t^2} \\
y &= \frac{2rs}{r^2 + s^2 + t^2} \\
z &= \frac{2rt}{r^2 + s^2 + t^2}
\end{aligned}
$$

A projective parameterization of the projective unit sphere is

$$
\begin{aligned}
x &= r^2 - s^2 - t^2 \\
y &= 2rs \\
z &= 2rt \\
w &= r^2 + s^2 + t^2
\end{aligned}
$$

Note that the parameter triple $(r, s, t) = (0, 1, 1)$ is mapped to the point $(-1, 0, 0)$ on the affine sphere that could not be reached with finite (s, t) values by the affine parameterization.

5.4.2 Parametric Curves

Some, but not all, algebraic curves possess a parametric representation. For example,

$$
\begin{aligned}
x(t) &= \frac{1 - t^2}{1 + t^2} \\
y(t) &= \frac{2t}{1 + t^2}
\end{aligned}
$$

is an affine parameterization of the unit circle in the affine plane. Again, we consider the parametric representation as a map, from a line with coordinate t to a curve in (x, y)-space. The point $(-1, 0)$ on the circle is a singularity for this parameterization.

Again, the curve can be projectively parameterized. The projective parameterization of the circle is given by

$$x(r,t) = \frac{r^2 - t^2}{r^2 + t^2}$$
$$y(r,t) = \frac{2rt}{r^2 + t^2}$$

The pair (r, t) defines a point on a projective line. The projective parameterization maps the point $(r, t) = (0, 1)$ to the singular point of the affine parameterization.

As an example of a parametric representation of a space curve, we mention the twisted cubic:

$$x(t) = t$$
$$y(t) = t^2$$
$$z(t) = t^3$$

A curve or surface parameterization is *faithful* if all but finitely many distinct parameter values correspond to distinct curve or surface points. For example, the parameterization

$$x(s) = -\frac{s^4 + 2s^3 + 3s^2 + 2s}{s^4 + 2s^3 + 3s^2 + 2s + 2}$$
$$y(s) = \frac{2(s^2 + s + 1)}{s^4 + 2s^3 + 3s^2 + 2s + 2} \tag{5.1}$$

of the unit circle is not faithful. To see this, observe that with $t = s^2 + s + 1$ we obtain from equation (5.1) the familiar parameterization of the circle. Thus, for all t, we have

$$(x(s_0), y(s_0)) = (x(s_1), y(s_1))$$

where s_0 and s_1 are the roots of $s^2 + s + 1 = t$.

5.4.3 Computer-Aided Geometric Design

In computer-aided geometric design (CAGD), there is a rich body of knowledge about special classes of parametric curves and surfaces. These classes are typically defined as linear combinations of certain *base functions*. Examples are Bezier curves and surfaces, and B-spline curves and surfaces. The importance of these curve and surface classes, briefly, stems from the following:

1. There is a method for constructing a curve or surface from a certain polygon or polyhedron, such that the shape of the polygon (polyhedron) gives a geometric intuition of, and control over, the shape of the curve (surface).

2. There are a number of elegant methods for evaluating and manipulating such curves and surfaces.

3. There are algorithms for aggregating larger curves or surfaces from patches of individual parametric curves or surfaces such that smoothness conditions between the patches are satisfied.

An in-depth discussion of these classes and their associated algorithms is beyond the scope of this book. At the end of this chapter, we cite a number of references on the subject.

5.5 Conversion from Implicit to Parametric Form

A useful capability in solid modeling is the conversion between implicit and parametric surface representations, since each form has different inherent strengths. Whereas all curves and surfaces with a rational parametric form can be converted to implicit form, at least in principle, not all implicit algebraic curves and surfaces possess a rational parametric form. In the case of curves, a complete characterization is given by *Noether's theorem*.

> **Theorem**
> A plane algebraic curve $f(x, y) = 0$ possesses a rational parametric form iff f has genus 0.

Roughly speaking, the curve genus measures the difference between the actual number of double points of f and the maximum number of double points a curve of the same degree as f may have. One knows that a plane curve of degree n can have no more than $(n-1)(n-2)/2$ double points, and this fact has an elementary proof. However, *counting* the number of double points of f is more subtle and involves the behavior at infinity as well as the internal structure of singular points. Algorithms for determining the genus exist but are nontrivial.

A similar characterization exists for surfaces, first given by Castelnuovo. For this characterization, two surface invariants are defined from which necessary and sufficient conditions for the existence of a parametric form are formulated. The invariants are not easily portrayed in intuitive terms.

The proof of Noether's theorem does not provide an efficient or simple computation for deriving a curve parameterization. However, for curves

	Implicit Form	Parametric Form	
Circle	$x^2 + y^2 - r^2 = 0$	$x(t) = r\,\dfrac{1 - t^2}{1 + t^2}$	$y(t) = r\,\dfrac{2t}{1 + t^2}$
Ellipse	$\dfrac{x^2}{a^2} + \dfrac{y^2}{b^2} - 1 = 0$	$x(t) = a\,\dfrac{1 - t^2}{1 + t^2}$	$y(t) = b\,\dfrac{2t}{1 + t^2}$
Hyperbola	$\dfrac{x^2}{a^2} - \dfrac{y^2}{b^2} - 1 = 0$	$x(t) = a\,\dfrac{1 + t^2}{1 - t^2}$	$y(t) = b\,\dfrac{2t}{1 - t^2}$
Parabola	$y^2 - 2px = 0$	$x(t) = \dfrac{t^2}{2p}$	$y(t) = t$

Table 5.1   Standard Parameterization of Conics

of degree 2 and 3, and for curves of special types such as *monoids*, simple techniques do exist. We define monoids later and describe how to parameterize them. Little appears to be known about the numerical behavior of these techniques, and the literature on this subject customarily assumes exact arithmetic.

5.5.1 Conics

We can use two basic approaches when parameterizing a conic:

1. Transform the conic into one for which a parametric form is already known, and then transform back this standard parameterization.

2. Parameterize the curve by a pencil of lines (defined later) through some curve point.

The first method requires a coordinate transformation of the conic that uses standard methods from linear algebra. The second method, with an appealingly simple underlying geometric idea, uses a modicum of coordinate transformations to simplify the implicit equation of the conic. It requires knowledge of a real curve point.

Since conics are well understood, the parameterizations for circle, ellipse, hyperbola, and parabola are well known when the curves are positioned suitably. We list them in Table 5.1.

A simple strategy for parameterizing a given conic is, therefore, first to transform the coordinate system so that the conic is properly positioned, then to retrieve a standard parameterization, and finally to apply the inverse transformation to the parametric representation.

First Method of Conic Parameterization

Any nondegenerate conic can be transformed into one of the conics in Table 5.1, using translations and rotations of the coordinate system. Formulae for computing the necessary transformation directly from the coefficients of the implicit curve equation are known, but are not reproduced here. Instead, we develop a more general method based on projective transformations, since it generalizes directly to quadric surfaces. Note, however, that projective transformations do not necessarily preserve the type of the conic. For example, it is possible that an ellipse is mapped to a hyperbola. For the purpose of curve parameterization, this is immaterial.

The general implicit conic equation, in homogeneous form, is

$$a_{11}x^2 + a_{22}y^2 + a_{33}w^2 + 2a_{12}xy + 2a_{13}xw + 2a_{23}yw = 0$$

It can be written as the *bilinear form*

$$(x \ y \ w) \begin{pmatrix} a_{11} & a_{12} & a_{13} \\ a_{12} & a_{22} & a_{23} \\ a_{13} & a_{23} & a_{33} \end{pmatrix} \begin{pmatrix} x \\ y \\ w \end{pmatrix} = 0$$

Let

$$A = \begin{pmatrix} a_{11} & a_{12} & a_{13} \\ a_{12} & a_{22} & a_{23} \\ a_{13} & a_{23} & a_{33} \end{pmatrix}$$

be the coefficient matrix of the conic. We seek a nonsingular matrix T such that $B = T^{-1}AT$ is diagonal. If the matrix A does not have full rank, then some diagonal elements of B will be zero. Since A is symmetric, it can be shown that such a matrix T exists and is real-valued.

The matrix T is a coordinate transformation, mapping the point $(x \ y \ w)$ to the new point $(x_1 \ y_1 \ w_1) = (x \ y \ w)T$. A conceptually simple method for finding it is to apply separate *Jacobi rotations* R, each designed to zero an off-diagonal element. For example, the element a_{12} is canceled by a rotation about the w axis of the form

$$R = \begin{pmatrix} \cos(\alpha) & \sin(\alpha) & 0 \\ -\sin(\alpha) & \cos(\alpha) & 0 \\ 0 & 0 & 1 \end{pmatrix}$$

The element a_{13} is canceled by a rotation about the y axis, and the element a_{23} by a rotation about the x axis. The rotation matrices can be found as follows. Let

$$A' = \begin{pmatrix} m & p \\ p & n \end{pmatrix}$$

be the 2×2 submatrix containing the element p we wish to cancel. Apply the rotation matrix

$$R^T = \begin{pmatrix} c & -s \\ s & c \end{pmatrix}$$

where $c = \cos(\alpha)$ and $s = \sin(\alpha)$. Then the $(1,2)$-element becomes

$$(R^T A' R)_{1,2} = (R^T A' R)_{2,1} = p(c^2 - s^2) - cs(n - m) = 0$$

Hence,

$$\frac{2cs}{c^2 - s^2} = \frac{2p}{n - m}$$

That is, to zero the element $(R^T A' R)_{1,2}$ in the matrix, we must choose an angle α such that

$$\tan(2\alpha) = \frac{2p}{n - m}$$

If $m = n$, then $\alpha = 45°$. Note that the angle α can always be restricted to be between $-45°$ and $45°$.

Let

$$B = \begin{pmatrix} \lambda_1 & 0 & 0 \\ 0 & \lambda_2 & 0 \\ 0 & 0 & \lambda_3 \end{pmatrix}$$

be the final diagonal matrix obtained. We distinguish the following cases:

- Rank 3; $\lambda_1, \lambda_2, \lambda_3 \neq 0$. The conic to be parameterized is irreducible.

- Rank 2; $\lambda_i, \lambda_j \neq 0$, $\lambda_k = 0$. The conic consists of two distinct lines.

- Rank 1; $\lambda_i \neq 0$, $\lambda_j, \lambda_k = 0$. The conic consists of two coincident lines.

If the conic consists of lines, then the original conic is reducible. In this case, each component should be parameterized separately as a line; only the rank 3 case is of interest.

The standard parameterization for the nondegenerate case depends on the signs of the λ_i. If all λ_i have the same sign, then the conic is imaginary. It is not possible to transform an imaginary conic to a real-valued one, or vice versa, since we apply real-valued rotation matrices. Hence, the original conic is also imaginary, so this case is not of interest.

If only λ_1 and λ_2 have the same sign, then the transformed conic is an ellipse or a circle. With $\mu_i = 1/\sqrt{|\lambda_i|}$, the conic is parameterized by

$$\begin{aligned} x(t) &= (1 - t^2)\mu_1 \\ y(t) &= 2t\mu_2 \\ w(t) &= (1 + t^2)\mu_3 \end{aligned}$$

If λ_1 has the opposite sign of λ_2 and λ_3, then the transformed conic is a hyperbola. With $\mu_i = 1/\sqrt{|\lambda_i|}$, it is parameterized by

$$
\begin{aligned}
x(t) &= (1 + t^2)\mu_1 \\
y(t) &= 2t\mu_2 \\
w(t) &= (1 - t^2)\mu_3
\end{aligned}
$$

Example 5.3: Consider the hyperbola $x^2 + 4xy + 3y^2 - 4 = 0$. Its matrix is

$$
A = \begin{pmatrix} 1 & 2 & 0 \\ 2 & 3 & 0 \\ 0 & 0 & -4 \end{pmatrix}
$$

Only a_{12} needs to be canceled. We determine

$$
\alpha = \frac{1}{2}\arctan(2) \approx 31.172°
$$

which yields as rotation matrix

$$
R^T = \begin{pmatrix} 0.851 & -0.526 & 0 \\ 0.526 & 0.851 & 0 \\ 0 & 0 & -4 \end{pmatrix}
$$

Then $B = R^T A R$ is

$$
B = \begin{pmatrix} -0.236 & 0.0 & 0 \\ 0.0 & 4.236 & 0 \\ 0 & 0 & -4 \end{pmatrix}
$$

It is diagonal and represents a hyperbola. As an affine curve, this conic is parameterized by

$$
\begin{aligned}
x_1(t) &= 4.117\,\frac{1 + t^2}{1 - t^2} \\
y_1(t) &= 0.972\,\frac{2t}{1 - t^2}
\end{aligned}
$$

The rotation matrix corresponds to the following coordinate transformation

$$
\begin{aligned}
x &= 0.526y_1 + 0.851x_1 \\
y &= 0.851y_1 - 0.526x_1
\end{aligned}
$$

from which we can recover a parameterization of the original hyperbola. $\diamondsuit$

Since a rotation affects off-diagonal elements other than the one we are zeroing out, a complete implementation of this approach must apply rotations iteratively, possibly more than once for each off-diagonal element. To understand the nature of the iteration, we recall the concept of matrix norms from Section 4.2.3 of Chapter 4. In particular, the *Frobenius norm* of the $m \times n$ matrix A is defined as

$$
\|A\|_F = \left(\sum_{i=1}^{m} \sum_{j=1}^{n} |a_{ij}|^2 \right)^{1/2}
$$

The Frobenius norm has the evident property that it is invariant under rotation. Hence, if $C = R^T A R$, then $\|A\|_F = \|C\|_F$. In the remainder of this section, we will use only the Frobenius norm and so will drop the subscript F.

We introduce a measure of how close the matrix A is to being diagonal and consider the quantity

$$
\text{off}(A) = \sum_{i \neq j} |a_{ij}|^2
$$

It is our plan to reduce this quantity with each rotation. If we can do that, then by repeated rotations we can minimize off(A), thereby making progress toward diagonalizing the matrix. Note that

$$
\|A\|^2 = \text{off}(A) + \sum_{i} |a_{ii}|^2
$$

Let $C = R^T A R$ be a rotation that zeros the ij-element in A. Then the Frobenius norms of A and C are equal. Observing how the diagonal elements a_{ii} and a_{jj} change, we note that

$$
\text{off}(C) = \text{off}(A) - 2|a_{ij}|^2 + 2|b_{ij}|^2 = \text{off}(A) - 2|a_{ij}|^2
$$

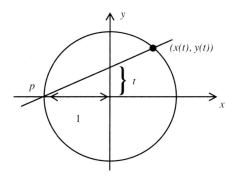

Figure 5.4   Parameterization of the Unit Circle

Hence, the quantity off(C) has decreased with twice the square of the entry in A that we zeroed. It follows that repeated rotations, each zeroing an off-diagonal element of largest magnitude, will drive off(A) to zero. For example, parameterizing the parabola $x^2 + 2xy + y^2 + 2y - 1 = 0$ in this way will require more than three rotations.

This iterative algorithm for diagonalizing A is numerically stable and has quadratic convergence. For the purpose of backsubstitution, the product of the individual rotation matrices should be accumulated.

Second Method of Conic Parameterization

A *pencil of lines* through a point p is a set of lines each containing p. The geometric idea on which the second parameterization method of conics is based can be stated as follows:

1. Pick a point $p = (u, v)$ on the conic and consider a pencil of lines through p. There is a one-parameter family of lines in the pencil.

2. The line $l(t)$ in the pencil will intersect the conic in p and in one other point $(x(t), y(t))$. This additional point provides the curve parameterization.

Therefore, a point p must be found, and the lines in the pencil must be quantified by a parameter t. For t, there is usually a natural choice. We demonstrate the idea with the circle $x^2 + y^2 - 1$. Thereafter, we show how the geometric idea expresses itself algebraically.

Consider the circle $x^2 + y^2 - 1 = 0$. We choose the point $p = (-1, 0)$ and consider the lines

$$l(t)\colon y = tx + t$$

that pass through p; see also Figure 5.4. Then the intersection points of the lines in the pencil and the circle are found by substituting for y and solving for x:

$$x^2(1 + t^2) + 2t^2 x + t^2 - 1 = 0$$

hence

$$x = \frac{-t^2 \pm \sqrt{t^4 + (1 - t^2)(1 + t^2)}}{1 + t^2} = \frac{-t^2 \pm 1}{1 + t^2}$$

Of the two roots, -1 represents the x coordinate of the fixed point p, whereas the other yields the x coordinate of the variable point $x(t)$ in which $l(t)$ also intersects the circle. In this way, we derive the familiar form

$$x(t) = \frac{1 - t^2}{1 + t^2}$$
$$y(t) = \frac{2t}{1 + t^2}$$

The procedure has a simple algebraic expression if the point p is chosen with care. To grasp this fact more generally, we pass to homogeneous coordinates (x, y, w).[5] Let

$$a_{11}x^2 + a_{22}y^2 + a_{33}w^2 + 2a_{12}xy + 2a_{13}xw + 2a_{23}yw = 0$$

be the homogenized equation. In general, we expect that none of the quadratic terms will vanish. However, if the conic contains one of the fundamental points, then the equation becomes linear in the corresponding variable. For example, if $(0, 0, 1)$ is a point on the conic, then the equation has no w^2 term. Similarly, if $(0, 1, 0)$ is on the conic, the y^2 term is absent. Thus, when a fundamental point is on the conic, then the conic equation will be linear in one variable, and that variable is then an explicit function of the other two. By considering the other two variables as projective parameter coordinates, therefore, we have a parameterization of the conic.

    Example 5.4: Given the circle $x^2 + y^2 - 2xw = 0$ that contains the origin $(0, 0, 1)$, we derive the parameterization:

$$x = s$$
$$y = t$$
$$w = (s^2 + t^2)/2s$$

This is a projective parameterization of the projective form of the conic. We set $s = 1$ to obtain affine parameter coordinates, and divide by w to

---

[5] Note that the homogenizing variable w is the third coordinate.

pass to affine curve coordinates. For the affine form of the circle, therefore, we obtain the affine parameterization

$$x(t) = 2/(1 + t^2)$$
$$y(t) = 2t/(1 + t^2)$$

Our strategy for parameterizing a conic is to translate or rotate the coordinate system so that the curve will pass through one of the three fundamental points, and then to parameterize the transformed curve. Applying the inverse coordinate transformation, we so obtain a parameterization for the original conic. The structure of the parameterization for conics is thus as follows:

1. If the curve already contains one of the fundamental points $(0, 0, 1)$, $(0, 1, 0)$, or $(1, 0, 0)$, then skip steps 2 and 4.

2. If the curve has a real point at infinity, change the coordinate system such that this point becomes $(0, 1, 0)$. If there is no real point at infinity, find a real point at finite distance and change the coordinate system such that the point becomes $(0, 0, 1)$.

3. Parameterize the curve.

4. Apply the inverse transformation to the parameterization.

Preference is given to finding a real point at infinity because that is a simpler computation.

A point at infinity can be found by setting $w = 0$ in the homogeneous conic equation. The resulting quadratic equation $a_{11}x^2 + 2a_{12}xy + a_{22}y^2 = 0$ is homogeneous in x and y, and has the solution

$$x = -a_{12} \pm \sqrt{a_{12}^2 - a_{11}a_{22}}$$
$$y = a_{11}$$

If the solution is complex, then no real points exist at infinity. This will be the case whenever the discriminant $a_{12}^2 - a_{11}a_{22}$ is less than zero. Otherwise, let $(u, v, 0)$ be the curve point corresponding to the real solution (u, v) of the homogeneous equation. Then the transformation

$$x = x_1 + uy_1$$
$$y = vy_1$$
$$w = w_1$$

is nonsingular and brings this point to $(0, 1, 0)$. After dehomogenizing, the transformed conic has the form

$$y_1(cx_1 + d) + q(x_1) = 0$$

where $q(x_1)$ is a quadratic polynomial in x_1. This curve is parameterized as $x_1 = t$, $y_1 = -q(t)/(ct + d)$. Using the transformation equations, a parameterization of the original curve is obtained.

If the curve has no real point at infinity and is not imaginary, then the conic must be an ellipse. A real point on it can be found by locating a point at which one of the partials vanishes, say $f_x = 0$. The point can then be brought to the origin by translation, after which the curve equation is parameterized as described before.

Example 5.5: Consider the conic $x^2 + 6xy + 5y^2 - 2x - 2y - 1 = 0$, whose homogeneous form is $x^2 + 6xy + 5y^2 - 2xw - 2yw - w^2 = 0$. The discriminant of $x^2 + 6xy + 5y^2$ is 4, so we expect two real solutions, corresponding to two points at infinity; that is, the conic is a hyperbola. One of the solutions is $(-1, 1)$, corresponding to the point $(-1, 1, 0)$ at infinity. The transformation

$$
\begin{aligned}
x &= x_1 - y_1 \\
y &= y_1
\end{aligned}
$$

maps the (affine) curve to

$$4x_1 y_1 + x_1^2 - 2x_1 - 1 = 0$$

which is parameterized as

$$
\begin{aligned}
x_1(t) &= t \\
y_1(t) &= \frac{1 + 2t - t^2}{4t}
\end{aligned}
$$

Backtransformation yields, for the original curve, the parameterization

$$
\begin{aligned}
x(t) &= \frac{5t^2 - 2t - 1}{4t} \\
y(t) &= \frac{1 + 2t - t^2}{4t}
\end{aligned}
$$

◇

Example 5.6: Consider the conic $x^2 + 4y^2 - 2x - 16y + 13 = 0$. Since $x^2 + 4y^2$ has a negative discriminant, the conic has no real points at infinity; thus, it is either an ellipse or an imaginary ellipse. The partial derivative by x defines the line $2x - 2 = 0$, and the intersection of this line with the conic determines the two points at which the curve has a tangent parallel to the x axis. We substitute 1 for x in the conic to locate these points, obtaining $4y^2 - 16y + 12$; hence, $(1, 3)$ is a point on the conic with tangent parallel to the x axis. We translate the curve by

$$
\begin{aligned}
x &= x_1 + 1 \\
y &= y_1 + 3
\end{aligned}
$$

and obtain

$$x_1^2 + 4y_1^2 + 8y_1 = 0$$

Note that this curve contains the origin, and that its homogeneous form is linear in w. We consider how the lines $x_1 - ty_1 = 0$ intersect this conic. Substituting, we obtain

$$t^2 y_1^2 + 4y_1^2 + 8y_1 = y_1(t^2 y_1 + 4y_1 + 8) = 0$$

Here, $y_1 = 0$ corresponds to the intersection at the origin; hence, the lines intersect the curve at $(0, 0)$ and at

$$
\begin{aligned}
y_1 &= \frac{-8}{t^2 + 4} \\
x_1 &= \frac{-8t}{t^2 + 4}
\end{aligned}
$$

This constitutes a parameterization of the translated curve. Translating back, we obtain the parameterization

$$
\begin{aligned}
x &= \frac{-8t}{t^2 + 4} + 1 &= \frac{t^2 - 8t + 4}{t^2 + 4} \\
y &= \frac{-8}{t^2 + 4} + 3 &= \frac{3t^2 + 4}{t^2 + 4}
\end{aligned}
$$

for the original conic. $\Diamond$

5.5.2 Quadrics

First Method

As in the case of conics, we can iteratively diagonalize the matrix representation of the quadric using rotations. Let

$$\begin{pmatrix} \lambda_1 & 0 & 0 & 0 \\ 0 & \lambda_2 & 0 & 0 \\ 0 & 0 & \lambda_3 & 0 \\ 0 & 0 & 0 & \lambda_4 \end{pmatrix}$$

be the diagonal matrix so obtained. We classify the surfaces first by rank.
Here, rank 2 and 1 are not of interest, since in this case the quadric surface
consists of two planes.

Rank 4 splits into several cases, according to the signature of the matrix;
that is, according to the distribution of signs of the diagonal elements. After
suitably renaming variables, and possibly multiplying the conic equation
with -1, we have three different cases to distinguish:

1. $\lambda_1, \lambda_2, \lambda_3, \lambda_4 > 0$: The quadric is imaginary. We denote this case by
   $(+, +, +, +)$.

2. $\lambda_1, \lambda_2, \lambda_3 > 0, \lambda_4 < 0$: The quadric is elliptic. We denote this case by
   $(+, +, +, -)$.

3. $\lambda_1, \lambda_2 > 0, \lambda_3, \lambda_4 < 0$: The quadric is hyperbolic. We denote this case
   by $(+, +, -, -)$.

Similarly, for rank 3, we distinguish the cases $(+, +, +, 0)$, and $(+, +, -, 0)$.
The case $(+, +, +, 0)$ means that the surface is imaginary. The projective
parameterization of the nonimaginary surfaces is given in Table 5.2. In
each case, we must multiply the ith coordinates with $\mu_i = 1/\sqrt{|\lambda_i|}$. Note
that the rank 3 surfaces are cones and cylinders.

Second Method

The second method for parameterizing conics also generalizes to quadrics:
A real point is picked on the surface, and a pencil of lines through this
point is considered. Again, the lines intersect the quadric in one additional
point, and we obtain in this way a surface parameterization. Since the lines
are in three-dimensional space, each member of the pencil must be fixed by
two independent parameters.

The algebraic method is closely analogous to the one for conics. We
wish to move a real point of the surface to one of the fundamental points
of projective three-dimensional space — that is, to $(0, 0, 0, 1)$, $(0, 0, 1, 0)$,

Signature	Parametric Form	
$(+,+,+,-)$	$x = r^2 - s^2 - t^2$	$y = 2rs$
	$z = 2rt$	$w = r^2 + s^2 + t^2$
$(+,+,-,-)$	$x = r^2 - s^2 + t^2$	$y = 2rs$
	$z = 2rt$	$w = r^2 + s^2 - t^2$
$(+,+,-,0)$	$x = r^2 - s^2 + t^2 - 2rt$	$y = 2rt - r^2 - s^2 - t^2$
	$z = 2sr - 2st$	$w = 1$

Table 5.2   Projective Parameterization of Quadric Surfaces

$(0,1,0,0)$, or $(1,0,0,0)$. Correspondingly, the equation simplifies with one of the quadratic terms vanishing in the homogeneous form. Thereafter, the parameterization proceeds as in the case of conics. For example, with the surface passing through $(0,1,0,0)$, its equation is linear in y. Hence, choosing $x = s$ and $z = t$ expresses y as a rational function of s and t.

A real surface point at infinity is found by investigating the homogeneous equation at $w = 0$. The substitution $w = 0$ gives a homogeneous form that describes a conic. This is the conic in which the quadric intersects the plane at infinity. This conic may have real points, found as described previously, and any such point can then be moved to $(0,1,0,0)$ by a coordinate transformation. Alternatively, we may deal with a closed surface (i.e., the ellipsoid), in which case we find a real point by locating where on the surface two of its partial derivatives vanish simultaneously. The details are quite straightforward.

5.5.3 Cubic Curves

Not all irreducible cubic curves have a rational parametric form. Those that do have a singular point that must be a double point. From a geometric point of view, the rational parameterization is analogous to conic parameterization: We select the double point on the cubic and consider a pencil of lines through it. Each line in the pencil must intersect the cubic in only one additional point. By parameterizing the pencil, we thus can parameterize the cubic. This idea is illustrated in Figure 5.5 for the curve $y^2 - x^2 - x^3 = 0$, whose double point is the origin. Thus, this curve is parameterized by the pencil of lines $y = tx$.

We describe an algorithm for parameterizing a cubic $f(x, y) = 0$. Using several birational transformations, the algorithm brings the cubic $f(x, y) = 0$ into the form

$$y_2^2 = g(x_2)$$

where the polynomial $g(x_2)$ has degree 4. If $g(x_2)$ has a double root, then

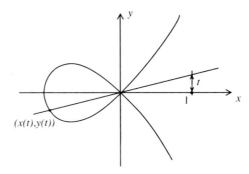

Figure 5.5   Parameterizing a Singular Cubic Curve

the cubic f is parameterizable; otherwise, a rational parametric form does not exist. As we will see, the parameterization process makes use of the parameterization algorithm for conics.

The curve transformations are as follows. First, we find a real point of the curve at infinity and bring it to $(0, 1, 0)$. This new coordinate system will be named (x_1, y_1). A real point at infinity must always exist, and when this point is $(0, 1, 0)$, then the cubic will not have a y_1^3 term. To understand this observation, we substitute $(0, 1, 0)$ into the homogeneous form F of the cubic. We obtain a value equal to the coefficient of the y_1^3 term in F. So, if $(0, 1, 0)$ is a curve point, the coefficient of y_1^3 must vanish.

Second, possibly after multiplying with a linear polynomial in x_1, the curve equation is changed to $y_2^2 - g(x_2) = 0$, where y_2 has the form $h(x_1)y_1 + k(x_1)$, where $h(x_1)$ is at most linear in x_1, and $k(x_1)$ is at most quadratic. Finally, if $g(x_2)$ has the double root α, then we let $y_3 = y_2/(x_2 - \alpha)$ and parameterize the resulting conic in y_3 and x_3. The conic parameterization, in turn, yields a parameterization for the cubic.

Consider a cubic $f(x, y)$ assuming that it is *regular* in both x and y; that is, both the x^3 and the y^3 term are present. To find a real point at infinity, we find a real root of the polynomial formed by all terms of degree 3 in f. Since this polynomial is a cubic homogeneous form, there is always a real root, say $(-v, u)$. We thus can write f as

$$f = (ux + vy)f_2(x, y) + g_2(x, y)$$

where f_2 is homogeneous of degree 2, and g_2 is at most of degree 2. The needed root, $(-v, u)$, could be found after substituting 1 for y, using a numerical subroutine or the Cardano formulae. We transform f by the nonsingular transformation

$$
\begin{aligned}
x &= x_1 - vy_1 \\
y &= uy_1
\end{aligned}
$$

Then the transformed cubic can be written as

$$
h_1(x_1)y_1^2 + h_2(x_1)y_1 + h_3(x_1) = 0
$$

where h_i is a polynomial of degree at most i. By multiplication with $4h_1(x_1)$, this equation can be rewritten as

$$
(2h_1(x_1)y_1 + h_2(x_1))^2 = (h_2(x_1))^2 - 4h_1(x_1)h_3(x_1)
$$

Setting $y_2 = 2h_1(x_1)y_1 + h_2(x_1)$ and $x_2 = x_1$, we thus obtain

$$
y_2^2 = h_4(x_2)
$$

where h_4 has degree 4 or less.

We investigate the roots of h_4. If there is at least one double root α, then we can set $y_3 = y_2/(x - \alpha)$ and so obtain the conic

$$
y_3^2 = q(x_2)
$$

This conic is parameterized, and, by backsubstitution, a parameterization of the original cubic is obtained. Note that if α is complex, then its conjugate $\tilde{\alpha}$ is also a double root and we set $y_3 = y_2/((x - \alpha)(x - \tilde{\alpha}))$. Thus a parameterization with real coefficients is possible. However, if h_4 has no multiple roots and has degree 3 or 4, then the curve $y_3^2 = h_4(x_1)$ has genus 1 and does not possess a rational parameterization. Since the original cubic f has been mapped to this curve birationally, it follows that f cannot be parameterized and is a nonsingular cubic.

Example Parameterization of a Cubic

Consider the cubic

$$f = 28y^3 + 26xy^2 + 7x^2y + x^3/2 + 28y^2 + 16xy + 7y + 3x/2$$

The degree form is $28y^3 + 26xy^2 + 7x^2y + x^3/2$ and has the root $(-2, 1)$. That is, we can write

$$f = (x + 2y)(14y^2 + 6xy + x^2/2) + 28y^2 + 16xy + 7y + 3x/2$$

We substitute

$$x = x_1 - 2y_1$$
$$y = y_1$$

to obtain

$$4(x_1 - 1)y_1^2 + 4(x_1^2 + 4x_1 + 1)y_1 + (x_1^3 + 3x_1)/2 = 0$$

After multiplication with $(x_1 - 1)$, we obtain the equivalent form

$$4(x_1 - 1)^2y_1^2 + 4(x_1 - 1)(x_1^2 + 4x_1 + 1)y_1 + (x_1^4 - x_1^3 + 3x_1^2 - 3x_1)/2 = 0$$

We set $y_2 = 2(x_1 - 1)y_1 + x_1^2 + 4x_1 + 1$ and obtain

$$y_2^2 = (x_1^4 + 17x_1^3 + 33x_1^2 + 19x_1 + 2)/2$$

The right-hand side has the double root $x_1 = -1$, so we set $y_3 = y_2/(x_1 + 1)$ to obtain

$$2y_3^2 = x_1^2 + 15x_1 + 2$$

This is a conic with the parameterization

$$x_1 = \frac{t^2 - 2}{2t + 15}$$
$$y_3 = -\frac{t^2 + 15t + 2}{\sqrt{2}(2t + 15)}$$

Recalling the substitution $y_3 = y_2/(x_1 + 1)$, we now obtain

$$y_2 = -\frac{(t^2 + 15t + 2)(t^2 + 2t + 13)}{\sqrt{2}(2t + 15)^2}$$

Since $y_2 = 2(x_1 - 1)y_1 + x_1^2 + 4x_1 + 1$, we obtain next

$$
\begin{aligned}
y_1 = \ & -[(\sqrt{2} + 1)t^4 + (8\sqrt{2} + 17)t^3 + (60\sqrt{2} + 45)t^2 + (44\sqrt{2} + 199)t \\
& + (109\sqrt{2} + 26)] / [\sqrt{2}(4t^3 + 22t^2 - 128t - 510)]
\end{aligned}
$$

Numerator and denominator have the common root $1 - 3\sqrt{2}$. Thus, the parametric expression for y_1 simplifies to

$$y_1 = \frac{(\sqrt{2} + 1)t^3 + (6\sqrt{2} + 12)t^2 + (30\sqrt{2} + 21)t + (11\sqrt{2} + 40)}{\sqrt{2}(4t^2 - (12\sqrt{2} - 26)t - (90\sqrt{2} + 30))}$$

From this parameterization, we finally obtain the parameterization of the original curve.

As an example of a nonsingular cubic, consider $y^2 - x^3 + x = 0$. It is already in the form $y_2^2 = x_2^3 - x_2 = h_4(x_2)$. Here, h_4 is of degree 3 with the distinct roots -1, 0, and 1, so the curve does not have a rational parametric form.

5.5.4 Monoids

A curve of degree n with a point of multiplicity $n - 1$ is called a *monoid*. Conics trivially are monoids, as are cubic curves possessing a double point (i.e., singular cubics). By Bezout's theorem, a line through an $(n - 1)$-fold point p intersects the curve in at most one additional point. Hence, a pencil of lines through p can be used to parameterize the monoid. The parameterization of conics and cubics has followed this strategy.

When the curve point of multiplicity $(n - 1)$ is the origin, then the equation of the monoid has the form

$$f(x, y) = h_n(x, y) - h_{n-1}(x, y) = 0$$

where h_n is homogeneous of degree n and h_{n-1} is homogeneous of degree $n - 1$. The curve parameterization is then simply

$$x(s, t) = s\frac{h_{n-1}(s, t)}{h_n(s, t)} \qquad\qquad y(s, t) = t\frac{h_{n-1}(s, t)}{h_n(s, t)}$$

This parameterization is projective, since it is derived from the pencil of lines

$$\begin{aligned} x(\lambda) &= s\lambda \\ y(\lambda) &= t\lambda \end{aligned}$$

We can make it an affine parameterization by choosing $s = 1$ or $t = 1$. For $s = 1$, we have

$$y = tx,$$

and, for $t = 1$,

$$x = sy.$$

Example 5.7: Consider the monoid

$$x^4 - 3x^3y + x^2y^2 + 2y^4 - x^3 - 3x^2y + y^2x = 0$$

Here, $h_4 = x^4 - 3x^3y + x^2y^2 + 2y^4$ and $h_3 = x^3 + 3x^2y - y^2x$. Choosing $s = 1$, we have $h_4(1, t) = 1 - 3t + t^2 + 2t^4$ and $h_3(1, t) = 1 + 3t - t^2$; hence, we obtain the parametric form

$$\begin{aligned} x(t) &= \frac{1 + 3t - t^2}{1 - 3t + t^2 + 2t^4} \\ y(t) &= \frac{t(1 + 3t - t^2)}{1 - 3t + t^2 + 2t^4} \end{aligned}$$

A surface of degree n is a *monoid* or *monoidal surface* if it contains a point of multiplicity $n - 1$. Monoidal surfaces include all quadrics, any cubic surface with a double point, any quartic surface with a triple point, and so on. When the $(n - 1)$-fold point is at the origin, the equation of such a surface becomes

$$f(x, y, z) = h_n(x, y, z) - h_{n-1}(x, y, z) = 0$$

where h_n has degree n and h_{n-1} has degree $n - 1$. The surface is parameterized by a pencil of lines through the origin. Each line in the pencil is determined by a point (r, s, t) of the projective plane and is given by the (parametric) equations

$$\begin{aligned} x(\lambda) &= r\lambda \\ y(\lambda) &= s\lambda \\ z(\lambda) &= t\lambda \end{aligned}$$

Therefore, the projective form of the surface parameterization is simply

$$
\begin{aligned}
x(r,s,t) &= r\,\frac{h_{n-1}(r,s,t)}{h_n(r,s,t)} \\[2mm]
y(r,s,t) &= s\,\frac{h_{n-1}(r,s,t)}{h_n(r,s,t)} \\[2mm]
z(r,s,t) &= t\,\frac{h_{n-1}(r,s,t)}{h_n(r,s,t)}
\end{aligned}
$$

and can be changed to the familiar affine parameterization by setting, for instance, $r = 1$.

Example 5.8: Consider the unit sphere

$$
x^2 + y^2 + (z - 1)^2 - 1 = 0
$$

which contains the origin. We have $h_2(x,y,z) = x^2+y^2+z^2$ and $h_1(x,y,z) = 2z$. Hence, this sphere is (projectively) parameterized by

$$
\begin{aligned}
x(r,s,t) &= \frac{2rt}{r^2 + s^2 + t^2} \\[2mm]
y(r,s,t) &= \frac{2st}{r^2 + s^2 + t^2} \\[2mm]
z(r,s,t) &= \frac{2t^2}{r^2 + s^2 + t^2}
\end{aligned}
$$

as is readily verified. An affine parameterization can be derived by setting one of the three parameters to 1. ◇

5.5.5 Parametric Domains

We mentioned previously that there is a rich literature on parametric curves and surfaces. To be more precise, the literature on that subject concentrates on *patches* of parametric curves and surfaces; that is, only a finite part of the curve or surface is considered. Typically, the patch is defined by restricting the parameter(s) to a *domain*. In the case of curves, the domain might be the interval $[0, 1]$; in the case of surfaces, the domain might be the unit square $[0, 1] \times [0, 1]$.

So far, we have discussed parameterizing curves and surfaces without regard to how the parameterization might be used. For example, if we consider a patch on the surface just parameterized, we may want to adjust the parameterization such that the patch is defined over a standard domain. We therefore consider the following problem.

Problem

Given a parameterized surface, and given four distinct surface points, by their parametric coordinates; reparameterize the surface, such that the parametric coordinates of the four given points are the corners of the unit square.

The reparameterization can be done based on a projective parameterization.

From the given projective parameterization (r, s, t), we derive another projective parameterization (u, v, w) such that the four corners are mapped as desired. Let the four corners be (r_i, s_i, t_i), in clockwise order. We seek a linear transformation A relating the two parameterizations as follows:

$$\rho \begin{pmatrix} r \\ s \\ t \end{pmatrix} = A \begin{pmatrix} u \\ v \\ w \end{pmatrix}$$

such that (r_1, s_1, t_1) is mapped to $(0, 0, 1)$, (r_2, s_2, t_2) is mapped to $(1, 0, 1)$, and so on. Note that, since (r, s, t) and $(\rho r, \rho s, \rho t)$ determine the same point on the projective plane, the proportionality factor ρ is needed. From projective geometry, we know that such a linear map exists, provided that no three of the points (r_i, s_i, t_i) are collinear. Thereafter, the (u, v, w) parameterization is dehomogenized by setting $w = 1$.

We formulate a system of linear equations determining A. The unknowns are the coefficients a_{jk} of A, and the proportionality factors ρ_i. For $i = 1, 2, 3, 4$, we write

$$\rho_i \begin{pmatrix} r_i \\ s_i \\ t_i \end{pmatrix} = A \begin{pmatrix} u_i \\ v_i \\ w_i \end{pmatrix} \tag{5.2}$$

We obtain 12 linear equations in 13 unknowns. Solving the system, we obtain A, and hence the new parameterization with the required domain.

Example 5.9: Consider the unit sphere parameterized as before:

$$x(r, s, t) = \frac{2rt}{r^2 + s^2 + t^2}$$
$$y(r, s, t) = \frac{2st}{r^2 + s^2 + t^2}$$
$$z(r, s, t) = \frac{2t^2}{r^2 + s^2 + t^2}$$

We wish to map a surface patch with the parametric corner coordinates $(0, 2, 1)$, $(1, 4, 1)$, $(3, 5, 1)$, and $(4, 1, 1)$; see also Figure 5.6. To find the

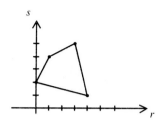

Figure 5.6   Patch Corners in Parameter Space

appropriate projective transformation, we formulate the linear equations (5.2) and obtain

$$
\begin{aligned}
0 &= a_{13} \\
2\rho_1 &= a_{23} \\
\rho_1 &= a_{33} \\
&\vdots \\
\rho_4 &= a_{31} + a_{33}
\end{aligned}
$$

Note that the a_{jk} are the entries of A. The solution yields the matrix

$$
A = \lambda \begin{pmatrix} 4 & 5 & 0 \\ -5 & 14 & 6 \\ -2 & 2 & 3 \end{pmatrix}
$$

Note that λ is a free constant. So, we can reparameterize the sphere by substituting $4u + 5v$ for r, $-5u + 14v + 6w$ for s, and $-2u + 2v + 3w$ for t. After dehomogenizing with $w = 1$, the resulting parameterization maps the corners of the domain $[0,1] \times [0,1]$ as desired. $\diamondsuit$

5.6 Conversion from Parametric to Implicit Form

Classical elimination theory provides tools for converting from rational parametric representations to implicit representations. Briefly, if a curve is given as

$$
\begin{aligned}
x(t) &= p(t)/r(t) \\
y(t) &= q(t)/r(t)
\end{aligned}
$$

then the pair of polynomial equations, obtained by clearing the denominator $r(t)$, describes the curve

$$x \cdot r(t) - p(t) = 0$$
$$y \cdot r(t) - q(t) = 0$$

These are polynomial equations in the variables x, y, and t. If t is eliminated from them, a single equation in x and y is obtained that is the implicit curve equation. Similarly, one eliminates the two parameters s and t from three polynomial equations obtained from a parametric surface representation, thus implicitizing a surface.

5.6.1 Resultants

One method for eliminating a variable from two polynomial equations is by forming the *resultant*. In the simplest case, there is only one variable to be eliminated; and thus we are, in effect, testing whether the two polynomials have a common root. We discuss this case in some detail. Let

$$f(x) = a_n x^n + a_{n-1} x^{n-1} + \ldots + a_0$$

and

$$g(x) = b_m x^m + b_{m-1} x^{m-1} + \ldots + b_0$$

be two univariate polynomials, of degree n and m. Clearly, f and g have a common root iff there are polynomials h_f and h_g of degree less than m and n, respectively, such that

$$f(x)h_f(x) = g(x)h_g(x) \tag{5.3}$$

We set

$$h_f(x) = u_{m-1} x^{m-1} + \ldots + u_1 x + u_0$$

and

$$h_g(x) = v_{n-1} x^{n-1} + \ldots + v_1 x + v_0$$

Then the coefficients u_k and v_k can be determined by symbolically multiplying out equation (5.3). The result is a polynomial in x all of whose coefficients must vanish. Each coefficient, in turn, is a linear form in the unknowns u_k and v_k. By setting the x coefficients to zero, we obtain a system of linear equations in u_k and v_k, and this system has a nontrivial solution iff equation (5.3) has a nontrivial solution. Now equation (5.3) has a nontrivial solution iff the linear system is underconstrained; that is, iff the system's determinant is zero. The system's determinant has the following form:

$$
\begin{vmatrix}
a_n & a_{n-1} & \cdots & a_0 & 0 & \cdots & 0 \\
0 & a_n & \cdots & a_1 & a_0 & \cdots & 0 \\
\vdots & & \ddots & & & \ddots & \\
0 & \cdots & 0 & a_n & a_{n-1} & \cdots & a_0 \\
b_m & b_{m-1} & \cdots & b_0 & 0 & \cdots & 0 \\
0 & b_m & \cdots & b_1 & b_0 & \cdots & 0 \\
\vdots & & \ddots & & & \ddots & \\
0 & \cdots & 0 & b_m & b_{m-1} & \cdots & b_0
\end{vmatrix}
$$

So, f and g have a common solution iff this determinant is zero. The determinant is called the *Sylvester resultant*, and we will denote it $Res_x(f, g)$.

In principle, the resultant can be applied to multivariate polynomials. A main variable x is identified, and the coefficients a_k and b_k are now polynomials in the remaining variables. In this case, a zero resultant does not necessarily imply a common solution to the two polynomials, since it is possible that the two lead coefficients a_n and b_m have a common solution. In that case, the resulting polynomial $Res_x(f, g)$ has additional factors identifying the common roots of the lead coefficients. Summarizing, the following theorem can be proved.

> **Theorem**
> Let $f(x_0)$ and $g(x_0)$ be multivariate polynomials of degree n and m, respectively, with coefficients that are polynomials in the variables $x_1, ..., x_n$. Then $Res_x(f, g) = 0$ iff there is a common solution of f and g, or the leading coefficients of f and g vanish simultaneously, or the coefficient polynomials of f or of g have a common root.

Consider the bivariate polynomials $f(x, y) = xy^2 - x^2y + y^2 + x^2 + 1$ and $g(x, y) = x^2y^2 - y^2 - 3xy + x$. We consider them polynomials in y with coefficients that are polynomials in x, and obtain as resultant

$$
Res_y(f, g) = \begin{vmatrix}
x+1 & -x^2 & x^2+1 & 0 \\
0 & x+1 & -x^2 & x^2+1 \\
x^2-1 & -3x & x & 0 \\
0 & x^2-1 & -3x & x
\end{vmatrix}
$$

$$
= (x+1)(x^7 - 3x^6 + x^5 + 2x^4 + 3x^3 + 11x^2 + x + 1)
$$

When formulating f and g as polynomials in y, the lead coefficients are $x+1$ and x^2-1, respectively. Both vanish simultaneously for $x=-1$, as reflected in the presence of the factor $x+1$.

Geometrically, the Sylvester resultant constitutes an orthographic projection along the axis of the variable that is eliminated. The following consideration shows that some extraneous factors have a geometric significance. Consider three polynomial equations in three variables — say, $f(x,y,z)=0$, $g(x,y,z)=0$, and $h(x,y,z)=0$. The three equations define three surfaces, and the common solutions to f, g, and h are the points at which all three surfaces intersect. We eliminate first z, obtaining two equations in x and y — say, $f_1(x,y)=Res_z(f,g)$ and $g_1(x,y)=Res_z(g,h)$. Note that the curve $f_1=0$ contains the projection of the space curve that is the intersection $f=0\cap g=0$. Similarly, $g_1=0$ contains the projection of the intersection $g=0\cap h=0$. A common intersection of the three surfaces must also be an intersection of the two plane curves f_1 and g_1. However, if there are two points $p=(a,b,c)$ and $q=(a,b,d)$ in 3-space, where $c\neq d$, and p is on the intersection $f\cap g$ while q is on the intersection $g\cap h$, then $p'=(a,b)$ is an intersection of $g_1=0$ with $h_1=0$ but is not a common intersection of the three surfaces. These "phantom" intersections must give rise to extraneous factors when we eliminate one of the variables from f_1 and g_1.

5.6.2 Implicitization of Curves and Surfaces

The resultant provides us with an algorithm to convert parametric curves and surfaces into implicit form. In the case of curves, we need to compute

$$f(x,y) = Res_t(xr(t) - p(t),\ yr(t) - q(t))$$

For example, recalling the parameterization of the unit circle (Table 5.1), we have

$$Res_t(x(1+t^2) - (1-t^2),\ y(1+t^2) - 2t) = 4(x^2 + y^2 - 1)$$

Here, no extraneous polynomial factors appear.

In the case of surfaces, we must eliminate two variables in succession. For example, the sphere that we parameterized as a monoid, with $r=1$, requires dealing with the equations

$$x(1+s^2+t^2) - 2t = 0 \tag{5.4}$$
$$y(1+s^2+t^2) - 2st = 0 \tag{5.5}$$
$$z(1+s^2+t^2) - 2t^2 = 0 \tag{5.6}$$

We begin by eliminating s from equations (5.4) and (5.5), and also from equations (5.5) and (5.6). This yields the equations

$$
\begin{aligned}
4t^2(y^2 + t^2x^2 + x^2 - 2tx) &= 0 \\
4t^2(t^2z^2 + z^2 - 2t^2z + t^2y^2) &= 0
\end{aligned}
$$

After dropping the common factor $4t^2$, we now eliminate t and obtain

$$
(x^2 + y^2 + z^2 - 2z)(y^6 + y^4(x^2 + z^2) - 2y^2z(y^2 + 2x^2) + 4x^2z^2) = 0
$$

Note that the second factor is extraneous.

We observe that surface implicitization using the Sylvester resultant is not an attractive method, since even in such simple examples complicated extraneous factors are generated. Since polynomial factorization is a difficult problem, it is not always easy to recognize the extraneous factors and to eliminate them. Moreover, the Sylvester resultant requires forming large matrices for higher-degree surfaces that can be costly to evaluate. We will discuss some alternatives in Sections 7.5.1 and 7.8.3 in Chapter 7.

5.7 Edge Identification

We have divided the representation of edges and faces into two parts: A description of the carrier (a space curve or surface) and a description of the boundary delimiting the area or interval of interest on the carrier. The preceding material in this chapter has dealt with techniques for representing the carrier, and has described elementary methods for manipulating these representations. We now turn to the boundary specification for edges. If curved edges are not specified carefully, the boundary description of objects could contain ambiguities.

In favorable cases, the carrier of the edge is a space curve that possesses a parameterization. In that case, one may represent the carrier parametrically and identify the edge by giving an interval of parameter values. This identifies the edge unambiguously. In general, however, the carrier is not parameterizable and so must be defined as the intersection of surfaces. In that case, the identification of the edge on the carrier is more delicate.

As a segment of a space curve, an edge boundary consists simply of the two bounding vertices; that is, of the two curve points. However, the global geometry of the carrier may be such that the two points do not identify a curve segment uniquely, so that additional information will be needed. In the following discussion, we assume that the edge carrier has been specified by an intersecting pair of surfaces.

5.7.1 Topological Aspects

Recall from Chapter 2, Section 2.4, the definition of a topologically valid solid. The definition considered two separate aspects:

1. The topological structure of solids was characterized abstractly, in the simplest case as a connected 3-manifold with compact boundary.

2. The relationship between the solid and the surrounding space was characterized by considering how the solid is embedded in three-dimensional space.

If we begin with a geometric description of the carrier, the specification of the edge as a segment on that carrier seems to be simply a matter of identifying a startpoint and an endpoint. However, there are complications.

If the curve is closed, then two points on it partition the curve into two segments, and we need to know which of the two segments is the edge. This problem did not occur with straight lines, for at most one of the line segments is finite.[6] This motivates orienting the carrier. If the carrier is a simple closed curve, distinct start and end vertices will specify a segment on it unambiguously.

If the space curve contains singularities, then it does not need to be homeomorphic to a circle. In that case, two points may partition the curve into more than two segments, so there could be several segments, each oriented from the start to the end vertex. An example is shown later in Figure 5.12. Here, we ask whether some segments can be ruled out because they would lead to geometric or topological inconsistencies later. We will show that a global resolution of edge ambiguities cannot be guaranteed.

The constructions demonstrate the need to identify segments of space curves by more information than just bounding vertices and orientation. Two methods have been proposed. One method uses an auxiliary vertex placed at the interior of the edge; the other method provides additional directional information at the two bounding vertices.

5.7.2 Edge Orientation

In Chapters 2 and 3, we oriented edges so that there could be a reference direction, giving meaning to concepts such as left and right adjacent faces. In the linear case, edges have distinct vertices u and v, and the edge (u, v) may simply be considered oriented from u to v. When extending this approach to curved edges, we must make some modifications: Since a curved edge may be closed, the specification (u, v) cannot imply an orientation. A subdivision of such edges is necessary to define an edge orientation at the same time, using this technique. A minimum of three vertices is needed on

---

[6]In projective space, a line is a closed curve. Two distinct points define two segments, but at most one is finite. This segment must be chosen because we assume that the boundary of solids is compact.

a closed curve. A disadvantage of this approach is that we must traverse an edge, say (u, v), before we can decide whether the initial direction of traversal was the correct one. This is unsatisfactory in general.

A better method for orienting edges is to orient the carrier directly. Let f and g be two surfaces whose intersection contains the edge. Let ∇f and ∇g be the surface gradients. We consider orienting the curve locally at the point p by the directed tangent

$$\mathbf{t}(p) = \nabla f(p) \times \nabla g(p)$$

As long as p is not singular on f or on g, and f and g are not tangent to each other at p, the vector $\mathbf{t}(p)$ exists. Let us call this convention the *cross-product method*.

The cross-product method has several properties that complicate its use. In particular,

$$\nabla f \times \nabla g = -(\nabla g \times \nabla f) = \nabla(-g) \times \nabla f$$

So, we must distinguish between f and $-f$, and hence must adopt the surface-orientation conventions of Section 3.2 in Chapter 3. Now we must give the two surfaces in order. We propose to fix this order *implicitly* as

(left face, right face)

declaring the carrier orientation to be $\nabla f \times \nabla g$, where $f = 0$ is the carrier of the left face, and $g = 0$ is the carrier of the right face, and both f and g have been oriented correctly.

However, this convention gives the expected results only when the angle between the face normals at p is acute. Otherwise, the order should be (right face, left face); see also Figure 5.7. Therefore, we specify the orientation by explicitly annotating the edge with the surface pair, ordered depending on the angle of intersection.

The angle between two curved faces varies along the edge, and our convention is defective if it changes from acute to obtuse, or vice versa, because then the carrier orientation as described by the gradient pair should be reversed. An example is shown in Figure 5.8, with the intersection of $f\colon z = 0$ and $g\colon z + y^2 - x^2 - x^3 = 0$, a plane curve, oriented uniformly as $\nabla f \times \nabla g$. The orientation reverses at the singularity at the origin where ∇f and ∇g are collinear. It is not difficult to see that a surface intersection curve must have a singularity at every point p at which the surface gradients are collinear. Hence, it is useful to require that there be no singularities in an edge interior. Thus, we require a vertex at every singular curve point that is part of the surface of the object that we wish to represent.

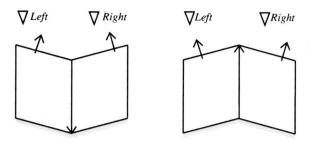

Figure 5.7   Implicit Edge Orientation as Left Face × Right Face

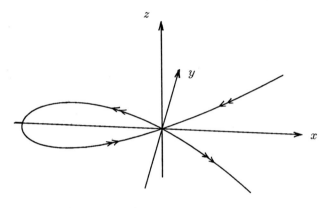

Figure 5.8   Intersection of f: $z = 0$ and g: $z + y^2 - x^2 - x^3 = 0$, Oriented as $\nabla f \times \nabla g$

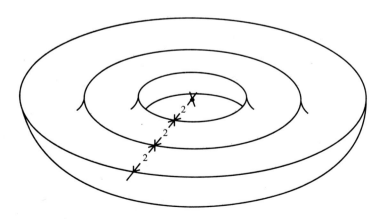

Figure 5.9   Grooved Toroidal Object

If the carrier is a parameterized space curve, then its parameterization implies an orientation. Most of the difficulties in specifying the edge unambiguously disappear in this case, for we consider the edge to be the curve segment defined by an interval of parameter values. Since not all algebraic space curves can be parameterized, however, this method is of limited utility.

5.7.3 Singularities on Edges

If an edge (u, v) is assumed to be oriented by the cross-product method, subject to the details just described, it is still possible that there are two or more curve segments that are both oriented from u to v. In this case, the edge may have been ambiguously defined, since we do not know locally which of the segments (u, v) is intended.

Conceivably, some of the segments cannot be used because of other properties of the boundary. For example, by choosing a particular segment e, we might not be able to find a consistent boundary for some of the faces. Possibly, then, such a local ambiguity could be resolved by global geometric properties of the data structure. We demonstrate now that global properties need not resolve ambiguities when we use implicit algebraic surfaces.

We assume that there are no curve singularities in the interior of edges, that every edge cycle contains at least three vertices, and that the segment orientation so implied is consistent with the local curve orientation by the cross-product method. With all these conventions, we now construct an ambiguous boundary representation.

We unambiguously construct an object with CSG operations. Then, we give a boundary representation for it and show that there is a second interpretation that defines a different solid. In the CSG definition, each primitive volume is specified by an implicit algebraic equation $f = 0$, and is the closure of the set of all points p for which $f(p) < 0$. Thus, we deal with regular sets, albeit not always of finite volume. Specifically, we use the *Cartesian* cylinder $C : y^3 + z^3 - 6yz = 0$, and the standard CSG primitives.

We construct the grooved toroidal object shown in Figure 5.9 by subtracting tori T_2 and T_3 from the halved torus $T_1 \cap H$, where H is the half-space $y \leq 0$. The corresponding CSG expression is $((T_1 \cap H) - T_2) - T_3$. The tori dimensions are as indicated in the figure. Next, we take the cylinder C, described previously and shown in Figure 5.10. The surface orientation of C is as indicated by the gradient vectors drawn in the figure. The intersection $(((T_1 \cap H) - T_2) - T_3) \cap C$ is as shown in Figure 5.11, and is the final object. We give a boundary description of the object in Tables 5.3–5.5. The boundary description could be the result of a conversion algorithm translating CSG trees to boundary representations, or the description could have been constructed directly from Figure 5.11 by an unwary designer.

In the description, we assume that the edges are oriented as specified by the vertex pair written, and this is consistent with the carrier orientation

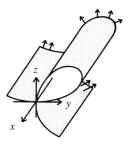

Figure 5.10   The Cartesian Cylinder C

by the cross-product of left-face gradient with right-face gradient, and by the cross-product of the surface gradients as indicated. Edge e_1, then, is oriented from vertex v_1 to vertex v_3. The opposite direction is indicated by negating the edge symbol; for instance, $-e_1$ denotes the edge e_1 in opposite direction.

We consider which curve segment constitutes an edge in the description given in the tables. The complete intersection curve of the torus T_1 with C is shown in Figure 5.12. Based on local information, the edge (v_6, v_4) can lie in one of four directions at v_6. One, in the $-x$ direction, must be excluded, since it does not directly connect to v_4. Another one, in the x direction,

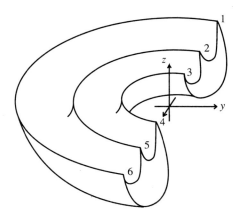

Figure 5.11   Object $(((T_1 \cap H) - T_2) - T_3) \cap C$

Vertex Coordinates	
v_1:	$(-6, 0, 0)$
v_2:	$(-4, 0, 0)$
v_3:	$(-2, 0, 0)$
v_4:	$(2, 0, 0)$
v_5:	$(4, 0, 0)$
v_6:	$(6, 0, 0)$

Vertex Incidences	
v_1:	$(e_1, -e_3, e_7)$
v_2:	$(e_3, -e_2, e_8)$
v_3:	$(e_2, -e_1, e_9)$
v_4:	$(e_5, -e_9, -e_4)$
v_5:	$(e_6, -e_8, -e_5)$
v_6:	$(e_4, -e_7, -e_6)$

Table 5.3 Vertex Tables of $(((T_1 \cap H) - T_2) - T_3) \cap C$

cannot be correct, since then the left and right faces of the edge would be incorrectly situated. They also would require a different edge orientation by the cross-product convention. The remaining two directions give consistent interpretations with the convention of outward-pointing normals, the topology of the boundary description, and the curve orientation by the cross-product method. For global topological consistency, the direction choices must agree at all vertices. We verify that there are two consistent interpretations of the boundary description. The second interpretation is shown in Figure 5.13. Note that the two interpretations are not congruent to each other and have different volumes.

Face Equation	
a:	$(x^2 + y^2 + z^2 - 4)^2 + 32(z^2 - x^2 - y^2 - 4) + 256 = 0$
b:	$-(x^2 + y^2 + z^2 - 1)^2 - 18(z^2 - x^2 - y^2 - 1) - 81 = 0$
c:	$-(x^2 + y^2 + z^2 - 1)^2 - 50(z^2 - x^2 - y^2 - 1) - 625 = 0$
d:	$y^3 + z^3 - 6yz = 0$
e:	$y^3 + z^3 - 6yz = 0$

Face Boundary	
a:	$(-e_1, e_7, e_4, -e_9)$
b:	$(-e_2, e_9, e_5, -e_8)$
c:	$(-e_3, e_8, e_6, -e_7)$
d:	(e_1, e_2, e_3)
e:	$(-e_4, -e_6, -e_5)$

Table 5.4 Face Tables of $(((T_1 \cap H) - T_2) - T_3) \cap C$

Edge	Incident Vertices	Left, Right Face	Carrier Orientation
e_1	(v_1, v_3)	(a, d)	$a \times d$
e_2	(v_3, v_2)	(b, d)	$b \times d$
e_3	(v_2, v_1)	(c, d)	$c \times d$
e_4	(v_6, v_4)	(e, a)	$e \times a$
e_5	(v_4, v_5)	(e, b)	$e \times b$
e_6	(v_5, v_6)	(e, c)	$e \times c$
e_7	(v_1, v_6)	(c, a)	$c \times a$
e_8	(v_2, v_5)	(b, c)	$b \times c$
e_9	(v_3, v_4)	(a, b)	$a \times b$

Table 5.5   Edge Table of $(((T_1 \cap H) - T_2) - T_3) \cap C$

5.7.4 Edge-Identification Information

The constructions in the previous section demonstrate that we must specify the following information to identify edge segments on space curves unambiguously:

1. The geometry of the carrier; for example, as the intersection of two surfaces

2. The bounding vertices of the edge

3. The intended curve branch

4. The orientation of the branch, at each vertex

The branch orientation and identification are needed because a vertex of the edge may be at a curve singularity.

Let (f, g) denote the intersection of the surfaces f and g, and consider a singular point p on it. At such a point, we have one or more distinct branches of the curve. In general, it is not possible to isolate one of the branches by selecting a better choice of g or by using additional surfaces to intersect with. If singular points are confined to vertices, then the edge segment is homeomorphic to a line, and therefore can be identified unambiguously by an interior point of the edge, as shown in Figure 5.14. The strength of this method is its simplicity. A drawback is its inconvenience: To locate the correct branch and direction at each vertex, we must trace the edge, beginning with the interior point, in both directions.

Another way to identify the branch is to give directional information at the vertices. In the simplest case, the desired branch is identified by

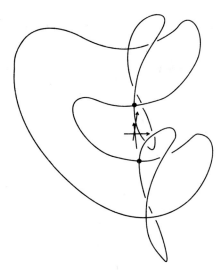

Figure 5.12   Complete Torus/Cylinder Intersection

the directed tangent at each vertex. This method suffices for all *nodal* singularities; that is, for singularities at which locally the curve consists of a number of continuous branches that intersect transversally. More difficult singularities are shown in Figures 5.15 and 5.16. The singularity in Figure 5.15 is a *cusp*. The curve has only one branch at the point and the branch is singular. The singularity in Figure 5.16 is a *tacnode*. Here, the curve

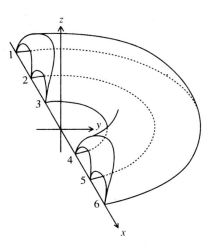

Figure 5.13   Second Interpretation of the Representation

Figure 5.14   Branch Identification by Interior Point

has two branches that intersect tangentially. Intuitively, such singularities require information about higher-order derivatives. This information may be based on the quadratic transformations explained in Section 6.5.2 of Chapter 6. Note that the singularities shown in Figures 5.15 and 5.16 arise for surfaces of fairly low degree: The cusp is the intersection of the cubic surface $y^2 - x^3 + z = 0$ with the plane $z = 0$, and the tacnode is the intersection of the parabolic cylinder $z - y^2 = 0$ with the quartic surface $z - x^4 - y^4 = 0$, approximately a figure of revolution.

The ambiguities constructed here depend on the fact that the curves and surfaces involved are not parametric. Indeed, when edges and faces can be defined in terms of domains on parametric curves and surfaces, the information listed here is easily derived from the parameterization and the domain. Unfortunately, many space curves are not parameterizable —

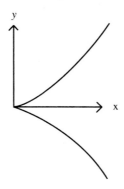

Figure 5.15   Cuspidal Singularity of $y^2 - x^3 + z = 0 \cap z = 0$

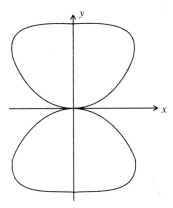

Figure 5.16   Tacnodal Singularity of $z - x^4 - y^4 = 0 \cap z - y^2 = 0$

even the intersection curves of parameterizable surfaces. For example, the intersection of two cylinders is, in general, a space curve that cannot be represented in a rational parametric form.

5.8 Notes and References

Many books on affine and projective spaces explain the details sketched in Section 5.2. See, for example, Klein (1925), or Semple and Kneebone (1952).

The sections on implicit and parametric representations present standard material from algebraic geometry. Brieskorn and Knörrer (1986) contains an exposition of many of these concepts, and illustrates them with many examples. More condensed and rigorous accounts can be found in van der Waerden (1939), Walker (1950), and many other books on algebraic curves and algebraic geometry. The following chapters present additional information on the intuition behind the algebraic concepts.

The geometry of conics has been studied in great detail by many authors. A nice exposition is found in Hilbert and Cohn-Vossen (1952). Formulae for determining the type of conics and quadrics directly from the coefficients of their equations, and methods for transforming conics to standard form through translation and rotation, can be found in mathematical handbooks, including Bronstein and Semendjajew (1961).

A good entry into the literature on special classes of parametric surfaces is the survey article by Böhm, Farin, and Kahmann (1984). Textbooks on the subject include Mortenson (1985), Bartels, Beatty, and Barsky (1987), and Farin (1988).

The first method for parameterizing conics and quadrics uses a method due to Jacobi. Our exposition is adapted from Golub and van Loan (1983). Jacobi rotations are numerically stable and the iteration has quadratic convergence. The second method for parameterizing conics and quadric surfaces is from Abhyankar and Bajaj (1987a).

Abhyankar and Bajaj (1987b) give the method for parameterizing cubic curves. Their paper also gives a technique for parameterizing cubic surfaces, but the resulting parameterization is not necessarily faithful. A different method for parameterizing cubic surfaces is given in Sederberg and Snively (1987).

Abhyankar and Bajaj (1987c,d) present techniques for parameterizing general algebraic curves. By extension, the method for parameterizing plane algebraic curves also determines whether the curve has genus zero.

Monoids were well known in the nineteenth century, and were used as a tool to classify algebraic space curves. In the more recent literature, they are presented again by Sederberg (1983), where they are called *dual forms* in recognition of the ease of converting between the parametric and the implicit form.

Classical elimination theory has developed a number of different resultant formulations, including formulations that achieve the elimination of two variables in a single step. An early systematic exposition can be found in Netto (1892). Technically, the resultant formulates a system of linear equations symbolically. Macaulay (1902 and 1916) recognized that the extraneous factors are related to the presence of dependent equations, and attempts to eliminate these factors by identifying them as suitable minors of a larger determinant.

Recent interest in elimination theory was stimulated by Sederberg's thesis (1983), which explains the resultant formulations of Sylvester, Bezout, and Dixon. Sederberg (1983) advocates the utility of resultants for implicitizing parametric curves and surfaces. However, as noted in Sederberg and Parry (1986a), using resultants becomes unattractive for curves of degree higher than 4. Many symbolic algebra systems such as Macsyma have implemented the Sylvester resultant.

Macaulay's idea of eliminating dependencies by dividing by a minor has been pursued algorithmically in Canny (1986). The conversion from parametric to implicit form can be done directly by formulating a linear system numerically rather than symbolically. In that case, no extraneous factors are present. See also Chuang and Hoffmann (1989).

The material on boundary-representation ambiguities is adapted from Hoffmann and Hopcroft (1987c). The proposal to identify edge segments by an interior, regular curve point is due to Requicha (1980b).

CHAPTER 6

Surface Intersections

Evaluating the intersection of two surfaces is a recurring operation in solid modeling — for example, when intersecting B-rep objects. Surface intersection is not an easy problem, and continues to be an active topic of research. Some of the reasons for this continued activity are not hard to identify: A good surface-intersection technique has to balance three conflicting goals: *efficiency*, *robustness*, and *accuracy*.

Typically, a numerical algorithm is efficient, but is not fully robust and so may fail in certain cases. Furthermore, the accuracy a numerical method can deliver varies with the surface degree, with the local surface geometry at the intersection curve, and with the angle at which the surfaces intersect. Algorithms based on exact arithmetic, on the other hand, are fully robust and accurate, but are normally slow. Perhaps the goals of efficiency, robustness, and accuracy cannot be met simultaneously without some compromises, and we might have to negotiate those compromises judiciously, as appropriate for the particular application. Further research is needed to clarify this picture.

In this chapter, we will look at tracing approaches to evaluating surface intersection. Surface intersections can be traced directly, or we can reformulate the intersection problem such that other curves are traced from which information about the surface intersection is computed. In the purest version, a curve-tracing scheme performs the following conceptual operation repeatedly:

At a point p on the intersection, a local approximation of the curve is constructed; for example, the curve tangent at p. By stepping along the approximation a specific distance, we obtain an estimate of a next curve point that we then refine using an iterative method.

Such an algorithm requires solving the following subproblems:

1. Find an initial point p on the intersection curve.

2. Determine a local approximant at p.

3. Select a suitable step size and step along the approximant.

4. Refine the new point estimate to a curve point.

We will not consider how to find an initial starting point, but will concentrate on the remaining steps.

Tracing schemes can be augmented and generalized. We consider two major ways to do this:

- Certain surface operations are naturally formulated using several algebraic equations in more than three variables. This motivates extending the numerical tracing schemes to work in n-dimensional spaces, where $n > 3$.

- Surface intersections can always be mapped to the equivalent problem of evaluating a plane algebraic curve. An attractive aspect of this approach is its ability to cope with singular curve points, a traditional weakness of numerical curve-tracing algorithms.

6.1 Chapter Overview

First, we explain a purely numerical tracing method for evaluating the intersection of two implicit surfaces, $f(x, y, z) = 0$ and $g(x, y, z) = 0$. Technically, the approximant used at a current curve point p is a truncated Taylor expansion of the intersection. The step length is determined adaptively, and the next point estimate is refined iteratively using the Newton–Raphson method. This method is efficient and, when implemented carefully, accurate. However, it is not fully robust and will fail in areas where the intersection curve is singular or nearly so.

The Taylor approximant used in the numerical method is derived by solving a certain system of linear equations whose coefficients depend on the partial derivatives of the two surfaces. It turns out that this formulation is a special case of solving a system of $n - 1$ algebraic equations in n variables, assuming that the equations are independent and the corresponding hypersurfaces intersect transversally. This observation can be applied in different ways. For example, we can formulate the intersection of two parametric surfaces equivalently as solving three algebraic equations in four variables. Other applications include intersecting derived surfaces, including offset surfaces. We explore such applications in Section 6.3. An advantage of the higher-dimensional formulation is that the algebraic degrees involved are often low, and this appears to increase the numerical accuracy of the method in many cases. A disadvantage is that the processing time at each point is greater, since the linear system solved to find the curve approximant is now of size $(n-1) \times n$, where n is the number of variables.

The intersection of two algebraic surfaces is an algebraic space curve, whether the surfaces have been specified implicitly or in parametric form. It is known that every algebraic space curve can be mapped to a plane algebraic curve. In consequence, surface intersection can be approached as follows:

1. Map the surface intersection to a plane algebraic curve $f(u, v) = 0$.

2. Evaluate the plane curve f.

3. Map the points of f back to points on the surface intersection.

In Section 6.4, we present a number of techniques for mapping surface intersections to plane algebraic curves. Using these mapping techniques, it is therefore possible to trace surface intersections by equivalently tracing plane curves. In Section 6.5, we describe a method for evaluating a plane algebraic curve that is capable of dealing with curve singularities. The idea of the method is as follows. Trace f with an ordinary numerical method. When approaching a singularity at a curve point p, apply a transformation that locally changes f to another curve g that is not singular at the corresponding point. Trace the transformed curve g and map each point of g back to f. After the singularity of f has been passed, resume tracing f. The method integrates numerical and symbolic computation. An advantage is its ability to cope with curve singularities. A disadvantage is that the map from a surface intersection to a plane algebraic curve can be difficult to construct.

Tracing a surface intersection in n-dimensional space and mapping the problem to a plane algebraic curve, are, in a sense, two extremes. Generally, when given $n-1$ equations in n variables, we have the option of eliminating none, some, or all but two of the variables. This implies that there are tradeoffs that should be explored. Such tradeoffs are not yet well understood.

6.2 Intersecting Two Implicit Surfaces Numerically

Given two implicit surfaces, $f(x, y, z) = 0$ and $g(x, y, z) = 0$, and a point $p = (p_x, p_y, p_z)$ on their intersection, we wish to trace the intersection curve, beginning at p. The tracing direction is fixed by the cross-product convention explained in the previous chapter. So, a *positive* trace proceeds in the direction $\nabla f \times \nabla g$, whereas a *negative* trace proceeds in the direction $-\nabla f \times \nabla g$.

We assume that, at each point p, the surface gradients ∇f and ∇g are linearly independent; that is, the two surfaces intersect transversally at p. In that case, the intersection curve is regular at p. If the gradients vanish or are linearly dependent, then the curve has a singularity at p and the numerical approach cannot be used without considerable changes and additions.

Assume that p is a regular point on the intersection of f and g. There is a neighborhood of p in which a local parameterization of the intersection curve exists. The local parameterization is a vector-valued function

$$\mathbf{r}(s) = \begin{pmatrix} r_x(s) \\ r_y(s) \\ r_z(s) \end{pmatrix}$$

of a scalar variable s. Note that $r_x(s)$ denotes the x component of the vector $\mathbf{r}(s)$. Analogously, $r_y(s)$ and $r_z(s)$ denote the y and z component, respectively.

It can be shown that the function $\mathbf{r}(s)$ is analytic in a neighborhood of p. By Taylor's theorem, therefore, this function may be written

$$\mathbf{r}(s) = \mathbf{r}(0) + s\mathbf{r}'(0) + \frac{s^2}{2}\mathbf{r}''(0) + \frac{s^3}{6}\mathbf{r}'''(0) + \cdots$$

where $p = \mathbf{r}(0)$. The value of the first derivative of $\mathbf{r}(s)$ at $s = 0$ is $\mathbf{r}'(0)$, that of the second derivative is $\mathbf{r}''(0)$, and so on. The tracing procedure repeats the following steps:

1. At the curve point p, construct a local approximant of $\mathbf{r}(s)$, to some order.[1]

2. Using this approximant and a step value s_0, determine the next point $q = \mathbf{r}(s_0)$.

3. By Newton iteration, bring q closer to the intersection of f and g.

Typically, the order of approximation is fixed. First-order approximations use the curve tangent at p as the local approximant. This is often implemented because the tangent is so easy to compute, as $\mathbf{t} = \nabla f \times \nabla g$.

---

[1] In the following discussion, $\mathbf{r}(s)$ will also denote the approximant.

Higher-order approximants allow larger steps. There is a tradeoff between the added time needed to compute a higher-order approximant, and the time saved by the ability to take larger steps. Degree-3 approximants seem to provide a good balance in that the determination of the approximant is not too costly, and the approximant accounts for both the curvature and the torsion at p.

6.2.1 Construction of the Approximant

We view the intersection of f and g as a vector function $\mathbf{r}(s)$, parameterized by the scalar variable s, with $p = \mathbf{r}(0)$, and write

$$\mathbf{r}(s) = \mathbf{r}(0) + s\mathbf{r}'(0) + \frac{s^2}{2}\mathbf{r}''(0) + \frac{s^3}{6}\mathbf{r}'''(0) + \cdots$$

since the curve is not singular at p by assumption. The approximant is an initial segment of this series and is determined by finding the components of the derivatives of $\mathbf{r}$, up to some order. Technically, this involves the formulation of a linear system, which always has the following structure:

$$\begin{aligned} \nabla f \cdot \mathbf{r}^{(m)}(0) &= b_{f,m} \\ \nabla g \cdot \mathbf{r}^{(m)}(0) &= b_{g,m} \end{aligned} \tag{6.1}$$

Here, $\mathbf{r}^{(m)}(s)$ denotes the mth derivative of $\mathbf{r}(s)$ by s. The coefficients $b_{f,m}$ and $b_{g,m}$ depend on the partial derivatives of f and g at p, and the derivatives of $\mathbf{r}$ up to order $m - 1$.

Since the system is underdetermined, it does not have a unique solution, and we must make certain choices. These choices have a geometric interpretation, and will result in an approximant where the values for $\mathbf{r}''$ and $\mathbf{r}'''$ are explicitly related to curvature and torsion at p.

Setting Up the Linear System

We determine the derivative values, $\mathbf{r}'(0)$, $\mathbf{r}''(0)$, $\mathbf{r}'''(0)$, from the partial derivatives of f and of g. When $p = (p_x, p_y, p_z)$ is a regular point of the surface f, by Taylor's theorem, there exists a neighborhood of p in that

$$f(x, y, z) = f(p_x + \delta_x, p_y + \delta_y, p_z + \delta_z) = \sum_{i,j,k} f_{i,j,k} \delta_x^i \delta_y^j \delta_z^k$$

for real numbers δ_x, δ_y, and δ_z. The coefficients $f_{i,j,k}$ in the sum denote expressions

$$f_{i,j,k} = \frac{1}{i!j!k!} \frac{\partial^{i+j+k}}{\partial x^i \partial y^j \partial z^k} f(p_x, p_y, p_z)$$

Let $f(p_x, p_y, p_z)$ and $f(p_x + \delta_x, p_y + \delta_y, p_z + \delta_z)$ be points on the curve $\mathbf{r}(s)$. Assuming that $p = \mathbf{r}(0)$ and $(p_x + \delta_x, p_y + \delta_y, p_z + \delta_z) = \mathbf{r}(s)$, we set

$$
\begin{aligned}
\delta_x &= \mathbf{r}'_x s + \mathbf{r}''_x s^2/2 + \mathbf{r}'''_x s^3/6 + \cdots \\
\delta_y &= \mathbf{r}'_y s + \mathbf{r}''_y s^2/2 + \mathbf{r}'''_y s^3/6 + \cdots \\
\delta_z &= \mathbf{r}'_z s + \mathbf{r}''_z s^2/2 + \mathbf{r}'''_z s^3/6 + \cdots
\end{aligned}
$$

where $\mathbf{r}'_x$ denotes the x-component of the vector $\mathbf{r}'$, and so on.[2] Then, we have

$$
\begin{aligned}
(\delta_x)^2 &= (\mathbf{r}'_x)^2 s^2 + \mathbf{r}'_x \mathbf{r}''_x s^3 + \cdots \\
(\delta_x)^3 &= (\mathbf{r}'_x)^3 s^3 + \cdots \\
\delta_x \delta_y &= \mathbf{r}'_x \mathbf{r}'_y s^2 + (\mathbf{r}''_x \mathbf{r}'_y + \mathbf{r}'_x \mathbf{r}''_y) s^3/2 + \cdots \\
\delta_x \delta_y \delta_z &= \mathbf{r}'_x \mathbf{r}'_y \mathbf{r}'_z s^3 + \cdots
\end{aligned}
$$

and so on.

Since the curve $\mathbf{r}$ is on f, substitution of these quantities must yield identically zero; hence, the coefficient of s^m must vanish for each m. For $m = 1, 2, 3$, we therefore obtain the equations

$$
\begin{aligned}
f_{1,0,0}\mathbf{r}'_x + f_{0,1,0}\mathbf{r}'_y + f_{0,0,1}\mathbf{r}'_z &= b_{f,1} \\
f_{1,0,0}\mathbf{r}''_x + f_{0,1,0}\mathbf{r}''_y + f_{0,0,1}\mathbf{r}''_z &= b_{f,2} \\
f_{1,0,0}\mathbf{r}'''_x + f_{0,1,0}\mathbf{r}'''_y + f_{0,0,1}\mathbf{r}'''_z &= b_{f,3}
\end{aligned}
$$

The righthand sides $b_{f,k}$ are computed from the partials of f and lower-order derivatives of $\mathbf{r}$

$$
b_{f,1} = 0
$$

$$
\begin{aligned}
b_{f,2} = -2[&f_{2,0,0}(\mathbf{r}'_x)^2 + f_{0,2,0}(\mathbf{r}'_y)^2 + f_{0,0,2}(\mathbf{r}'_z)^2 \\
&+ f_{1,1,0}\mathbf{r}'_x\mathbf{r}'_y + f_{1,0,1}\mathbf{r}'_x\mathbf{r}'_z + f_{0,1,1}\mathbf{r}'_y\mathbf{r}'_z]
\end{aligned}
$$

$$
\begin{aligned}
b_{f,3} = -6[&f_{2,0,0}\mathbf{r}'_x\mathbf{r}''_x + f_{0,2,0}\mathbf{r}'_y\mathbf{r}''_y + f_{0,0,2}\mathbf{r}'_z\mathbf{r}''_z + f_{1,1,0}(\mathbf{r}''_x\mathbf{r}'_y + \mathbf{r}'_x\mathbf{r}''_y)/2 \\
&+ f_{1,0,1}(\mathbf{r}''_x\mathbf{r}'_z + \mathbf{r}'_x\mathbf{r}''_z)/2 + f_{0,1,1}(\mathbf{r}''_y\mathbf{r}'_z + \mathbf{r}'_y\mathbf{r}''_z)/2 \\
&+ f_{3,0,0}(\mathbf{r}'_x)^3 + f_{0,3,0}(\mathbf{r}'_y)^3 + f_{0,0,3}(\mathbf{r}'_z)^3 \\
&+ f_{2,1,0}(\mathbf{r}'_x)^2\mathbf{r}'_y + f_{1,2,0}\mathbf{r}'_x(\mathbf{r}'_y)^2 + f_{2,0,1}(\mathbf{r}'_x)^2\mathbf{r}'_z \\
&+ f_{1,0,2}\mathbf{r}'_x(\mathbf{r}'_z)^2 + f_{0,2,1}(\mathbf{r}'_y)^2\mathbf{r}'_z + f_{0,1,2}\mathbf{r}'_y(\mathbf{r}'_z)^2 + f_{1,1,1}\mathbf{r}'_x\mathbf{r}'_y\mathbf{r}'_z]
\end{aligned}
$$

---

[2] We write $\mathbf{r}$ instead of $\mathbf{r}(0)$, $\mathbf{r}'$ instead of $\mathbf{r}'(0)$, and so on.

With the $b_{f,m}$ as the right-hand sides, we can rewrite these equations in vectorial notation as

$$\nabla f \cdot \mathbf{r}' = b_{f,1}$$
$$\nabla f \cdot \mathbf{r}'' = b_{f,2}$$
$$\nabla f \cdot \mathbf{r}''' = b_{f,3}$$

The equations for g are developed analogously. In particular, we have

$$\nabla g \cdot \mathbf{r}' = b_{g,1}$$
$$\nabla g \cdot \mathbf{r}'' = b_{g,2}$$
$$\nabla g \cdot \mathbf{r}''' = b_{g,3}$$

where

$$b_{g,1} = 0$$

$$b_{g,2} = -2[g_{2,0,0}(\mathbf{r}'_x)^2 + g_{0,2,0}(\mathbf{r}'_y)^2 + g_{0,0,2}(\mathbf{r}'_z)^2$$
$$+ g_{1,1,0}\mathbf{r}'_x\mathbf{r}'_y + g_{1,0,1}\mathbf{r}'_x\mathbf{r}'_z + g_{0,1,1}\mathbf{r}'_y\mathbf{r}'_z]$$

$$b_{g,3} = -6[g_{2,0,0}\mathbf{r}'_x\mathbf{r}''_x + g_{0,2,0}\mathbf{r}'_y\mathbf{r}''_y + g_{0,0,2}\mathbf{r}'_z\mathbf{r}''_z + g_{1,1,0}(\mathbf{r}''_x\mathbf{r}'_y + \mathbf{r}'_x\mathbf{r}''_y)/2$$
$$+ g_{1,0,1}(\mathbf{r}''_x\mathbf{r}'_z + \mathbf{r}'_x\mathbf{r}''_z)/2 + g_{0,1,1}(\mathbf{r}''_y\mathbf{r}'_z + \mathbf{r}'_y\mathbf{r}''_z)/2$$
$$+ g_{3,0,0}(\mathbf{r}'_x)^3 + g_{0,3,0}(\mathbf{r}'_y)^3 + g_{0,0,3}(\mathbf{r}'_z)^3$$
$$+ g_{2,1,0}(\mathbf{r}'_x)^2\mathbf{r}'_y + g_{1,2,0}\mathbf{r}'_x(\mathbf{r}'_y)^2 + g_{2,0,1}(\mathbf{r}'_x)^2\mathbf{r}'_z$$
$$+ g_{1,0,2}\mathbf{r}'_x(\mathbf{r}'_z)^2 + g_{0,2,1}(\mathbf{r}'_y)^2\mathbf{r}'_z + g_{0,1,2}\mathbf{r}'_y(\mathbf{r}'_z)^2 + g_{1,1,1}\mathbf{r}'_x\mathbf{r}'_y\mathbf{r}'_z]$$

We put these equations into matrix form. A is a 2×3 matrix whose rows are the gradients of f and of g, and all partials of f and of g are evaluated at p. Then the system is

$$A\mathbf{r}^{(m)} = \begin{pmatrix} b_{f,m} \\ b_{g,m} \end{pmatrix}$$

Although this system is only 2×3, solving it without giving proper attention to its numerical properties will waste accuracy in the solution. Hence, we should carefully choose a numerically stable solution technique. A good choice is *singular value decomposition*, sketched in Section 6.1.4.

As output, singular value decomposition delivers, in our case, two scalars, σ_1 and σ_2; three orthonormal vectors in three-dimensional space, U_1, U_2,

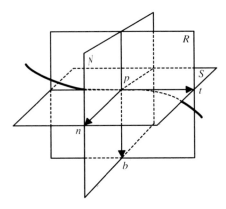

Figure 6.1   The Space-Curve Triad

U_3; and an orthogonal 2×2 matrix V. From these quantities, we construct a solution of the form

$$\mathbf{r}^{(m)} = \alpha_m U_1 + \beta_m U_2 + \gamma_m U_3$$

where the coefficients α_m and β_m are determined by V, σ_1, and σ_2. The details are deferred to Section 6.2.4.

Choosing the Undetermined Coefficients

The linear system is underdetermined and has an infinity of solutions. So, choices must be made for the γ_m to arrive at a canonical solution. Our strategy is to choose values such that the derivative values reveal some of the intrinsic geometric structure of the curve at the point p.

From differential geometry, we recall that at the point p of a space curve, the *moving triad* forms a natural local coordinate system.[3] The triad consists of three orthonormal vectors, the *tangent vector* $\mathbf{t}$, the *principal normal vector* $\mathbf{n}$, and the *binormal vector* $\mathbf{b}$, where $\mathbf{b} = \mathbf{t} \times \mathbf{n}$. Their directions are defined by the tangent, the curvature, and the torsion of the space curve.

The curve *tangent t* at the point p is the limiting position of curve secants (p, q), where q approaches p. The plane perpendicular to t is the *normal plane N* at p. We consider a plane through the tangent and an additional curve point r. As r approaches p, this plane approaches as limit position

---

[3]The moving triad is also called the *Frenet frame*.

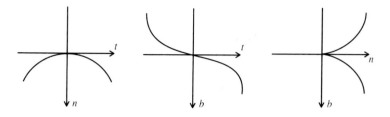

Figure 6.2   Local Curve Projections

the *osculating plane* S. The perpendicular to t in the osculating plane is the *principal normal* n. The plane perpendicular to both N and S is the *rectifying plane* R. The perpendicular to t in the rectifying plane is the *binormal* b; see also Figure 6.1. At a regular point, the curve intersects the osculating plane but remains on one side of the rectifying plane.

We consider three points r, p, and q on the curve. They define a circle. As r and q approach p, the limit position of the circle is the *circle of curvature* and lies in S. Its radius ρ is the *radius of curvature* at p. Now consider four curve points. If the points are not coplanar, they define a sphere. As three of the points approach the fourth point p, the limiting position of this sphere is the *osculating sphere*. The center of the osculating sphere is in the normal plane, and the sphere intersects the osculating plane in the circle of curvature.

Intuitively, the torsion at p is obtained by considering how the osculating plane changes with p. Consider the angle between the osculating planes at p and a nearby curve point q. As q approaches p, the ratio between this angle and the arc length (p, q) approaches as limit the torsion T of the curve at p.

We orient the curve at p by choosing a direction for the tangent t, and we denote the unit vector in this direction by $\mathbf{t}$. Then, we orient the normal toward the concave curve side; that is, toward the center of the circle of curvature. The unit vector in this direction will be $\mathbf{n}$. Finally, we orient the binormal by the vector $\mathbf{b} = \mathbf{t} \times \mathbf{n}$, as shown in Figure 6.1. With these conventions of orientation, the projection of the space curve onto each of the three planes is locally as shown in Figure 6.2.

As the point p moves on the space curve the vectors $\mathbf{t}$, $\mathbf{n}$, and $\mathbf{b}$ vary obeying the *Frenet–Serret formulae*.

$$\frac{d\mathbf{t}}{ds} = \kappa\mathbf{n} \qquad \frac{d\mathbf{b}}{ds} = -T\mathbf{n} \qquad \frac{d\mathbf{n}}{ds} = T\mathbf{b} - \kappa\mathbf{t} \qquad (6.2)$$

Here, s is the arc length, $\kappa = 1/\rho$ is the curvature, and T is the torsion of the curve.

Now U_3, as determined by singular value decomposition, is a unit vector in the tangent direction. So, we choose $\gamma_1 = \pm 1$, depending on the tracing direction, and observe that $\mathbf{r}' = \pm U_3$. By choosing γ_2 and γ_3 properly, we relate the higher-order derivatives $\mathbf{r}''$ and $\mathbf{r}'''$ to the moving triad at p. Since

$$\mathbf{r}'' = \frac{d\mathbf{t}}{ds} = \kappa \mathbf{n}$$

$\mathbf{r}''$ should be perpendicular to $\mathbf{t}$. So, we choose $\gamma_2 = 0$. Hence, the curvature at p will be

$$\kappa = \sqrt{\alpha_2^2 + \beta_2^2}$$

Finally, we have

$$\mathbf{r}'''(s) = \frac{d}{ds}(\kappa \mathbf{n}) = \frac{d\kappa}{ds}\mathbf{n} + \kappa \frac{d\mathbf{n}}{ds} = \kappa'\mathbf{n} + \kappa T\mathbf{b} - \kappa^2 \mathbf{t}$$

But $\mathbf{r}''' = \alpha_3 U_1 + \beta_3 U_2 + \gamma_3 \mathbf{t}$, so, by orthogonality, we have $\gamma_3 = -\kappa^2$. Moreover, we can compute the torsion at p by projecting $\mathbf{r}'''$ onto $\mathbf{b}$ and dividing the length of the projected vector by κ.

Recall that the method for determining the quantities γ_1, γ_2, and γ_3 just presented is not the only one. We can understand different strategies by interpreting them geometrically. For simplicity, we consider first-order approximants and interpret the effect of choosing a value for γ_1. Now, with $\gamma_1 = 1$, the estimated curve point obtained as

$$q = \mathbf{r}(0) + s\,\mathbf{r}'(0)$$

has distance s from p. If $0 < \gamma_1 < 1$, then the distance is less than s; with $\gamma_1 > 1$, it is greater than s. Hence, the choices for γ_m determine how $\mathbf{r}(s)$ is parameterized.

6.2.2 Selection of Step Size

We have constructed an approximant $\mathbf{r}(s)$ to the curve at p; now we must choose a step length s_0 to obtain a subsequent curve-point estimate $\mathbf{r}(s_0)$. Choosing a safe step length requires understanding the radius of convergence of the full Taylor series. To this end, we consider each coordinate of $\mathbf{r}$ separately as a function of s. For each coordinate of $\mathbf{r}(s)$, we have a function

$$F(s) = \sum_{n=0}^{\infty} a_n s^n \tag{6.3}$$

This series will converge absolutely for all values of s that satisfy $|s| < R$, and will diverge for all values $|s| \geq R$, where

$$R = \lim \sup |a_n|^{1/n}$$

We assume that $R = 0$ whenever $|a_n|^{1/n}$ is unbounded. Therefore, the radius of convergence for the full Taylor series of $\mathbf{r}$ is the minimum R of the three coordinate functions $F(s)$.

In practice, the determination of R is difficult except in those cases where simple recurrences or closed-form expressions can be given for the coefficients a_n. Thus, we opt for a simpler heuristic in which the contribution of the quadratic and cubic terms to the next point estimate is kept small. For example, since $\mathbf{r}'$ has unit length, we may choose s_0 such that both

$$\frac{\|s_0^2 \mathbf{r}''(0)\|}{2} < \frac{|s_0|}{10} \quad \text{and} \quad \frac{\|s_0^3 \mathbf{r}'''(0)\|}{6} < \frac{|s_0|}{10}$$

Since the step sizes could become arbitrarily small, a minimum step size should also be specified. This simple strategy does well in many cases.

6.2.3 Newton Iteration

At the point p, we have constructed a third-order approximant $\mathbf{r}(s)$, we have determined adaptively a step length s_0, and now we have a new point estimate $q = \mathbf{r}(s_0)$. Using Newton iteration, we refine this estimate until we are on the intersection of f and g with acceptable accuracy. The iteration is based on the following, first-order approximation of the two surfaces:

$$\nabla f(q_k) \cdot \Delta_k = -f(q_k)$$
$$\nabla g(q_k) \cdot \Delta_k = -g(q_k)$$

where $\Delta_k = (\delta_x, \delta_y, \delta_z)^T$. Note that this system has the same structure as does system (6.1). Solving it for Δ_k, we obtain the next point estimate as

$$q_{k+1} = q_k + \Delta_k$$

As in the approximant construction, we solve the linear system using singular value decomposition. For the solution Δ_k, we set the coefficient of U_3 to zero, since it represents lateral movement that will not improve the

quality of the new estimate significantly. We continue with the iteration
until

$$\|q_{k+1} - q_k\| < 10^{-t}\|q_k\|$$

where t is a precision parameter. Typically, we have $t = 10$ for double-
precision floating-point computations, and we require two or three iterations to achieve this accuracy.

6.2.4 Singular Value Decomposition

Singular value decomposition is a method for solving systems of linear equations that may be singular. It is a numerically stable method of considerable
flexibility, and is a part of many widely available software libraries.

Using Singular Value Decomposition

Assume that we are given the linear system

$$A\mathbf{r} = \mathbf{b} \tag{6.4}$$

From the system matrix A, the singular-value-decomposition algorithm constructs three matrices U, S, and V such that

$$A = VSU^T \tag{6.5}$$

where the matrices have the following properties:

1. The matrices U and V are orthogonal; that is, UU^T and VV^T are the
   identity matrices.

2. The matrix S is diagonal and its diagonal entries are nonnegative and
   decreasing.

When we are using the method for the intersection of two implicit surfaces,
the matrix V is 2×2, U is 3×3, and S is

$$S = \begin{pmatrix} \sigma_1 & 0 & 0 \\ 0 & \sigma_2 & 0 \end{pmatrix}$$

where $\sigma_1 \geq \sigma_2 \geq 0$. If the surfaces intersect transversally, moreover, then
$\sigma_2 > 0$. Using equation (6.5), we transform system (6.4) to

$$S(U^T\mathbf{r}) = V^T\mathbf{b}$$

Let U_i be the ith column in U, and denote by $(V^T\mathbf{b})_i$ the ith component of the vector $V^T\mathbf{b}$. Since U is orthogonal, the vectors U_i are also orthogonal. Then it can be proved that the solution of system (6.4) is

$$\mathbf{r} = \alpha U_1 + \beta U_2 + \gamma U_3$$

where the scalar coefficients α and β are given by

$$\alpha = (V^T\mathbf{b})_1/\sigma_1$$
$$\beta = (V^T\mathbf{b})_2/\sigma_2$$

The last coefficient γ is arbitrary, and the column vector U_3 is in the null space of A. When intersecting two implicit surfaces, the null space at a regular curve point is spanned by $\nabla f \times \nabla g$. Hence, U_3 is the tangent direction to the curve at $p = \mathbf{r}(0)$. Note, however, that the direction of U_3 could be equal to or opposite the direction $\nabla f \times \nabla g$.

First Phase of the Algorithm

The singular-value-decomposition algorithm transforms the matrix A in two phases. Let A be $m \times n$, where $m \le n$. In the first phase, A is changed to a matrix B in lower bidiagonal form. This is done using *Householder* transformations that multiply A left and right with certain orthogonal matrices.

$$B = \begin{pmatrix} a_{11} & 0 & 0 & \ldots & 0 & 0 & 0 & \ldots \\ a_{21} & a_{22} & 0 & \ldots & 0 & 0 & 0 & \ldots \\ 0 & a_{32} & a_{33} & \ldots & 0 & 0 & 0 & \ldots \\ \vdots & \vdots & \vdots & & \vdots & & \vdots & \vdots \\ 0 & 0 & 0 & \ldots & a_{m-1\,m-1} & 0 & 0 & \ldots \\ 0 & 0 & 0 & \ldots & a_{mm-1} & a_{mm} & 0 & \ldots \end{pmatrix}$$

At each step, we zero all elements to the right of the ith diagonal element by multiplying A from the right with a matrix U_i, and then zero all elements below the $(i+1, i)$-element by multiplying from the left with V_i.

A Householder transformation is essentially a reflection about the direction of a column vector $\mathbf{n}$, and is effected by a matrix of the form

$$P = I - \frac{2\mathbf{n}\mathbf{n}^T}{\mathbf{n}^T\mathbf{n}}$$

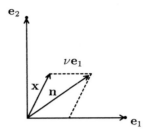

Figure 6.3   The Vector **n**

P is symmetric and orthogonal. Given a column vector $\mathbf{x}$, the vector $\mathbf{n}$ can be chosen such that $P\mathbf{x}$ is a multiple of the unit vector $\mathbf{e}_1 = (1, 0, 0, \dots)^T$. To do so, we use

$$\mathbf{n} = \mathbf{x} + \nu\mathbf{e}_1$$

where ν is $\|\mathbf{x}\|_2$; see also Figure 6.3. A calculation shows that the matrix P so constructed from $\mathbf{n}$ has the desired effect on $\mathbf{x}$.

We use Householder transformations to zero out blocks of entries in the matrix A. First, we zero all elements to the right of the (i, i)-element. Let $\mathbf{x} = (x_1, \dots, x_i, x_{i+1}, \dots, x_n)$ be the ith row in the matrix. We multiply A from the right with an $n \times n$ matrix U_i of the form

$$U_i = \begin{pmatrix} I & 0 \\ 0 & P \end{pmatrix}$$

where I is the $(i - 1) \times (i - 1)$ identity matrix, and P is the Householder matrix for $(x_i, x_{i+1}, \dots, x_n)^T$. Next, we zero all elements below the $(i + 1, i)$-element by multiplying from the left with a matrix V_i. If $(y_1, \dots, y_i, y_{i+1}, \dots, y_m)^T$ is the ith column of A, then we multiply with

$$V_i = \begin{pmatrix} I & 0 \\ 0 & P \end{pmatrix}$$

where I is $i \times i$ and P is the Householder matrix for $(y_{i+1}, \dots, y_n)^T$. In this way, we can change A to a lower bidiagonal form.

Second Phase of the Algorithm

In the second phase of singular value decomposition, an iteration is done to diagonalize the output from the first phase. The iteration uses *Givens* rotations, and it has similarities with the procedure to diagonalize a real symmetric matrix discussed in Chapter 5, Section 5.5.1.

We consider a rotation matrix that differs from the identity only in the four entries (i,i), (i,j), (j,i), (j,j):

$$
J(i, j, \theta) =
\begin{pmatrix}
1 & & & & & & \\
& \ddots & \vdots & & \vdots & & \\
& \cdots & c & \cdots & -s & \cdots & \\
& & \vdots & \ddots & \vdots & & \\
& \cdots & s & \cdots & c & \cdots & \\
& & \vdots & & \vdots & \ddots & \\
& & & & & & 1
\end{pmatrix}
$$

where $s = \sin(\theta)$ and $c = \cos(\theta)$. By a computation analogous to the derivation of Jacobi rotations, we can show that the jth element of the row vector $\mathbf{x} = (..., x_i, ..., x_j, ...)$ is canceled in $\mathbf{x}J(i, j, \theta)$, provided θ is such that

$$
\begin{aligned}
\cos(\theta) &= x_i/(x_i^2 + x_j^2) \\
\sin(\theta) &= x_j/(x_i^2 + x_j^2)
\end{aligned}
$$

The resulting vector is equal to $\mathbf{x}$ except for the ith and the jth components.

We apply Givens rotations as follows: In the lower bidiagonal matrix B, we initially zero the element b_{21} with a rotation $J(1, 2, \theta)^T B$. Since B is not symmetric, this results in a nonzero entry b_{12}. We cancel the element a_{12} with a rotation $J(1, 2, \theta)$. This reintroduces a_{21} and an element a_{31}. The element a_{31} is canceled next in $J(1, 3, \theta)^T B$, introducing a nonzero element a_{23}. We handle a_{23} just like we have a_{12}, pushing the unwanted element to position a_{34} with two rotations. In this manner, the unwanted element is percolated down. When it reaches the position $a_{n-1,n}$, it disappears with the next rotation, leaving us again with a matrix in lower bidiagonal form. This sequence is illustrated in Figure 6.4. It can be shown that, when suitably starting out the initial rotation to cancel a_{21}, the magnitude of the off-diagonal entries is diminished with each such sequence of Givens rotations.

$$
\begin{pmatrix} * & & \\ + & * & \\ & * & * \end{pmatrix}
\Longrightarrow
\begin{pmatrix} * & + & \\ 0 & * & \\ & * & * \end{pmatrix}
\Longrightarrow
\begin{pmatrix} * & 0 & \\ * & * & \\ + & * & * \end{pmatrix}
$$

$$
\Longrightarrow
\begin{pmatrix} * & & \\ * & * & + \\ 0 & * & * \end{pmatrix}
\Longrightarrow
\begin{pmatrix} * & & \\ * & * & 0 \\ & * & * \end{pmatrix}
$$

Figure 6.4   Sequence of Givens Rotations in Phase 2 of Singular Value Decomposition

Implementation

Our description of the singular-value-decomposition algorithm leaves out a number of important implementation details. First, the structure of the Householder matrices is such that they do not need to be formed explicitly. The vector **n** can be used directly, and this results in an $O(n^2)$ cost for each transformation step of A. Similar considerations apply to the second phase. Moreover, we should partition the matrix at each zero off-diagonal entry, treating the resulting blocks of submatrices separately, and permute rows and columns suitably so that the diagonal elements of S are nonincreasing.

6.3 Tracing in Higher Dimensions

The numerical tracing method we have described is not limited to evaluating the intersection of two implicit surfaces in 3-space; but it is easily generalized to intersecting $n-1$ hypersurfaces in n-space, where $n > 3$. We sketch this generalization and discuss several applications.

6.3.1 The Method

We generalize the material of Section 6.2 to the problem of tracing the intersection of a system of $n - 1$ algebraic hypersurfaces in n-dimensional space. Let

$$
\begin{aligned}
f_1(x_1, x_2, ..., x_n) &= 0 \\
f_2(x_1, x_2, ..., x_n) &= 0 \\
&\vdots \\
f_{n-1}(x_1, x_2, ..., x_n) &= 0
\end{aligned}
$$

be the surfaces that must be intersected. We assume that we are given a regular point p on the intersection. The algorithm considers a local parameterization of the intersection, in a neighborhood of p, as a vector function $\mathbf{r}(s)$ of a scalar variable s. Note that $\mathbf{r}(s)$ now has n scalar components, one for each variable x_i. We proceed as follows:

1. At the curve point p, determine an initial segment of the Taylor expansion of $\mathbf{r}(s)$ at p, by solving a linear system of the form

$$A\mathbf{r}^{(m)} = \mathbf{b}_m$$

   The rows of A are the gradients of the f_i, and the entries of $\mathbf{b}_m$ depend on the partial derivatives of the f_i and the derivatives of $\mathbf{r}$ up to order $m - 1$.

2. Determine a suitable step value s_0, and derive a new curve point estimate $q = \mathbf{r}(s_0)$.

3. Refine the estimate q to a curve point using Newton iteration.

As before, the linear systems are derived by considering the Taylor expansion at p for each surface f_i, and deriving from it expressions for the curve derivatives $\mathbf{r}'$, $\mathbf{r}''$, and so on. Let $f_i^{(k)}$ denote the partial derivative of f_i by x_k, and $f_i^{(k,j)}$ denote the partial derivative of $f_i^{(k)}$ by x_j. Moreover, let $\mathbf{r}_i$ denote the ith component of $\mathbf{r}$. Then, the first derivative of $\mathbf{r}(s)$ is determined from $n - 1$ equations of the form

$$f_i^{(1)}\mathbf{r}_1' + f_i^{(2)}\mathbf{r}_2' + \cdots + f_i^{(n)}\mathbf{r}_n' = 0$$

The second derivative is determined from $n - 1$ equations of the form

$$f_i^{(1)}\mathbf{r}_1'' + f_i^{(2)}\mathbf{r}_2'' + \cdots + f_i^{(n)}\mathbf{r}_n'' = b_{i,2}$$

where the right-hand side is

$$
\begin{aligned}
b_{i,2} = \quad &-(f_i^{(1,1)}\mathbf{r}_1'^{\,2} + f_i^{(2,2)}\mathbf{r}_2'^{\,2} + \cdots + f_i^{(n,n)}\mathbf{r}_n'^{\,2}) \\
&-2(f_i^{(1,2)}\mathbf{r}_1'\mathbf{r}_2' + f_i^{(1,3)}\mathbf{r}_1'\mathbf{r}_3' + \cdots + f_i^{(1,n)}\mathbf{r}_1'\mathbf{r}_n' \\
&\qquad\quad +f_i^{(2,3)}\mathbf{r}_2'\mathbf{r}_3' + \cdots + f_i^{(2,n)}\mathbf{r}_2'\mathbf{r}_n' \\
&\qquad\qquad\qquad\qquad \ddots \\
&\qquad\qquad\qquad\qquad\qquad +f_i^{(n-1,n)}\mathbf{r}_{n-1}'\mathbf{r}_n')
\end{aligned}
$$

The third-order derivative of $\mathbf{r}$ can be obtained analogously.

Using singular value decomposition to solve the system, there are free parameters to be chosen corresponding to the γ_m in the three-dimensional case. Here we choose $\gamma_1 = \pm 1$ and $\gamma_2 = 0$.[4] A suitable stepping length may be determined with the same heuristics as those used in the three-dimensional case. Thereafter, Newton iteration is used to refine the new curve-point estimate. The details are straightforward.

6.3.2 Numerically Intersecting Two Parametric Surfaces

The traditional approach to intersecting two parametric surfaces is to use subdivision and piecewise linear approximation. When an initial intersection point p is known, however, the numerical approach becomes directly applicable, greatly simplifying the problem.

Let the surfaces be given as

$$
\begin{aligned}
x &= G_{1,1}(u_1, v_1) & x &= G_{2,1}(u_2, v_2) \\
y &= G_{1,2}(u_1, v_1) \quad \text{and} \quad & y &= G_{2,2}(u_2, v_2) \\
z &= G_{1,3}(u_1, v_1) & z &= G_{2,3}(u_2, v_2)
\end{aligned}
$$

Then the intersection is given by the equations

$$
\begin{aligned}
F_1(u_1, v_1, u_2, v_2) &= G_{1,1}(u_1, v_1) - G_{2,1}(u_2, v_2) &= 0 \\
F_2(u_1, v_1, u_2, v_2) &= G_{1,2}(u_1, v_1) - G_{2,2}(u_2, v_2) &= 0 \\
F_3(u_1, v_1, u_2, v_2) &= G_{1,3}(u_1, v_1) - G_{2,3}(u_2, v_2) &= 0
\end{aligned}
$$

that is, by three equations in the four unknowns u_1, v_1, u_2, and v_2. These equations define a curve $\mathbf{r}(s)$ in four-dimensional space:

$$
\mathbf{r}(s) = \begin{pmatrix} u_1(s) \\ v_1(s) \\ u_2(s) \\ v_2(s) \end{pmatrix}
$$

---

[4]A generalization of the Frenet–Serret formulae to n dimensions exists and can be used to devise a strategy for determining γ_3. Alternatively, we can designate a subset of three coordinates and determine γ_3 based on them alone, using the method of Section 6.2. This alternative is natural in some applications, including offset surface intersection, discussed later.

The surface intersection is recovered from $\mathbf{r}(s)$ using the functions $G_{j,k}$

$$
\begin{pmatrix} x \\ y \\ z \end{pmatrix} = \begin{pmatrix} G_{1,1}(u_1(s), v_1(s)) \\ G_{1,2}(u_1(s), v_1(s)) \\ G_{1,3}(u_1(s), v_1(s)) \end{pmatrix} = \begin{pmatrix} G_{2,1}(u_2(s), v_2(s)) \\ G_{2,2}(u_2(s), v_2(s)) \\ G_{2,3}(u_2(s), v_2(s)) \end{pmatrix}
$$

Example 6.1: Consider intersecting two bicubic surfaces. Assume that the first surface is given by

$$
\begin{aligned}
x &= G_{1,1}(u_1, v_1) &&= 3v_1(v_1 - 1)^2(u_1 - 1)^3 + 3u_1 \\
y &= G_{1,2}(u_1, v_1) &&= 3u_1(u_1 - 1)^2 v_1^3 + 3v_1 \\
z &= G_{1,3}(u_1, v_1) &&= (u_1^2 - 5u_1 + 5)v_1^3 - 3(u_1^3 + 6u_1^2 - 9u_1 + 1)v_1^2
\end{aligned}
$$

and the second surface by

$$
\begin{aligned}
x &= G_{2,1}(u_2, v_2) &&= u_2^3 v_2^2 - u_2^3 \\
y &= G_{2,2}(u_2, v_2) &&= u_2^2 v_2 + 2u_2^3 v_2^3 \\
z &= G_{2,3}(u_2, v_2) &&= u_2 v_2^3 + u_2^2 v_2
\end{aligned}
$$

Then the equations to be traced are

$$
\begin{aligned}
3v_1(v_1 - 1)^2(u_1 - 1)^3 + 3u_1 - u_2^3 v_2^2 + u_2^3 &= 0 \\
3u_1(u_1 - 1)^2 v_1^3 + 3v_1 - u_2^2 v_2 - 2u_2^3 v_2^3 &= 0 \\
(u_1^2 - 5u_1 + 5)v_1^3 - 3(u_1^3 + 6u_1^2 - 9u_1 + 1)v_1^2 - u_2 v_2^3 - u_2^2 v_2 &= 0
\end{aligned}
$$

The points obtained by the trace have the coordinates (u_1, v_1, u_2, v_2) and trace simultaneously the image of the intersection curve in both parameter spaces. The curve in 3-space is recovered from (u_1, v_1) via the coordinate functions $G_{1,j}$, or from (u_2, v_2) via $G_{2,j}$, where $j = 1, 2, 3$. $\Diamond$

6.3.3 Surface Operations in Higher Dimensions

Some surface-intersection problems can be expressed straightforwardly as the simultaneous intersection of $n-1$ hypersurfaces in n-dimensional space, where $n > 3$. Given such a formulation, we can use the generalized tracing method. As an illustration, we consider offset surface intersection. Other surface operations may be similarly expressed and treated; see the notes at the end of the chapter.

A number of geometric operations on solid models require *offsetting* a given surface by some distance r. That is, given a surface f, we wish to determine a surface g such that, for every point p of f, there is a point q on g such that the distance between p and q is exactly r, and the line $\overline{(p,q)}$ is perpendicular to f at p.

There are methods for determining an implicit equation for the r-offset g of f. Here, f could be implicit or parametric. However, offsetting may entail considerable symbolic computation, and it may therefore be advantageous to circumvent determining g explicitly, and to reformulate the problem in a higher-dimensional space.

Offset Surface Construction Using Envelopes

Consider a parametric surface f given by

$$
\begin{aligned}
x &= f_1(s,t) \\
y &= f_2(s,t) \\
z &= f_3(s,t)
\end{aligned}
$$

Let $\mathbf{n}(s,t) = (n_x(s,t), n_y(s,t), n_z(s,t))$ be the unit normal to f; that is, $\mathbf{n}$ is a vector of length 1. Then, the points

$$
\begin{aligned}
x &= f_1(s,t) + rn_x(s,t) \\
y &= f_2(s,t) + rn_y(s,t) \\
z &= f_3(s,t) + rn_z(s,t)
\end{aligned}
\tag{6.6}
$$

are on the r-offset of f. The formula (6.6) can be used as the definition of the r-offset of f, but the disadvantage is that this formulation is not algebraic, since $\mathbf{n}$ involves a square root. In fact, examples can be constructed such that the surface described by (6.6) is not algebraic. It is, however, part of an algebraic surface. To find this algebraic surface, we must consider the points at distance r on *both sides* of f. We describe a method for determining the two-sided offset surface.

We consider a family of spheres S of radius r, each of whose centers is constrained to lie on the surface f. The *envelope* of this family contains the set of points whose distance from f is r. Figure 6.5 illustrates this concept in two dimensions. Intuitively, the envelope points are determined by intersecting a sphere in generic position with two adjacent spheres, differentially moved in independent directions on the surface. Using techniques from differential geometry, we can prove that we find these points by solving a system of algebraic equations.

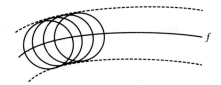

Figure 6.5   Offset Curve as Envelope of Circles

Theorem
The envelope points of a family of surfaces $S(x, y, z, \alpha_1, \alpha_2)$, parameterized by α_1 and α_2, satisfy the three equations

$$S = 0 \tag{6.7}$$

$$\frac{\partial S}{\partial \alpha_1} = 0 \tag{6.8}$$

$$\frac{\partial S}{\partial \alpha_2} = 0 \tag{6.9}$$

The theorem generalizes to all dimensions. In our situation, we apply the theorem as follows. Given the parametric surface f as

$$x = f_1(s, t)$$
$$y = f_2(s, t)$$
$$z = f_3(s, t))$$

we consider the spheres

$$S : (x - f_1(s, t))^2 + (y - f_2(s, t))^2 + (z - f_3(s, t))^2 - r^2 = 0$$

Note that $\alpha_1 = s$ and $\alpha_2 = t$. We form the partial derivatives of S by s and by t and obtain

$$S_s : -2(x - f_1)\frac{\partial f_1}{\partial s} - 2(y - f_2)\frac{\partial f_2}{\partial s} - 2(z - f_3)\frac{\partial f_3}{\partial s}$$

$$S_t : -2(x - f_1)\frac{\partial f_1}{\partial t} - 2(y - f_2)\frac{\partial f_2}{\partial t} - 2(z - f_3)\frac{\partial f_3}{\partial t}$$

By eliminating s and t from the three equations, an algebraic description of the offset surfaces is obtained.

For implicit f, equations (6.8) and (6.9) should be replaced with the directional derivatives in two independent tangent directions on the surface f, and an additional equation is needed that expresses that the centers of the sphere must lie on the implicit surface. The pattern is as follows:

$$
\begin{aligned}
S: \ (x - u_1)^2 + (y - u_2)^2 + (z - u_3)^2 - r^2 &= 0 \\
f(u_1, u_2, u_3) &= 0 \\
\nabla_u S \cdot \mathbf{t}_1 &= 0 \\
\nabla_u S \cdot \mathbf{t}_2 &= 0
\end{aligned}
\qquad (6.10)
$$

Here, $\mathbf{t}_1$ and $\mathbf{t}_2$ are two linearly independent tangent vectors to f at the point (u_1, u_2, u_3), and

$$
\nabla_u S = \left(\frac{\partial S}{\partial u_1}, \frac{\partial S}{\partial u_2}, \frac{\partial S}{\partial u_3} \right)
$$

Elimination of u_1, u_2, and u_3 from the set of equations (6.10) results in an implicit equation describing the offset of f.

We could now eliminate s and t in the parametric case, or eliminate u_1, u_2, and u_3, in the implicit case. The result, in each case, is an implicit equation for the offset surface which then is intersected with some other surface, say g. However, the symbolic computations incurred by the elimination step could be forbidding. So, we will intersect g with the system of equations describing the offset, thus tracing the intersection in a dimension higher than three. Example 6.2 illustrates the method. Such a trace derives the following additional information:

- In the parametric case, each point is traced in five dimensions, and has the coordinates (x, y, z, s, t). Here, $p = (x, y, z)$ is the point on the intersection of the offset surface of f with g. The point (s, t) in parameter space determines the *footpoint* of p; that is, the point on f at distance r from p.

- In the implicit case, each point is traced in six dimensions, and has the coordinates (x, y, z, u_1, u_2, u_3). Again, $p = (x, y, z)$ is the point on the offset surface intersection with g, and (u_1, u_2, u_3) is its footpoint on f.

Note that we can intersect two offset surfaces with each other by combining the respective systems of equations. This raises the dimensionality of the problem, but not its difficulty.

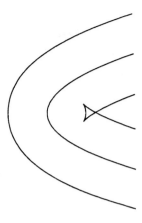

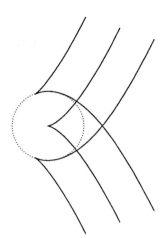

Figure 6.6 Interior Offset Part at Self-Intersections

Figure 6.7 Additional Offset Points at Singularity

It is important to note the following points about the envelope method for formulating offsets:

1. The offset surface may self-intersect. In applications, self-intersections are undesirable, and "interior" surface parts may be obtained that one wants to eliminate. See Figure 6.6 for an illustration in two dimensions. Neither formulation (6.6) nor the envelope method will automatically eliminate those interior parts.

2. In constructing an algebraic description of offset surfaces, we operate implicitly over the field of complex numbers, and we obtain certain surface components at infinity. Both result in additional points that are described by the equations.[5] Figure 6.7 shows an example in two dimensions. Those points are not generated in formulation (6.6). On the other hand, that formulation cannot handle singularities.

In our view, these phenomena are due to the fact that algebraic computations implicitly require projective spaces over an algebraically closed ground field, as explained in Section 7.2.1 in Chapter 7. Insisting on working in real affine spaces substantially reduces the available mathematical machinery.

Example 6.2: Consider the ellipsoid $f = 2x^2 + 9y^2 + 18z^2 - 18$. We plan to intersect its offset by 1 with a cylinder $h = (x-3)^2 + y^2 - 1$. We

---

[5]In the case of parametric curves, some of these additional points can be eliminated by dividing out certain factors. See also the notes at the end of the chapter.

consider a sphere of radius 1 centered at the point $p = (u_1, u_2, u_3)$ of the ellipsoid:

$$S: \quad \begin{aligned} (x - u_1)^2 + (y - u_2)^2 + (z - u_3)^2 - 1 &= 0 \\ 2u_1^2 + 9u_2^2 + 18u_3^2 - 18 &= 0 \end{aligned}$$

Here, the second equation ensures that p lies on the ellipsoid. To find the directional derivatives of S, we must determine two independent tangent directions to the ellipsoid at p. Now the gradient at p is

$$\nabla f = (4u_1, 18u_2, 36u_3) = 2(2u_1, 9u_2, 18u_3)$$

Hence, perpendiculars to ∇f will be tangent directions. We choose

$$\begin{aligned} \mathbf{t}_1 : \quad & (-9u_2, 2u_1, 0) \\ \mathbf{t}_2 : \quad & (0, -18u_3, 9u_2) \end{aligned}$$

and observe that $\mathbf{t}_1 \perp \nabla f$, $\mathbf{t}_2 \perp \nabla f$, and that $\mathbf{t}_1$ and $\mathbf{t}_2$ are linearly independent when $u_2 \neq 0$. Moreover,

$$\nabla_u S = 2(-(x - u_1), -(y - u_2), -(z - u_3))$$

Equations (6.8) and (6.9) specialize to

$$\begin{aligned} \nabla_u S \cdot \mathbf{t}_1 &= 9(x - u_1)u_2 - 2(y - u_2)u_1 \\ \nabla_u S \cdot \mathbf{t}_2 &= 18(y - u_2)u_3 - 9(z - u_3)u_2 \end{aligned}$$

Therefore, the intersection with h is described by the equations

$$\begin{aligned} (x - u_1)^2 + (y - u_2)^2 + (z - u_3)^2 - 1 &= 0 \\ 2u_1^2 + 9u_2^2 + 18u_3^2 - 18 &= 0 \\ 9(x - u_1)u_2 - 2(y - u_2)u_1 &= 0 \\ 18(y - u_2)u_3 - 9(z - u_3)u_2 &= 0 \\ (x - 3)^2 + y^2 - 1 &= 0 \end{aligned} \qquad (6.11)$$

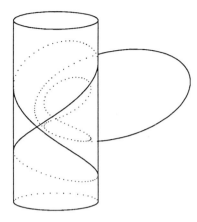

Figure 6.8   Intersecting a Cylinder with an Offset of an Ellipsoid

These are five equations in the six unknowns x, y, z, u_1, u_2, u_3. Here, x, y, and z are the coordinates, in 3-space, of the intersection curve of the offset of f with g. Moreover, $q = (u_1, u_2, u_3)$ is the footpoint of $p = (x, y, z)$ on f; that is, it is a point on f such that the surface normal through q passes through p, and such that the Euclidian distance $\overline{(p, q)}$ is the offset distance. Rather than eliminating the unknowns u_1, u_2, and u_3, we trace the intersection curve in six dimensions, tracking simultaneously the intersection of the offset with g, as well as the footpoint curve on f. Figure 6.8 shows this trace. $\diamondsuit$

6.4 Mapping Surface Intersections to Plane Curves

A general approach to surface-intersection evaluation is to map the surface intersection to a plane curve $h(u, v) = 0$. The approach is appealing for a number of reasons. For one, a plane curve can be traced through singularities, as explained later in this chapter. An analogous process for surface intersection could be devised in principle, but it would be substantially more complex because it would have to map the intersecting surfaces simultaneously such that the singularity of their intersection would be resolved.

On the other hand, the mapping approach has to face a number of difficulties that reduce its attractiveness. These include the cost of constructing the map, the numerical inaccuracies that might arise in the substitution process, and, finally, the high degree of h, which is, in general, the product of the surface degrees and usually leads to numerical difficulties. We discuss several techniques that can be applied in various situations. None of them avoid all the problems mentioned.

6.4.1 Substitution Maps

In a substitution map, we substitute the parametric form of one surface into the implicit form of the other, thereby obtaining a plane curve in the parameter space of the first surface. If we intersect a parametric with an implicit surface, the cost of constructing the map is just the cost of doing the substitution. Otherwise, we must add the cost of converting the representation of one of the surfaces from parametric to implicit, or vice versa. In most of those situations, the cost of the representation conversion will dominate.

Intersecting Two Parametric Surfaces

When intersecting two parametric surfaces, we implicitize one of them. Implicitization is always possible, and can be done either by resultant computations or by Gröbner bases techniques. The resultant-based computation suffers from the extraneous factor problem. If the implicitized surface is

$$f(x, y, z) = 0$$

and the parametric surface is

$$
\begin{aligned}
x &= g_1(u, v) \\
y &= g_2(u, v) \\
z &= g_3(u, v)
\end{aligned}
$$

then the plane algebraic curve is

$$h(u, v) = f(g_1(u, v), g_2(u, v), g_3(u, v)) = 0$$

We can then trace $h = 0$ in u, v space, and map each point via the rational functions g_i.

Example 6.3: Consider the intersection of the parametric surfaces

$$
f : \begin{cases} x = st \\ y = st^2 \\ z = s^2 \end{cases}
\quad \text{and} \quad
g : \begin{cases} x = u^2 - v^2 \\ y = 2uv \\ z = u^2 + v^2 \end{cases}
$$

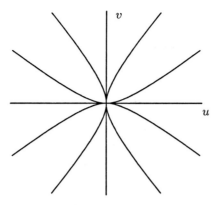

Figure 6.9   Trace of $(u^2 - v^2)^4 - 4u^2v^2(u^2 + v^2) = 0$

We implicitize the surface f using the Gröbner bases method discussed in Section 7.5.1 of Chapter 7. and obtain the implicit form

$$x^4 - y^2z = 0$$

Substitution of the second surface into this implicit form yields the plane curve

$$h: \ (u^2 - v^2)^4 - 4u^2v^2(u^2 + v^2) = 0$$

Each point (u, v) of h corresponds to the point $(u^2 - v^2, 2uv, u^2 + v^2)$ on g, which must also be on f; hence, it is a point on the intersection. A trace of h is shown in Figure 6.9. $\diamondsuit$

Intersecting Two Implicit Surfaces

When intersecting two implicit surfaces, we would like to parameterize one of them. Not every implicit surface possesses a rational parametric form, however, so this approach needs to be modified. It can be shown that the intersection of two implicit surfaces always lies on a parameterizable surface. That is, given the surfaces

$$\begin{aligned} f(x, y, z) &= 0 \\ g(x, y, z) &= 0 \end{aligned}$$

there is a surface h that is parameterizable and contains the intersection of f and g. The surface has the form

$$h(x, y, z) = h_1 f + h_2 g = 0$$

where the coefficients h_1 and h_2 are polynomials. The computation for obtaining h is conceptually simple, as is the parameterization, since h will be a monoid whose singular point we will know.

We describe the derivation of h. First, we *homogenize* f and g, obtaining $F(w, x, y, z)$ and $G(w, x, y, z)$. As long as $w \neq 0$, the curve $F \cap G$ is identical to $f \cap g$. We select one of the variables as *main variable*, and rewrite F and G as polynomials in this variable, say w:

$$F = u_n w^n + u_{n-1} w^{n-1} + \cdots + u_1 w + u_0$$
$$G = v_{n'} w^{n'} + v_{n'-1} w^{n'-1} + \cdots + v_1 w + v_0$$

Without loss of generality, we can assume that $n \geq n' > 1$, and determine the polynomials

$$F_1 = u_n w^{n-n'} G - v_{n'} F$$
$$G_1 = (u_0 G - v_0 F)/w$$

In effect, in F_1, we cancel the highest terms in w; in G_1, we cancel the lowest term. Note that both F_1 and G_1 contain the intersection curve of F and G, since they are algebraic combinations of the two surfaces.

Both F_1 and G_1 have degree at most $n - 1$ in w. If one of them is linear in w, then we stop; we have found the desired surface. If neither is linear, then we repeat the calculation using F_1 and G_1 in place of F and G. Since at each step the maximum degree in w is lowered by at least one, the computation derives the desired monoid equation after at most n steps, in the form

$$w H_{m-1}(x, y, z) + H_m(x, y, z) = 0$$

This surface is then parameterized by

$$w(u, v, s) = -H_m(u, v, s)/H_{m-1}(u, v, s)$$
$$x(u, v, s) = u$$
$$y(u, v, s) = v$$
$$z(u, v, s) = s$$

as described in Section 5.5.4 of Chapter 5. The parametric forms are now substituted into the equation of G and give a plane curve in homogeneous form. After dehomogenizing, this is the desired plane curve.

Example 6.4: Consider the intersection curve of the cylinder $f = x^2 + (z+1)^2 - 1 = 0$ and the sphere $g = x^2 + y^2 + (z+2)^2 - 4 = 0$. Homogenizing, we obtain $F = x^2 + z^2 + 2zw$ and $G = x^2 + y^2 + z^2 + 4zw$. The intersection curve is an irreducible degree-4 space curve with a nodal singularity at the origin. We select z as the main variable. Accordingly, we compute

$$\begin{aligned} F_1 &= G - F = y^2 + 2zw \\ G_1 &= [(x^2 + y^2)F - x^2 G]/z = y^2 z + 2(y^2 - x^2)w \end{aligned}$$

Both polynomials are linear in z. F_1 is simpler and has the parameterization

$$\begin{aligned} z &= -\frac{s^2}{2u} \\ w &= u \\ x &= v \\ y &= s \end{aligned}$$

Substitution into G yields the plane curve

$$s^4 + 4u^2(v^2 - s^2) = 0$$

Dehomogenizing with $u = 1$ yields $s^4 - 4(v^2 - s^2) = 0$. Both the space curve and its planar image are shown in Figure 6.10. $\diamondsuit$

Example 6.4 is favorable because the degree of the plane curve obtained is the minimum degree possible. In general, the monoid method will introduce extraneous factors and will yield plane curves of higher degree than needed. An example of this phenomenon is easily constructed.

We intersect the torus

$$(x^2 + y^2 + z^2 - w^2)^2 + 8w^2(z^2 - x^2 - y^2 - w^2) + 16w^4 = 0$$

with the ellipsoid

$$36(x - w)^2 + 4(y - w)^2 + 9z^2 - 36w^2 = 0$$

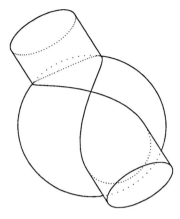
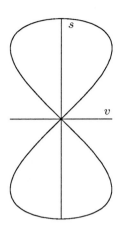

Figure 6.10   Space Curve and Its Planar Image in Parameter Space of Monoid

We apply the monoid construction,[6] and obtain in three steps a rational surface of degree 8. The respective degrees obtained in each step are as follows:

$$F_i \text{ degrees}: \quad 4 \quad 6 \quad 8$$
$$G_i \text{ degrees}: \quad 5 \quad 4 \quad 9$$

Note that the degree drop in the second stage is due to a common factor of degree 4 of the w^0 coefficients.

We use the monoid of degree 8 and substitute its parametric form into the equation of the ellipsoid. This yields a plane curve of degree 16 that factors. The curve has three components, of degree 2, 6, and 8, respectively. The degree-2 component is $36x^2 + 4y^2 + 9z^2$, and is the intersection of the ellipsoid with the plane at infinity. We can verify that this curve is not on the torus, and conclude that the degree-2 component is an extraneous factor. By Bezout's theorem, we expect an intersection curve of degree 8. In conjunction with the rejection of the degree-2 component, this implies that the degree-6 component is also extraneous, so the degree-8 component is the sought curve. It is shown in Figure 6.11.

6.4.2 Projection Methods

The second general approach to mapping a space curve to a plane curve is to use projection. In principle, the construction of these maps is straightfor-

---

[6]In practice, one should parameterize the ellipsoid or the torus, since both are rationally parameterizable.

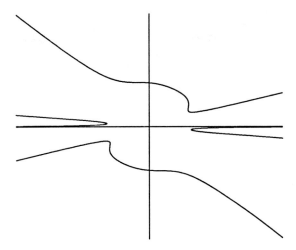

Figure 6.11   Ellipsoid/Torus Intersection in Parameter Space

ward. The main problem, however, is that the point from which to project must be chosen carefully: A poorly chosen point will result in a map that cannot be inverted. Such a projection map would not permit mapping the points of the plane curve back to space-curve points, so that the plane-curve trace would yield no information.

If we assume that the two surfaces intersect transversally — that is, that the surface gradients are linearly independent almost everywhere — and that the curve itself is irreducible, then it can be shown that a good projection point can be chosen by the following computation:

1. Transform the surface equations by a nonsingular linear transformation with symbolic coefficients.

2. Project the intersection by a resultant computation.

3. Choose random numeric values for the coefficients and verify that the projection does not degenerate.

Note that step 3 succeeds with a probability of one. Almost all assignments will result in a nonsingular linear transformation. Moreover, assignments failing to produce a good projection are in directions at which infinitely many curve-point pairs line up. Those directions constitute a ruled surface, and any view point not on that surface yields a suitable projection.

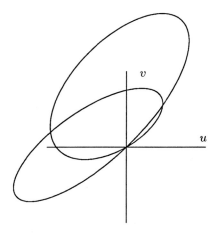

Figure 6.12   Projection of the Cylinder/Sphere Intersection

Example 6.5:   We consider the surfaces of Example 6.4, intersecting

$$f: \quad x^2 + (z+1)^2 - 1$$
$$g: \quad x^2 + y^2 + (z+2)^2 - 4$$

Instead of substituting with symbolic coefficients a_{ij}, we substitute

$$x = u + v + w$$
$$y = u + 2v + 4w$$
$$z = u - 2v - w$$

For random values, we expect that none of the a_{ij} are zero, and that none of the coefficient expressions vanish, after substitution. This is also the case for this substitution, although it is not based on random values.

With this substitution, we obtain the polynomial $F(u, v, w)$ from f, and the polynomial $G(u, v, w)$ from g. We eliminate one of the variables — say, w — obtaining a polynomial $H(u, v) = Res_w(F, G)$, where

$$
\begin{aligned}
H(u,v)/4 = \;& 400v^4 - 960uv^3 - 952v^3 + 1256u^2v^2 + 1848uv^2 + 490v^2 \\
& -816u^3v - 1554u^2v - 784uv + 289u^4 + 588u^3 + 294u^2
\end{aligned}
$$

Recall that the initial form of a polynomial consists of the terms of lowest degree. Consequently, the initial form of the curve H is $h_0 = 490v^2 - 784uv + 294u^2$. The initial form factors $h_0 = 98(v - u)(5v - 3u)$; that is, the singularity of H at the origin is a node.

The curve H is shown in Figure 6.12. It has three singularities. The one at the origin corresponds to the singularity of the surface intersection. The other two have been introduced by the projection.

We stated that the projection will succeed with high probability. As example of a poor projection point, consider the assignment

$$x = w, \qquad y = v, \qquad z = u$$

Here we obtain the plane curve

$$(v^2 + 2u)^2$$

That is, we obtain a double parabola. There is no rational map from this plane curve to the space curve, so tracing the parabola would be useless.
$\diamondsuit$

6.5 Plane Algebraic Curves

We now consider how to trace a plane algebraic curve $f(x, y) = 0$. Tracing a plane algebraic curve is fundamental, because every algebraic space curve can be mapped birationally to a plane algebraic curve. This observation has been used in various ways in the surface-intersection problem, and continues to be researched as an approach to intersection evaluation. The method to be described can trace through curve singularities of arbitrary structure.

As before, the bulk of the tracing will be done numerically, and the routines continue to be structured as before:

1. Construct a local approximant at the curve point p.

2. With a selected step size, derive a new curve-point estimate q.

3. Refine the estimate q iteratively, obtaining a curve point.

The numerical tracing routine performs very well, except at singularities. All purely numerical tracing routines fail at a singular curve point for the same reason: Technically, the routines depend on the underlying assumption that there exists a system of linear equations that determines the local structure of the curve with sufficient accuracy. In our case, this was the system of equations (6.1). At a singular point, however, these equations are nonlinear, as explained later, and approaching the problem as a linear one would be inappropriate. Hence, we seek methods for analyzing singularities.

Rather than dealing directly with nonlinear equations, we will apply a classical result from algebraic geometry that states that every algebraic curve $f(x,y) = 0$ can be transformed birationally into a curve $g(x,y) = 0$ that is devoid of singularities. Thus, we plan to trace g in the vicinity of singular points of f, and to map the points of g back to corresponding points of f.

It would be nice if we needed to trace only g. Unfortunately, g cannot be so used, since we might have to pass through infinity. So, we trace f whenever possible and trace only the critical segments of f on g — the segments containing singularities.

6.5.1 Place of a Curve

In this section, we define the notion of a *place* of an algebraic curve. We need this concept to analyze the nature of singularities and to elucidate the effect of quadratic transformations used by the tracing algorithm to resolve singularities.

Definition of Place of a Curve

At the point $p = (a_0, b_0)$ of the plane algebraic curve $f(x,y) = 0$, we define the formal power series

$$
\begin{aligned}
x(s) &= a_0 + a_1 s + a_2 s^2 + \cdots \\
y(s) &= b_0 + b_1 s + b_2 s^2 + \cdots
\end{aligned}
\tag{6.12}
$$

and require that $f(x(s), y(s)) \equiv 0$. We think of the pair as a *local parameterization* of f. It is called a *place* of f at p, and exists because of Newton's theorem.

Newton's theorem generalizes the implicit function theorem: The implicit function theorem states that, for a regular curve point p at which the partial derivative f_y is not zero, there exists a neighborhood U in which an analytic function $y = h(x)$ can be defined such that $f(x, h(x)) \equiv 0$, for all x in U. By introducing a new variable s and defining two analytic functions $x = h_1(s)$ and $y = h_2(s)$, such that $f(h_1(s), h_2(s)) \equiv 0$, the hypothesis $f_y \neq 0$ can be abolished. Furthermore, by allowing possibly more than one pair of functions of the form of equation (6.12) at p, the assumption that p is not singular can be removed. So generalized, we obtain Newton's theorem, which says, roughly, that given a polynomial $f(x,y)$ and a point $p = (a_0, b_0)$ on it, there exist power series of the form of equation (6.12) such that

$$
f(x(s), y(s)) \equiv 0
\tag{6.13}
$$

These power series can be viewed as formal series, in which case equation (6.13) is an algebraic identity; or they can be considered as defining analytic functions, in which case their convergence properties must be considered as well. In the following discussion, we adopt the former point of view.

The notion of place is more specific than that of a curve point. At a regular curve point p, the curve f has only one place, and that place can be shown to be essentially the Taylor expansion of f at p. At singular points, the curve may have several places. When considered within the disk of convergence, a place is simply an analytic curve branch.

Basic Properties of Places and Singularities

A place is *regular* if a_1 and b_1 are not simultaneously zero; otherwise, it is *singular*. We say that the place is *centered* at (a_0, b_0). For example, the place

$$
\begin{aligned}
x(s) &= s \\
y(s) &= s + \frac{1}{2}s^2 - \frac{1}{8}s^3 \pm \ldots
\end{aligned}
$$

is regular, whereas the place

$$
\begin{aligned}
x(s) &= s^2 \\
y(s) &= s^3
\end{aligned}
$$

is singular. If a curve has exactly one regular place centered at (a_0, b_0), then (a_0, b_0) is a regular curve point. Otherwise, it is a singular curve point. Thus, a singular curve point is one at which the curve has either one singular place or at which the curve has two or more places. In the latter case, none, some, or all of the places could be singular as well.

The definition of a singular curve point in terms of places can be shown to be equivalent to the definition in terms of vanishing partial derivatives. We define the *derivative* $h'(s)$ of the series $h(s) = a_0 + a_1 s + a_2 s^2 + a_3 s^3 + \cdots$ as

$$
h'(s) = a_1 + 2a_2 s + 3a_3 s^2 + \cdots
$$

Then, it can be shown that at the regular curve point (a_0, b_0) the partial derivatives of f are proportional to the derivatives of the place; that is,

$$
\begin{aligned}
f_x(a_0, b_0) &= \alpha x'(0) \\
f_y(a_0, b_0) &= \alpha y'(0)
\end{aligned}
$$

where $\alpha \neq 0$.

The *order* of a power series $a_1 s + a_2 s^2 + a_3 s^3 + \cdots$ is the minimum index k such that $a_k \neq 0$. Similarly, the *order* of a place centered at the origin is the smallest index k such that a_k and b_k are not both zero. The order of a regular place is always one, the order of a singular place is always greater than one. A place

$$
\begin{aligned}
x(s) &= a_1 s + a_2 s^2 + \cdots \\
y(s) &= b_1 s + b_2 s^2 + \cdots
\end{aligned}
$$

intersects a curve $g(x,y) = 0$ at the origin with *multiplicity* k if k is the order of the power series $g(x(s), y(s))$. Intersection multiplicity is also called *order of contact*.

Example 6.6:   The place $(x(s) = s^2, y(s) = s^3)$ intersects the line $x + y$ with multiplicity 2, since $x(s) + y(s) = s^2 + s^3$ has order 2. However, the line $y = 0$ intersects the place with multiplicity 3. $\diamondsuit$

Let $P_1 = (x_1(s), y_1(s))$ and $P_2 = (x_2(s), y_2(s))$ be two places centered at the origin. We would like to define their intersection multiplicity at the origin as k whenever the first $k + 1$ coefficients of $x_1(s)$ and $x_2(s)$ and of $y_1(s)$ and $y_2(s)$ agree. This problem is not quite so simple, because there are different ways to write the power series. Moreover, since the line $x + y = 0$ has the place $(x(s) = s, y(s) = s)$ at the origin, such a definition would not be compatible with the intersection multiplicity of places with curves. The proper definition requires reparameterizing the two places such that a canonical form is obtained, after which the multiplicity — or, equivalently, the order of contact — can be defined as the order of a certain power series. The details are omitted.

A key theorem from algebraic geometry states that two places either are in contact of finite order, or else are equal. Later on, we will use this theorem to show that the different places centered at the same singular point of a curve can be "separated." Such a separation is one of the key aspects of resolving curve singularities. Note that the theorem is reminiscent of Bezout's theorem.

If we think of a place as an analytic branch, then it makes sense to define its tangent. Intuitively, a tangent to the place

$$
\begin{aligned}
x(s) &= a_0 + a_1 s + a_2 s^2 + \cdots \\
y(s) &= b_0 + b_1 s + b_2 s^2 + \cdots
\end{aligned}
$$

is a line through (a_0, b_0) that intersects the place with a higher multiplicity; that is, it is in higher order of contact with the place than almost all other lines.

Example 6.7:   Consider the place $(x(s) = s^2, y(s) = s^3)$, centered at the origin. Let

$$
ux + vy = 0
$$

be a line through the origin, where u and v are not both zero. We have

$$ux(s) + vy(s) = us^2 + vs^3$$

So, the line intersects the place with multiplicity 2, except when $u = 0$, for then the intersection multiplicity is 3. Therefore, $y = 0$ is tangent to the place (s^2, s^3). $\diamondsuit$

It can be proved that there is exactly one tangent to a place. Moreover, it can be proved that at a regular curve point the tangent to the place is the curve tangent, and that at a singular point p the curve tangents consist of the tangents to the places of the curve that are centered at p. In particular, if the origin is a point on f, then the tangent lines to f at the origin are the linear factors of the initial form of f. Thus, the notion of tangency to a place is more specific than is the concept of tangent space introduced in Section 5.3.1 of Chapter 5.

A Method for Computing Places

Given a point $p = (a_0, b_0)$, one way to determine the place(s) of $f(x, y)$ is to set up the series of equations (6.12) formally, to substitute them into f, and to set the coefficients of the resulting power series to zero. For example, let $f = y^2 - x^2 - x^3$, and consider the point $(0, 0)$. We substitute $\sum_{i \geq 1} a_i s^i$ for x, and $\sum_{i \geq 1} b_i s^i$ for y, and set the coefficient of each power of s to zero. This yields the following system

$$
\begin{aligned}
a_1^2 - b_1^2 &= 0 \\
2b_1 b_2 - 2a_1 a_2 - a_1^3 &= 0 \\
2b_1 b_3 + b_2^2 - 2a_1 a_3 - a_2^2 - 3a_1^2 a_2 &= 0 \\
2b_1 b_4 + 2b_2 b_3 - 2a_1 a_4 - 2a_2 a_3 - 3a_1^2 a_3 - 3a_1 a_2^2 &= 0 \\
&\vdots
\end{aligned}
\tag{6.14}
$$

which has the solutions

$$
\begin{aligned}
x(s) &= s \\
y(s) &= s + \frac{1}{2}s^2 - \frac{1}{8}s^3 \pm \cdots
\end{aligned}
$$

and

$$
\begin{aligned}
x(s) &= s \\
y(s) &= -s - \frac{1}{2}s^2 + \frac{1}{8}s^3 \mp \cdots
\end{aligned}
$$

Each solution is a distinct regular place of f at the origin. Since f has more than one place, it is singular at $(0,0)$, which is also evident from the nonlinear initial form $y^2 - x^2 = (y - x)(y + x)$ and from the graph of the curve shown in Section 6.5.3 in Figure 6.14 on the left.

The system of equations derived in this way agrees formally with the system of equations (6.1), formulated in Section 6.2. The connection becomes evident when considering the derivatives of a place

$$
\begin{aligned}
x'(s) &= a_1 + 2a_2 s + 3a_3 s^2 + \ldots \\
y'(s) &= b_1 + 2b_2 s + 3b_3 s^2 + \ldots
\end{aligned}
$$

Higher-order derivatives are defined analogously. Then, the system of equations (6.14) can be shown to be of the form

$$
\nabla f \cdot \mathbf{r}^{(m)} = b_{f,m}
$$

with $\mathbf{r} = (x(s), y(s))$. Thus, the difference between the regular and the singular case is simply that in the regular case this system is linear, whereas in the singular case it is nonlinear.

Places on Space Curves

The notion of place generalizes directly to higher-dimensional algebraic curves. As before, the system of equations (6.1) can be formulated and solved for each space-curve point. For regular curve points, the system is linear; for singular curve points, it is nonlinear. When solving such a system, the following theorem is helpful.

> **Theorem**
> Let $(x_1(s), x_2(s), ..., x_n(s))$ be a place of an algebraic space curve. Then the parameter s can be chosen such that one of the coordinates x_j has the form
>
> $$
> x_j(s) = s^k
> $$

For a regular curve point, k will be 1, so this theorem specializes to the implicit function theorem.

6.5.2 Quadratic Transformations

Let $f(x, y) = 0$ be a plane algebraic curve on which the origin $(0,0)$ is a singular point. We wish to construct a birational transformation τ from the curve f to a curve g with the following properties. The transformation is bijective in a neighborhood of the origin, except, possibly, at the origin.[7] Moreover, each place of f centered at the origin is mapped to a regular place of g, and the center of each such place is a regular point of g.

Intuitively, τ separates all places of f at the origin, and, if any one of them is a singular place, it is transformed by τ into a nonsingular place centered at a regular curve point of g. Thus, τ "resolves" the singularity into several regular curve branches situated at different nonsingular points. Note that we consider only singularities at the origin. This is sufficient, because a singular curve point can always be brought to the origin by a change of coordinates.

The birational map effecting a resolution of the singularity is constructed incrementally from two quadratic transformations T_1 and T_2:

$$T_1 : \quad x_1 = x$$
$$y_1 = y/x$$

$$T_2 : \quad x_2 = x/y$$
$$y_2 = y$$

Initially, we restrict attention to T_1. Its inverse is evidently $x = x_1$ and $y = x_1 y_1$. The basic properties of T_1 are as follows:

1. T_1 maps the set $\{(x,y) \mid x \neq 0\}$ bijectively onto the set $\{(x_1, y_1) \mid x_1 \neq 0\}$.

2. The points $(0, y)$ with $y \neq 0$ are mapped to infinity in the (x_1, y_1)-plane.

3. As we approach the origin on a curve branch, the limit of the image points is the image of the origin on the branch. This limit depends on the direction of approach: If the branch has a tangent with slope m at the origin, then that branch will intersect the y_1 axis in $(0, m)$.

Figure 6.13 shows the effect of T_1 on select lines. The coordinate lines $x = m$ are mapped to $x_1 = m$ for $m \neq 0$. The coordinate lines $y = m$ are mapped to the hyperbolas $y_1 x_1 = m$. Finally, the lines $y = mx$ are mapped to the lines $y_1 = m$ for $m \neq 0$. The effect of T_2 is analogous.

6.5.3 Branch and Curve Desingularization

Assume that $f(x, y) = 0$ has a singularity of order k at the origin, and that the initial form of f is not y^k. When T_1 is applied to f, then the *total*

---

[7]Strictly speaking, τ is not bijective on certain lines. When constructing τ, we will ensure that these "exceptional lines" are not tangent to the branch we trace.

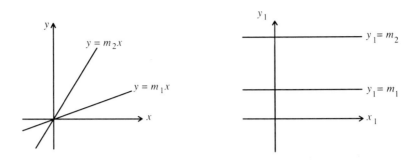

Figure 6.13   Quadratic Transformation $T_1 : (x, y) \to (x, y/x)$

transform of f is $x_1^k g(x_1, y_1) = 0$. The lines $x_1^k = 0$ are not of interest, and we consider $g(x_1, y_1) = 0$ as the *proper transform* of *f*. In favorable cases, the points of g corresponding to the origin of the (x, y)-plane are not singular. Figures 6.14 and 6.15 show two examples. In more complicated situations, there are singularities at the corresponding points of g, but the structure of these singularities has been simplified in some sense. This statement can be made precise, but requires considerable mathematical machinery, so we restrict our exposition to a somewhat simplistic but intuitive version.

Intuitively, then, there are a number of places at the singularity at the origin that are mapped as follows by T_1: Two places of contact order k will be mapped to two places with order of contact at most $k - 1$. Moreover, the image of a singular place will be a place that, if still singular, has a singularity that is structurally simpler. Remarkably, singular places become

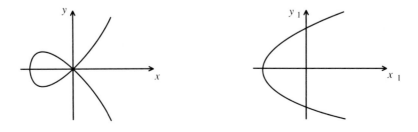

Figure 6.14   Resolution of a Nodal Singularity

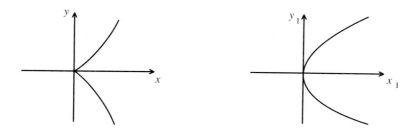

Figure 6.15 Resolution of a Cuspidal Singularity

regular after finitely many applications of quadratic transformations T_1 and/or T_2. Moreover, since different branches cannot have infinite-order contact, they must separate after finitely many quadratic transformations.

So far, we have not commented on the use of T_2. Briefly, if a place has the y axis as tangent, T_1 maps it to infinity where it cannot be further analyzed without passing to the projective plane. Thus, we transform such a branch with the help of T_2.

6.5.4 Tracing with Desingularization

The idea of tracing with desingularization is as follows:

1. Beginning at a regular curve point p, we trace f using the numerical procedure outlined previously.

2. When approaching a singularity q, the numerical trace is suspended at a point r prior to reaching q. Then f is translated such that q becomes the origin.

3. Depending on the tangent direction of the branch we are currently tracing, we transform f to g with T_1 or T_2. Then, beginning at the point r_1 of g corresponding to r, we trace g until we have crossed the singularity, mapping the points on g to f by the inverse of T_1 or T_2.

See also Figure 6.16 for an illustration of the idea. This procedure must be implemented recursively, since a single quadratic transformation may not suffice to resolve the singularity. The major practical concerns are locating the singularity while tracing, and accounting for the intended direction of the trace. Since we do a coordinate transformation to bring the singularity to the origin, we also have to cope with imprecise coordinates of the singularity.

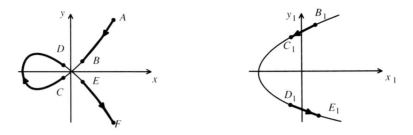

Figure 6.16   Tracing with Desingularization

6.5.5 Locating Singularities

When we are numerically tracing f, an impending singularity is detected from the condition number of the matrix

$$\begin{pmatrix} f_x & -f_y \\ f_y & f_x \end{pmatrix}$$

The singular point is the simultaneous intersection of $f = 0$, $f_x = 0$, and $f_y = 0$, and can be found iteratively or by direct methods.

Least-Squares Approach

An iterative approach can be based on a least-squares formulation as follows: Beginning with a nearby curve point p_0, we construct a sequence of points p_0, p_1, p_2, ... converging to the singularity. Let $p_{i+1} = p_i + (\delta_x, \delta_y)$. Then we solve the linear system

$$\begin{pmatrix} f_x & f_y \\ f_{xx} & f_{xy} \\ f_{xy} & f_{yy} \end{pmatrix} \begin{pmatrix} \delta_x \\ \delta_y \end{pmatrix} = - \begin{pmatrix} f \\ f_x \\ f_y \end{pmatrix}$$

We rewrite this system in matrix notation as

$$A\Delta = \mathbf{b}$$

where $\Delta = (\delta_x, \delta_y)^T$. This overconstrained system corresponds to the least-squares problem

$$A^T A \Delta = A^T \mathbf{b}$$

For higher-order singularities, higher-order partials may also vanish. Thus, if A does not have full rank, we extend the system by adding, for each vanishing partial h, the equation

$$h_x \delta_x + h_y \delta_y = -h$$

In this manner, a matrix $A^T A$ of full rank is obtained.

Numerically, the least-squares problem is best solved by singular value decomposition of $A\Delta = \mathbf{b}$, since the formation of AA^T significantly diminishes the obtainable precision. Nevertheless, the method has difficulties with flat cusps — for example, with singularities such as $y^2 - x^{2m+1} = 0$, $m \gg 1$.

Using Constrained Minimization

We may consider locating a singularity as a constrained-minimization problem:

> **Problem**
> Minimize $f_x^2 + f_y^2$ subject to the constraint $f(x, y) = 0$.

With the help of Lagrangian multipliers, this problem can be converted to an unconstrained minimization problem by minimizing

$$L = f_x^2 + f_y^2 + \lambda f$$

where λ is the Lagrange multiplier. An extremum of L then satisfies the following equations:

$$
\begin{aligned}
L_x &= 0 \\
L_y &= 0 \qquad\qquad (6.15)\\
L_\lambda &= 0
\end{aligned}
$$

These are three algebraic equations in three variables; that is, they represent the intersection of three algebraic surfaces in (x, y, λ)-space. Given an initial guess (x_0, y_0), the intersection will include a nearby curve singularity. An initial guess for λ must also be given; it could be 1, for instance.

Newton's method cannot be used to solve the system of equations (6.15) without attention to some details. To understand the reason, we expand the partials of the goal function L from which the matrix for the Newton iteration is formed.

$$\begin{aligned}
L_x &= 2(f_x f_{xx} + f_y f_{xy}) + \lambda f_x \\
L_y &= 2(f_x f_{xy} + f_y f_{yy}) + \lambda f_y \\
L_\lambda &= f
\end{aligned}$$

The matrix of the linear system used in Newton's method is therefore

$$\begin{pmatrix}
u_{11} & u_{12} & f_x \\
u_{21} & u_{22} & f_y \\
f_x & f_y & 0
\end{pmatrix} \tag{6.16}$$

where

$$\begin{aligned}
u_{11} &= 2(f_{xx}^2 + f_x f_{xxx} + f_{xy}^2 + f_y f_{xxy}) + \lambda f_{xx} \\
u_{12} &= 2(f_{xx} f_{xy} + f_x f_{xxy} + f_{xy} f_{yy} + f_y f_{xyy}) + \lambda f_{xy} \\
u_{21} &= 2(f_{xx} f_{xy} + f_x f_{xxy} + f_{xy} f_{yy} + f_y f_{xyy}) + \lambda f_{xy} \\
u_{22} &= 2(f_{xy}^2 + f_x f_{xyy} + f_{yy}^2 + f_y f_{yyy}) + \lambda f_{yy}
\end{aligned}$$

Since $f_x \to 0$ and $f_y \to 0$ as we approach the singularity, the last row vanishes and matrix (6.16) becomes singular. However, the last row governs the change in λ, which is irrelevant as long as we stay on the curve f. So, we could restrict attention to the 2×2 submatrix

$$\begin{pmatrix}
u_{11} & u_{12} \\
u_{21} & u_{22}
\end{pmatrix} \tag{6.17}$$

This modification will not help for higher-order singularities where, in addition to f_x and f_y, the higher-order partials f_{xx}, f_{xy}, and f_{yy} vanish as well.

Reduction to Root Finding

Locating the singularities of the curve $f(x, y) = 0$ can be reduced to finding the roots of a univariate polynomial as follows. By forming the resultant $Res_y(f, f_x)$, we obtain a univariate polynomial $P(x)$. Its roots are the x coordinates of those curve points at which f_x vanishes. The partial derivative f_x vanishes at all singular curve points, and it vanishes at all regular curve points at which the curve tangent is parallel to the x axis. So, we must determine $P(x)$, and, for each root a, we need to test whether there is a singular curve point (a, y_a). The ordinates y_a can be determined as the roots of the polynomial $f(a, y)$.

Example 6.8: Consider the curve

$$f = x^3 + 3x^2 y + 3xy^2 + y^3 - 3x^2 - 2xy - 3y^2 + 5x - 3y - 4$$

The partial derivatives are

$$\begin{aligned} f_x &= 3x^2 + 6xy + 3y^2 - 6x - 2y + 5 \\ f_y &= 3x^2 + 6xy + 3y^2 - 2x - 6y - 3 \end{aligned}$$

The y-resultant of f and f_x is

$$Res_y(f, f_x) = 432x^4 - 2464x^3 + 5256x^2 - 4968x + 1755$$

with the two real roots

$$\begin{aligned} a_1 &= 1.5 \\ a_2 &= 1.2037037... \end{aligned}$$

For the abscissa a_1 the only ordinate value is $b_1 = -0.5$. For the other real root, we obtain the ordinate values $b_{21} = -1.0925926$, $b_{22} = -0.5290596$, and $b_{23} = -0.5290596$. Here, f_x does not vanish at (a_2, b_{22}) and at (a_2, b_{23}), and f_y does not vanish at (a_2, b_{21}); hence, all three points are regular. However, both f_x and f_y vanish at (a_1, b_1), which therefore is a singularity of f. ◇

From a practical perspective, the cost of computing $P(x)$ can be expected to be noticeable. On the other hand, the computation needs to be done only once. A second reduction method to root finding, based on Gröbner bases techniques, will be discussed in Section 7.4.3 of Chapter 7.

6.5.6 Bringing the Singularity to the Origin

When we are determining the locus of a nearby singularity numerically, the resulting coordinates will be imprecise. However, the validity of the transformations T_1 and T_2 depends on the origin being a singularity. Intuitively, small perturbations in the position of the singularity will introduce low-order terms with small coefficients in the translated polynomial $\bar{f}$. These

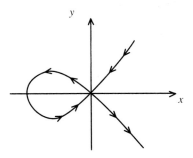

Figure 6.17   Curve Orientation of $f = y^2 - x^2 - x^3$ by $(-f_y, f_x)$

terms should be eliminated. To identify them, we recall that the term $cx^i y^j$ occurs in f iff the partial derivative

$$\frac{1}{i! j!} \frac{\partial^{i+j}}{\partial x^i \partial y^j} f(0,0) = c$$

Since the value of partial derivatives is invariant under translation, it follows that the term $cx^i y^j$ should be absent in $\bar{f}$ iff the corresponding partial vanishes at the singularity located prior to translation. Vanishing low-order partials are discovered as part of the least-squares iteration, but must be determined explicitly in the case of other methods for determining the singularity.

6.5.7 Preserving the Direction of Tracing

At nonsingular points, we locally orient f by the tangent vector $(-f_y, f_x)$. At a singularity, curve segments locally belonging to the same analytic branch may be oriented in an opposite direction, necessitating a reversal of the nominal tracing direction. An example is shown in Figure 6.17. We establish a relationship between the orientation of the curve f and the orientation of its proper transform g with the goal of recognizing when to reverse the tracing direction after having passed through a singular point.

Let $p = (a_0, b_0)$ be a nonsingular point of f, where $a_0 \neq 0$. Let

$$x(s) = a_0 + a_1 s + a_2 s^2 + \dots$$
$$y(s) = b_0 + b_1 s + b_2 s^2 + \dots$$

be the place of f centered at p. The place defines a branch orientation by increasing s. This orientation agrees with the standard orientation $(-f_y, f_x)$ whenever

$$\text{sign}(f_x(a_0, b_0)) = \text{sign}(b_1)$$
$$\text{sign}(f_y(a_0, b_0)) = \text{sign}(-a_1)$$

Otherwise, it is opposite. At the corresponding point $p_1 = (a_0, b_0/a_0)$ of g, the transformed curve g has the place

$$
\begin{aligned}
x_1(s) &= x(s) \\
y_1(s) &= y(s)/x(s) = c_0 + c_1 s + c_2 s^2 + \ldots
\end{aligned}
$$

Since $x(s) = x_1(s)$, the curve and its transform are oriented the same way, by increasing s. Moreover, dividing $y(s)$ by $x(s)$, we obtain

$$
\begin{aligned}
c_0 &= b_0/a_0 \\
c_1 &= (b_1 a_0 - a_1 b_0)/a_0^2
\end{aligned}
$$

and so on. Hence, relating this to the standard orientation by a proportionality constant α, we have

$$
\begin{aligned}
g_y &= \alpha f_y \\
g_x &= \alpha(x f_x + y f_y)/x^2
\end{aligned}
$$

If $\text{sign}(\alpha) = 1$, then both f and g are traced in the same direction, relative to the standard orientation; otherwise, we trace g in the opposite direction. Since no orientation reversal can happen on the fully desingularized branch, we obtain the following recursive algorithm for maintaining a consistent direction of traversal:

1. Traverse f in the direction $u(-f_y, f_x)$, where $u = 1$ or $u = -1$.

2. When changing over to the proper transform g of f, compute the sign of α for the corresponding points p of f and p_1 of g at which we switch.

3. If $\alpha > 0$, the transform g is traversed in the direction $u(-g_y, g_x)$; otherwise, it is traversed in the opposite direction.

4. Assume recursively that we have the traversal direction $u'(-g_y, g_x)$ at a regular point p_1' of g. When reverting to tracing f at the corresponding point p', compute the sign of α again, and, if necessary, complement u.

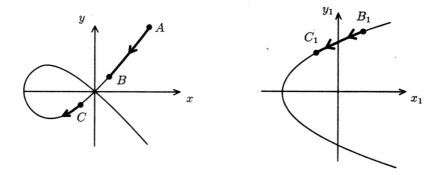

Figure 6.18   Correlation of Standard Curve Orientations

Example 6.9: Figure 6.18 illustrates the method for maintaining consistent traversal direction in the presence of singularities. Assume we are tracing the curve $f : y^2 - x^2 - x^3 = 0$ beginning at the point A in the direction $(-f_y, f_x)$. At point B, we switch to tracing the proper transform $g : y_1^2 - 1 - x_1 = 0$ because of the impending singularity at the origin. We determine the proportionality factor between the partials of f at B and the partials of g at the corresponding point B_1. We find that α is positive, and trace g in the direction $(-g_y, g_x)$. At the point C_1 of g, we determine that we have safely passed the singularity and switch back to tracing f at the corresponding point C. Again, we investigate α to find that this time it is negative. Therefore, we continue traversing f in the direction $(f_y, -f_x)$. $\diamondsuit$

6.6 Remarks on Surface Intersection

Sections 6.4 and 6.5 showed how to reduce surface intersection to the evaluation of a plane algebraic curve. As mentioned before, the ability of the plane-curve tracing method to cope with complicated singularities is a strong advantage of this approach, especially since, until now, a comprehensive method for handling surface-intersection singularities has not been developed and implemented. However, the approach has to cope with a number of practical difficulties, including the following:

1. Implicitizing a parametrically defined surface entails substantial symbolic computation for surfaces such as bicubic patches.

2. Although it is conceptually trivial to substitute a parametric into an implicit form, it is subtle in practice, because of possible floating-point errors. Exact arithmetic is, of course, free from such errors, but is more expensive.

3. The plane algebraic curve eventually obtained is typically of very high
   algebraic degree. For example, the intersection of two bicubic surface
   is in general an algebraic curve of degree 324. At such high degrees,
   severe numerical problems are often encountered.

Many of these difficulties are remedied by tracing in higher dimensions. For
instance, the intersection of two bicubics is easily traced in four dimensions,
and ordinary double-precision floating-point arithmetic delivers accurate
results. On the other hand, higher-dimensional approaches are traditionally
perceived as being slow. Probably, this perception can be corrected with a
sophisticated implementation of the method. However, the method raises
a number of research issues to which there are, at this time, only partial
answers. We mention the following issues:

1. Finding a starting point for the trace is harder in higher dimensions.
   It is certain that subdivision and domain-shrinking techniques can be
   generalized directly; however, unless care is exercised, the complexity
   of these methods grows exponentially with the dimension.

2. In a higher-dimensional space, complicated singularities might be
   present on the intersection curve. These could be difficult to analyze and resolve.

3. By elimination, it is always possible to reduce the number of equations and variables at the expense of raising the degree of the algebraic equations. The tradeoff entailed by this strategy is not understood, and no method is known for introducing additional variables
   and equations that lowers the algebraic degrees of the equations.

More research and experimentation is needed to understand these issues in
depth, and to assess the proper role of the different approaches to surface
intersection.

6.7 Notes and References

In many cases, initial starting points for the trace will be intersections of
the curve to be traced with another surface. In that case, the methods from
Section 7.4 in Chapter 7 could be used. There are other methods, including
subdivision strategies, lattice methods, and homotopy continuation. See,
for example, Pratt and Geisow (1986) and Morgan (1987).

The material of Section 6.2 is mostly from Bajaj, Hoffmann, Hopcroft,
and Lynch (1988). Our exposition of singular value decomposition is based
on Golub and van Loan (1983). For an elementary introduction to differential geometry and the properties of the moving triad, see Hilbert and
Cohn-Vossen (1952). Montaudouin, Tiller, and Vold (1986) discuss step-
size selection in the context of an explicit approximant to a plane curve;

that is, they use an approximant of the form $y = a_0 + a_1 x + a_2 x^2 + \cdots$, based on the implicit function theorem.

The idea of tracing surface intersections in higher dimensions is mentioned in Bajaj, Hoffmann, Hopcroft, and Lynch (1988), where it is applied to the numerical intersection of parametric surfaces. Hoffmann (1988) discusses applications of the higher-dimensional formulation, including offsets, equal-distance surfaces, and variable-radius blending surfaces. The paper explores the suitability of using the higher-dimensional formulation as a representation for such surfaces, and reports experiences with an implementation. Subdivision and approximation methods for surfaces defined as $n - 2$ algebraic equations in n variables are currently being explored.

Farouki and Neff (1989) discuss the algebraic formulation of offsets of rational plane curves, and show that the extraneous points at singularities can be eliminated by dividing out common factors of the derivatives of the coordinate functions. It is unclear whether this approach generalizes to implicit algebraic curves. The envelope theorem is discussed in Spivak (1975), Volume 2. Farouki and Neff (1989) contains figures similar to our figures 6.6 and 6.7.

There is a rich literature on quadratic transformations and on the desingularization of plane algebraic curves. For a projective version, see, for example, van der Waerden (1939). For an affine version, see, for example, Abhyankar (1983). Semple and Kneebone (1959) give a lucid description of the effect of quadratic transformations on the curve places at a singularity. Roughly speaking, the effect of quadratic transformations on the power series is akin to a shifting operation in which the coefficients a_0 and b_0 are dropped, and the remaining coefficients shift to the left. Since each place has a regular structure for sufficiently high exponents of s, repeated quadratic transformations eventually strip off the leading, irregular coefficient structures, leaving only the trailing, regular part. When that has happened, the place has been desingularized, and the various places can be separated. See Walker (1950) for a discussion of places, order of contact of places, tangents to places, and other properties.

The formulation of nonlinear equations for determining the places at a singularity, and the correspondence with the system of equations (6.1), is from Hoffmann (1988), who also notes the monoid computation when seeking to map the intersection of implicit surfaces to plane curves. The monoid computation was well known in the nineteenth-century geometry literature, where it was used as a technical device for classifying different types of space curves of low degree. See, for example, Snyder and Sisam (1914). Owen and Rockwood (1987) analyze singularities on surface/surface intersections by constructing locally a second-order approximant to each surface and analyzing the possible types of singularities of the approximants. The method cannot deal with all types of singularities.

Mapping surface intersections to plane algebraic curves has been advocated repeatedly — by Geisow (1983), by Farouki (1986a), and by many other authors. The approach has many appealing aspects, but so far does not seem to have had a deep effect on practice. Because substitution is such a natural conceptual operation, some authors overlook that it may introduce substantial floating-point errors. A good discussion of this and related practical points can be found in Prakash and Patrikalakis (1988).

The section on projection methods presents material from Abhyankar and Bajaj (1987d). Garrity and Warren (1988) propose a different method for projecting implicit surface intersections to plane algebraic curves. Their method removes the requirement that the two surfaces must intersect transversally in an irreducible space curve, and is based on a classical theorem that says that all but finitely many points on a line are good projection points, provided the line does not intersect the space curve.

Locating singularities precisely is one of the main practical concerns when implementing the plane curve trace. The least-squares approach is from Bajaj, Hoffmann, Hopcroft, and Lynch (1988). Its convergence can be slow, but the use of overrelaxation could improve the convergence rate. Using constrained optimization is a natural idea. Prakash and Patrikalakis (1988) use the technique with good success for ordinary singularities. In the case of higher-order singularities, they suggest an adaptive extension of the goal function to be minimized. The extension uses higher-order partial derivatives in a manner similar to the least-squares method described. Sederberg (1988) proposes a subdivision scheme for locating singularities that assumes that the curve has been expressed in a special Bernstein basis form. For a method to translate a polynomial into Bernstein form see, for example, Waggenspack and Anderson (1986).

CHAPTER 7
Gröbner Bases Techniques

Beginning with Descartes, mathematics has been developing tools to formulate and prove geometric theorems algebraically, and, vice versa, to express geometric facts in algebraic terms in an effort to interpret algebraic theorems geometrically. The resulting discipline of *algebraic geometry* is of interest to us because it delivers a symbolic representation of geometric objects that allows us to compute with geometric objects using symbolic manipulation. We have made periodic use of this fact in the preceding chapters, formulating algorithms that accept algebraic equations as input and deliver, as output, other algebraic equations. Examples have included converting between implicit and parametric forms, approximating surface intersections by parametric expressions, mapping space curves to plane curves, and so on.

In this chapter, we examine these computations in more detail. More specifically, we concentrate on computing with *ideals*. Ideals are sets of polynomials that describe elementary geometric objects symbolically, and are a natural representation of geometric objects. We can often find the solution of a system of linear equations more conveniently by considering linear combinations of the given equations. Likewise, when solving systems of algebraic equations, considering algebraic combinations of them may lead to an easier solution, as long as the solution set is not altered. The set of all such algebraic combinations is an ideal.

The algorithms of this chapter are very general and are capable of solving, in principle, a wide spectrum of difficult and important problems. Such generality does not come without its price, however, for some of the computations can be very space and time intensive. Therefore, we must weigh carefully where and when to apply these techniques. However, research is appearing that aims at *specializing* the algorithms given here in situations not requiring the full generality they currently embody. This work could result in highly efficient and sophisticated tools for addressing some of the difficult mathematical problems faced by geometric and solid modeling.

7.1 Chapter Overview

The algorithms to be discussed require a working knowledge of algebra and algebraic geometry. As in Chapter 5, we therefore begin with an informal review of the needed vocabulary and concepts, for the benefit of the nonspecialist. The purpose of the informality is to develop the intuition underlying these terms and ideas. So, we relate the mathematical concepts to applications that are already quite familiar. Once armed with the road maps provided here, the reader can consult books on algebra or algebraic geometry for further details.

The central data structure in the chapter is a special set of polynomials defining an ideal. This set is a *Gröbner basis* of the ideal. An ideal has many generating sets defining it, but the advantage of a Gröbner basis is that many algorithmic problems can be solved easily once a Gröbner basis is known.

We are interested in those algorithmic problems that arise from applications in geometric and solid modeling. However, the concept of a Gröbner basis is best grasped by considering first a more abstract problem; namely, the question whether a given polynomial g is in a given ideal I. Assuming that the ideal is given by the polynomials $\{f_1, ..., f_r\}$, we ask whether the polynomial g can be written as an algebraic combination of the f_j; that is, whether $g = h_1 f_1 + \cdots + h_r f_r$ for some polynomials h_j. This problem of *ideal membership* can be answered using a Gröbner basis of the ideal.[1]

With this problem as the focus, we explain in Section 7.3 what a Gröbner basis is, how to construct it, that the basis depends on certain term orderings, and how to use it to decide ideal membership.

Solving systems of algebraic equations is a fundamental activity in geometric and solid modeling. Section 7.4 therefore discusses how to solve systems of algebraic equations using Gröbner bases. We give a general algorithm and discuss as geometric applications how to find all points in which three or more surfaces intersect, and how to find all singular points of an algebraic curve. This section also contains an example discussing some of the subtleties that arise when we use Gröbner bases methods to solve

---

[1]This problem has a geometric significance: Roughly speaking, g can be so written whenever the surface $g = 0$ contains all points that are the common intersection of the surfaces $f_j = 0$. Section 7.2.6 explains why this interpretation is not exact.

a system of algebraic equations, in which the individual equations contain symbolic parameters. This situation arises, for example, when we wish to find the singularities of a family of curves, or to locate surface intersections for families of intersecting surfaces.

Section 7.5 considers operations on curves and surfaces such as implicitization, inversion, and offsetting. These are mathematically demanding problems for which Gröbner bases methods provide uniform solutions.

Section 7.6 briefly sketches the applicability of Gröbner bases methods to geometric theorem proving. The techniques developed for this problem have bearing on the robustness problem in geometric modeling in that they can provide general reasoning capabilities for the problems discussed in Chapter 4 in Section 4.4, on representations and models.

Constructing a Gröbner basis can be resource intensive, because of both the need for exact arithmetic and the possibility of generating and analyzing many polynomials. This fact hinders using Gröbner bases in practice. For this reason, Section 7.7 reviews known complexity results and discusses our experience with using Gröbner bases in geometric applications. It turns out that recent research on basis conversion has significantly improved the efficiency of this approach. Section 7.8 explains the method and gives a variant that can handle large-scale elimination problems. This material, we believe, is of great practical consequence and is paradigmatic of possible specializations that could be efficient and of widespread applicability.

7.2 Algebraic Concepts

7.2.1 Fields, Rings, and Polynomials

The simplest object we consider is described by a single algebraic equation of the form

$$f(x_1, ..., x_n) = 0$$

where f is a polynomial in n variables. We think of the variables as *coordinates* in an n-dimensional Cartesian space. Depending on the interpretation of the coordinates, the space corresponds to affine or to projective space. When substituting specific values for the x_i satisfying the equation, we obtain certain *points* on the $(n-1)$-dimensional *hypersurface* implicitly defined by f. For example, in 3-space, the equation

$$x^2 + y^2 + z^2 - 1 = 0$$

defines the unit sphere.

So far, we have tacitly assumed that the possible values for the x_i are real numbers. But we can use different sets of values, thereby giving a different meaning to f and to the space containing the hypersurface it defines. Such a set of possible values must be drawn from a *field*; that is, it must have elements that may be added, subtracted, multiplied, and divided. We usually fix the field of coordinate values, concentrating on the geometry of the Cartesian space, and call it the *ground field*.

A field can be finite, or it can be infinite. Simple examples of a finite field include the integers modulo a fixed prime number p. For our purposes, the field **R** of real numbers is of primary interest. However, algebraic geometry has considered mostly the field **C** of complex numbers. For instance, when considering the equation

$$x^2 + y^2 = 0$$

over **C**, this equation describes the two complex lines

$$x + iy = 0 \qquad \text{and} \qquad x - iy = 0$$

intersecting at the origin. Over the reals, the equation would describe just one point; namely, the origin. Therefore, we have to be aware that subtle problems can arise when we try to apply classical algebraic geometry to real spaces. The reason algebraic geometry has been developed primarily for the ground field **C** is that then certain fundamental theorems have uniform validity; for example, theorems on the dimensionality of hypersurfaces.

Let us denote the ground field by k, avoiding for the moment a commitment to a specific one. A *univariate polynomial* over k has the form

$$\sum_{i=0}^{m} a_i x^i$$

where x is a variable symbol, and the *coefficients* a_i are numbers in k. The set of all univariate polynomials in x is denoted by $k[x]$. We can add and subtract polynomials from each other and we can multiply them, but we cannot, in general, divide two polynomials. A set in which addition, subtraction, and multiplication are defined is called a *ring*. The set $k[x]$ is a ring.

Whether a polynomial can be factored will depend on the ground field k. The polynomial

$$x^2 + 1$$

does not factor over the reals, but it will factor as $(x - i)(x + i)$ over the complex numbers. A polynomial that factors nontrivially is called *reducible*. One that cannot be factored is *irreducible*. The example $x^2 + 1$ shows that reducibility is a relative notion that depends on the ground field.

7.2.2 Field Extensions and Rational Functions

A field may be considered a subfield of a larger field, provided the arithmetic operations are compatible in both fields. For example, the field **R** is a subfield of **C**. It can be convenient to think of this relationship as a process of enlarging the smaller field by adding new elements to it. This process is referred to as a field *extension*. A field extension may be done for pragmatic reasons. For instance, complex numbers were "invented" so that the polynomial $x^2 + 1$ would have roots. More generally, the *fundamental theorem of algebra* states that, over the complex numbers, every univariate polynomial can be factored into linear factors.

When extending a field, we *adjoin* the elements of the larger field. To keep things simple, we adjoin only as many elements as are needed. That is, when adjoining a new element u to a field k, we include automatically all elements that must be added as consequence of the field operations — that is, all elements obtained from u and the elements in k by successive additions, subtractions, multiplications, and divisions. Thus, when extending **R** to **C**, we adjoin the imaginary unit i. In fact, it turns out that all other complex numbers then can be expressed as $a + bi$, were a and b are reals. If the field k is extended by some new element u, the new field is denoted $k(u)$.

There are two types of field extensions: *algebraic extensions* and *transcendental extensions*. In an algebraic extension, we adjoin an element that is the root of a specific polynomial $q \in k[x]$. It can be shown that all elements of the extension field so obtained can be expressed in the form $a_0 + a_1 u + a_2 u^2 + ... + a_{m-1} u^{m-1}$, where the degree of q is m.

For example, an algebraic extension of **R** is **C**, which has the additional property that every polynomial in **R**$[x]$ factors into linear components. When extending the reals to the complex numbers, we adjoin the root i of $x^2 + 1$. Therefore, all complex numbers can be expressed as $a + bi$. If we begin with the field **Q** of *rational* numbers, we might also adjoin a root of $x^2 - 2$, and obtain the field **Q**$(\sqrt{2})$. All elements in this field can be written as $a + b\sqrt{2}$, where a and b are rational numbers. We might then extend the resulting field by adjoining a root of some other polynomial.

By adjoining to **Q** the roots of all univariate polynomials with rational coefficients, we get the field of *algebraic numbers*. After that, we would still miss some real numbers, such as π, that are *transcendental*. The second type of field extension, then, is a transcendental extension in which the element adjoined to the field k does not satisfy any algebraic relation — that is, is not the root of any polynomial in $k[x]$. When adjoining a transcendental x to k, new elements are obtained from the transcendental and the elements of k by successive additions, subtractions, multiplications, and divisions. These new elements can be written uniquely as ratios of relatively prime polynomials in the transcendental, $p(x)/q(x)$, where q is not the zero polynomial. The set of all these ratios is denoted $k(x)$. It is a field because there is a natural division operation defined on these ratios. Note that the assumption that x is transcendental (i.e., is not the root of some polynomial) implies that we do not accidentally divide by zero (i.e., by a root of $q(x)$).

Transcendental field extension might seem a rather remote concept. From our perspective, however, transcendental extensions correspond to computing with symbolic parameters. For example, consider a sphere of radius r. We write

$$x^2 + y^2 + z^2 - r^2 = 0$$

as its equation. We consider this a polynomial over x, y, and z, but conceptualize r as a *parameter*, and treat it differently from the variables x, y, and z. When computing with this equation, perhaps for purposes of defining another surface whose shape depends somehow on the radius of the sphere, we may freely form expressions involving r, such as

$$y^2 + z^2 - \frac{r}{r^2 + 1} = 0$$

defining, say, a cylinder whose radius is a rational function of r. Although we do not think of instantiating these surfaces with transcendental numbers, we compute with r as though it were transcendental.

7.2.3 Multivariate Polynomials and Ideals

We form *multivariate* polynomials with more than one variable symbol. Using the symbols $x_1, ..., x_n$, such a polynomial is written

$$\sum_{j=1}^{m} a_j x_1^{e_{1,j}} x_2^{e_{2,j}} \cdots x_n^{e_{n,j}}$$

where the coefficients a_j are in the ground field k. The exponents $e_{i,j}$ are, of course, nonnegative integers.

Just as in the univariate case, we can add, subtract, and multiply multivariate polynomials, but we cannot, in general, divide two multivariate polynomials. The set of all multivariate polynomials in the variables $x_1, ..., x_n$ is denoted $k[x_1, ..., x_n]$ and forms a ring.

We saw in the case of univariate polynomials that the reducibility of a polynomial (i.e., whether it can be factored) depends on the ground field. This is still the case for multivariate polynomials, but there are also multivariate polynomials that cannot be factored over any ground field. Such polynomials are called *absolutely* irreducible. The polynomial $x^2 + y^2 + z^2 - 1$ is absolutely irreducible.

We fix a ground field k, and consider the n-dimensional affine space k^n over k. The points in this space are n-tuples $(x_1, x_2, ..., x_n)$, where the

x_i take on values in k. We consider the hypersurface $f = 0$ defined by a multivariate polynomial f. We assume that f is irreducible; that is, that it does not factor. We observe that any *multiple cf* of f defines the same hypersurface, where c is a nonzero field element. Moreover, for any polynomial g, the hypersurface $gf = 0$ certainly includes the hypersurface $f = 0$. This raises the question of whether there exists a *unique* algebraic representation for the hypersurface $f = 0$. The answer is yes, but the unique representation requires a *set* of polynomials, rather than a single one.

Consider the surface $f = 0$, and let g be any polynomial. All surfaces $gf = 0$ will contain the surface $f = 0$. Moreover, for fixed f in $k[x_1, ..., x_n]$, the intersection of all surfaces $gf = 0$, where g varies over $k[x_1, ..., x_n]$, is precisely the surface $f = 0$. So, for fixed f, we consider the set

$$I\langle f \rangle = \{gf \in k[x_1, ..., x_n] \mid f \text{ fixed}\}$$

as the description of the surface. In Section 7.2.6, we explain that this description is not always unique.

$I\langle f \rangle$ has the property that the sum and difference of any two polynomials in the set is again in $I\langle f \rangle$. Moreover, the product of any polynomial in $k[x_1, ..., x_n]$ with an element of $I\langle f \rangle$ is again in $I\langle f \rangle$. Sets with these properties are called *ideals*.

Now consider a finite set F of polynomials $f_1, f_2, ..., f_r$ in $k[x_1, ..., x_n]$. We form all *algebraic combinations* of the f_i; that is, we form the set of polynomials

$$I\langle F \rangle = \{g_1 f_1 + g_2 f_2 + \cdots + g_r f_r \mid g_i \in k[x_1, ..., x_n]\}$$

Clearly, $I\langle F \rangle$ is an ideal. We say that $I\langle F \rangle$ is the *ideal generated by F*, and that F is a *generating set* of $I\langle F \rangle$. Generating sets are not unique, and a basic theme of this chapter is to find generating sets that have special properties that are useful for solving geometric problems.

The nonuniqueness of generating sets has been used implicitly; for instance, in surface intersection. When determining the intersection of two quadrics f and g, we may proceed as follows. First, replace one of the quadrics with a *ruled* quadric surface $f' = \lambda f + \mu g$, where λ and μ are suitable numbers; that is, with a cylinder, a cone, or a hyperboloid. Then compute $f' \cap g$ instead of $f \cap g$. The same intersection is obtained, but the reformulated problem simplifies the treatment of special cases. Algebraically, we have replaced the generators $\{f, g\}$ of the ideal describing the intersection curve with the generators $\{f', g\}$.

7.2.4 The Residue Class Ring of an Ideal

Given an ideal I in the ring $k[x_1, ..., x_n]$ of multivariate polynomials over the ground field k, we consider the *residue class ring* R_I of I. The elements in R_I are equivalence classes of polynomials in $k[x_1, ..., x_n]$; that is, they are disjoint subsets of $k[x_1, ..., x_n]$, where two polynomials p and q are in the same equivalence class iff their difference $p-q$ is in the ideal I. Computations in residue class rings will be considered later, in Section 7.8.1.

We denote the elements of R_I with $[p]$, where p is any polynomial in the equivalence class $[p]$. The operations on the equivalence classes are induced in the natural way via

1. $[p] + [q] = [p + q]$

2. $[p][q] = [pq]$

As an example, let I be the ideal generated by $\{x^2, y\}$. The elements in I have the form $ux^2 + vy$, where u and v are polynomials in $k[x, y]$. It is easy to see that $p - q$ is in the ideal I whenever p and q have the same constant term and the same x term; that is, $p = a + bx + ...$ and $q = a + bx + ...$, for numbers a and b in k. Hence two such polynomials are in the same equivalence class.

The residue class ring R_I of an ideal may be considered to be a vector space over the ground field k. Moreover, if I is a zero-dimensional ideal — that is, if there are only finitely many points $(a_1, ..., a_n) \in k^n$ satisfying every polynomial in I — then the residue class ring can be shown to be a finite-dimensional vector space.

7.2.5 Algebraic Sets and Varieties

We consider the ideal $I \subset k[x_1, ..., x_n]$ generated by the set $F = \{f_1, ..., f_r\}$. Let $p = (a_1, ..., a_n)$ be a point in k^n such that $g(p) = 0$ for every $g \in I$. The set of all such points p is the *algebraic set* $V(I)$ of I. Clearly, for p to be in the algebraic set $V(I)$, it suffices that $f_i(p) = 0$ for every generator f_i in F.

In three dimensions, the algebraic surface $f = 0$ is the algebraic set of the ideal $I\langle f \rangle$. The intersection of two algebraic surfaces f and g in 3-space is an algebraic space curve. Hence, such a curve is the algebraic set of the ideal $I\langle \{f, g\} \rangle$.[2] It is not true that every algebraic space curve can be defined as the intersection of two surfaces. Additional surfaces may be required in certain cases. An example is the *twisted cubic*, a curve parametrically defined as

$$
\begin{aligned}
x &= t \\
y &= t^2 \\
z &= t^3
\end{aligned}
$$

See also Figure 7.1. To define it, we need to intersect three algebraic sur-

---

[2]In the following, we will write $I\langle f, g \rangle$ instead of $I\langle \{f, g\} \rangle$.

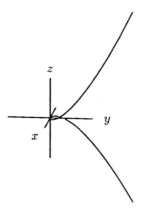

Figure 7.1   Twisted Cubic (t, t^2, t^3)

faces. For example, we could intersect a paraboloid with two cubic surfaces

$$x^2 - y = 0 \cap y^3 - z^2 = 0 \cap z - x^3 = 0$$

Later, we explain why two surfaces alone do not suffice, which motivates us to consider ideals with generating sets that contain more than two polynomials.

When we are given a set $F = \{f_1, ..., f_r\}$ of generators, we expect in general that the algebraic set defined by it in k^n has dimension $n - r$. This is an analogy to linear algebra, where a set of r linear equations in n variables defines, in general, a linear subspace of dimension $n - r$. Just as in linear algebra, this requires that the equations $f_i = 0$ be *algebraically independent*. However, the matter becomes more complicated in the algebraic case, in that the algebraic set of the ideal $I\langle F\rangle$ could consist of several components, some of which might have different dimensions.

Let us consider the algebraic set $V(I)$ defined by the ideal I in k^n. It is possible that $V(I)$ is the union of two or more point sets, each of which can be defined separately by an ideal. In this case, we say that the set $V(I)$ is *reducible*. The notion is analogous to polynomial reducibility: A multivariate polynomial f that factors describes a surface consisting of several components. Each component belongs to an irreducible factor of f. In the same spirit, the reducibility of an algebraic set $V(I)$ mirrors the fact that we can *decompose* the ideal I into several components, although this no longer looks like polynomial factorization in general. Each such ideal

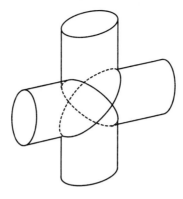

Figure 7.2   Reducible Intersection of Two Cylinders

component defines a component of the algebraic set $V(I)$. If an algebraic set $V(I)$ cannot be decomposed, we say that $V(I)$ is a *variety*, or, more simply, that it is *irreducible*.

As an example, consider the intersection curve of the two cylinders

$$
\begin{aligned}
f_1 : \ x^2 + y^2 - r^2 &= 0 \\
f_2 : \ y^2 + z^2 - r^2 &= 0
\end{aligned}
$$

Since the cylinders intersect through their axes and have equal radii, the intersection consists of two ellipses in the planes

$$g_1 : \ x + z = 0 \qquad \text{and} \qquad g_2 : \ x - z = 0$$

as shown in Figure 7.2. Each ellipse can be described separately, as the intersection of one of the cylinders with one of the planes. One of them is the intersection of f_1 with g_1; that is, it is the algebraic set belonging to the ideal generated by $\{f_1, g_1\}$. The other ellipse is the algebraic set of the ideal generated by $\{f_1, g_2\}$. Each ellipse is irreducible. Hence, we can summarize the situation as follows: The ideal $I_1 = I\langle f_1, f_2 \rangle$ is reducible, and decomposes into the ideals $I_2 = I\langle f_1, g_1 \rangle$ and $I_3 = I\langle f_1, g_2 \rangle$; the algebraic set $V(I_1)$ is the union of the two varieties $V(I_2)$ and $V(I_3)$.

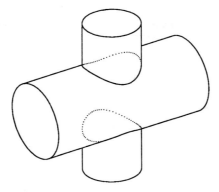

Figure 7.3   Irreducible Intersection of Two Cylinders

Now consider the intersection of two cylinders, one with the radius 1, the other with the radius $\sqrt{2}$.

$$f_1 : \ x^2 + y^2 - 1 \ = \ 0$$
$$f_2 : \ y^2 + z^2 - 2 \ = \ 0$$

Here the intersection curve, shown in Figure 7.3, appears to be reducible. However, it is not reducible, and the two components cannot be defined separately by polynomials. To understand this fact, we recall Bezout's theorem from Section 5.3.3 in Chapter 5. The theorem states that two irreducible surfaces of degree m and n intersect in a curve of degree mn. So, the curve shown in Figure 7.3 has degree 4. The union of two curves of degree m and n is a reducible curve of degree $m + n$. Were the intersection curve shown in Figure 7.3 reducible, the two components would each have to have degree 2, since neither can be of degree 1. But every degree 2 space curve is planar, and the components in the figure evidently are not planar. Hence, the intersection is irreducible.

Recall the earlier assertion that the twisted cubic cannot be defined algebraically as the intersection of two surfaces. It can be shown that this curve has degree 3, since a plane in general position will intersect it in three points. By Bezout's theorem, therefore, the curve would have to be the intersection of a plane and a cubic surface. But the twisted cubic is not a plane curve, so this would be a contradiction.

7.2.6 Prime Ideals and Radicals

Let V be a variety; that is, an irreducible algebraic set in k^n. This means that there is an ideal $I \subset k[x_1, ..., x_n]$ defining V. In fact, there may be several such ideals, for the ideal I may contain redundancies not reflected in V as a set of points. We consider the intersection curve V of the cylinder f_1 above with the plane g_1. We know it is an ellipse, and is a variety. The ideal $J_1 = I\langle f_1, g_1 \rangle$ defines V, but so does the ideal $J_2 = I\langle f_1, g_1^2 \rangle$. J_1 and J_2 are different ideals, since J_2 does not contain g_1, but contains the higher powers of g_1. On the other hand, every polynomial in J_2 is also in J_1, so J_2 is a proper subset of J_1.

Viewed geometrically, as an algebraic set of J_1, the ellipse V is the intersection of a cylinder with a plane, whereas, understood as an algebraic set of J_2, it is the intersection of a cylinder with the *double* plane $g_1^2 = 0$. In the latter case, we should consider the points of V to count double, once for each of the two planes $g_1 = 0$. Hence, the variety V does not reflect the algebraic *multiplicity* of the ideal elements.

To associate with an algebraic set V a unique ideal, we introduce the notion of *radical ideal*. An ideal I is a radical ideal of V if $V = V(I)$ and I is *maximal*. That is, every other ideal J with $V = V(J)$ is contained in I. Given an algebraic set V, there is a unique radical ideal $I = Rad(V)$ such that $V = V(I)$. If V is a variety, then the radical ideal is a *prime* ideal. A *prime ideal* I has the property that, whenever a reducible polynomial is in I, then at least one of its factors is in I. The ideal J_1 is a prime ideal. The ideal J_2 is not. We can see that J_2 is not prime, because g_1^2 is in J_2, but neither of its two linear factors is.

The distinction between an algebraic set as a set-theoretic object and as an algebraic object is important. Viewed set-theoretically, the points in the set have no multiplicity — hence the concept of radical ideals. Viewed as an algebraic object, the points may have higher multiplicity. The twisted cubic illustrates this distinction. Viewed set-theoretically, we argued that it cannot be defined as the intersection of two algebraic surfaces, because of Bezout's theorem. However, if the curve points are considered as having a higher multiplicity, then the twisted cubic (t, t^2, t^3) is in fact the intersection of

$$y^2 - xz = 0 \cap x^3 - 2xyw + zw^2 = 0$$

The two surfaces are tangent to each other in the curve, so each curve point has multiplicity 2 and Bezout's theorem is satisfied. In general, it is not known whether every algebraic space curve can be defined as the intersection of only two surfaces, in this sense.

Note that the problem should be considered projectively. Again, the twisted cubic illustrates the situation. In affine space, the twisted cubic (t, t^2, t^3) is the intersection of

$$y^2 - z^3 = 0 \cap x - y^2 = 0$$

When embedded into projective space, however, the surfaces intersect at infinity in a triple line.

7.3 Gröbner Bases

An ideal can have many different generating sets. Depending on the use to which we want to put them, some generating sets will be better than others. We consider first in detail the problem of testing whether a given polynomial g is in some ideal I. We consider a class of generating sets that allows conceptually simple algorithms to decide ideal membership. These generating sets are Gröbner bases, and although ideal membership is not a central problem in solid modeling, Gröbner bases are also advantageous for many of the problems that are important to geometric and solid modeling. We seek a solution to the *ideal membership problem*.

> **Problem**
> Given a finite set of polynomials $F = \{f_1, \ldots, f_r\}$ and a polynomial g, decide whether g is in the ideal generated by F; that is, whether g can be written in the form $g = h_1 f_1 + h_2 f_2 + \cdots + h_r f_r$, where the h_i are polynomials.

The difficulty of the problem is to determine the coefficient polynomials h_i. When no special assumptions can be made about the generators, deciding whether g is in the ideal is not easy. For instance, even when the f_i are all quadratic and the polynomial g is quartic, we cannot assume a priori that the coefficient polynomials are of degree 2 or less.

We will solve the ideal membership problem by repeatedly *rewriting* g until g has been simplified to the point where the original question can be answered by inspection. Specifically, we will repeatedly subtract from g multiples of the f_i. Since these multiples are in $I\langle F \rangle$, it is clear that the rewritten g is in the ideal iff g is in the ideal. Moreover, if g is in the ideal, then there must exist some rewriting sequence that reduces g to zero. Whether such a rewriting sequence can be found easily depends on specific properties of the generators.

7.3.1 Lexicographic Term Ordering and Leading Terms

Assume that we are rewriting some polynomial $g \in I\langle F \rangle$ with the goal of reducing it to zero. At each rewriting step, we would like assurance that we are making progress toward this goal. This means that, at each step, we want to obtain a polynomial that is in some sense *simpler* than the preceding one. So, we must define an appropriate notion of "this polynomial is simpler than that one." We develop it from an ordering of individual terms in polynomials. This gives us first a concept for judging whether a single term is more complicated than another one. Moreover, given f and g, we will declare that f is more complicated than g if the most complicated term of g precedes the most complicated term of f in the term ordering. The term ordering to be introduced now is only one possibility. Later, we will also introduce different orderings.

Assume that all polynomials are in $k[x_1, ..., x_n]$. A product of the form

$$x_1{}^{e_1} x_2{}^{e_2} \cdots x_n{}^{e_n}$$

with $e_i \geq 0$, is called a *power product*. We define a *lexicographic ordering*, written $\prec$, of the power products as follows:

1. $1 \prec x_1 \prec x_2 \prec \ldots \prec x_n$.

2. If $u \prec v$, then $uw \prec vw$ for all power products w.

3. If u and v are not yet ordered by rules 1 and 2, then order them lexicographically as strings.[3]

For instance, with $n = 2$, setting $x_1 = x$ and $x_2 = y$, we have the following ordering of power products:

$$1 \prec x \prec x^2 \prec \ldots \prec x^k \prec \ldots \prec y \prec xy \prec x^2 y \prec \ldots \prec y^2 \prec xy^2 \prec \ldots$$

Every term in a polynomial g consists of a coefficient and a power product. The term whose power product is largest with respect to the ordering $\prec$ is called the *leading term* of g, written $lt(g)$. Among all the terms of g, $lt(g)$ is considered the most complicated term. The leading term consists of the *leading coefficient*, $lcf(g)$, and the *leading power product*, $lpp(g)$.

Definition
The polynomial f is *simpler* than the polynomial g if $lpp(f) \prec lpp(g)$.

Example 7.1: Assuming $x \prec y$, the leading term of $g = 2y^3 - xy^2 + x^2$ is $2y^3$. The leading coefficient of g is 2, and the leading power product is y^3. The leading term of $h = 3xy^3 - x^2 + 1$ is $3xy^3$, with the leading power product xy^3. Since $y^3 \prec xy^3$, we consider h to be more complicated than g. $\diamond$

7.3.2 Rewriting and Normal-Form Algorithms

We are given a polynomial g, and a set of polynomials $F = \{f_1, ..., f_r\}$. We plan to rewrite g using the polynomials in F, simplifying g at each step, until it cannot be further simplified. When g cannot be further simplified,

---

[3]The power product $x_1^{a_1} x_2^{a_2} \cdots x_n^{a_n}$ precedes $x_1^{b_1} x_2^{b_2} \cdots x_n^{b_n}$ lexicographically as a string if there is $1 \leq r \leq n$ such that $a_r < b_r$ and $a_{r+1} = b_{r+1}, \ldots, a_n = b_n$.

we say that g is in *normal form* with respect to F. A normal form of g with respect to F is denoted by $NF(g, F)$. The rewriting is done as follows:

> *Input*: A set F of polynomials, and a polynomial g.
>
> *Output*: A normal form $NF(g, F)$ of g with respect to F.
>
> *Method*:
>
> 1. Set $g_0 = g$ and $i = 0$.
> 2. For $i = 0, 1, 2, \ldots$ repeat step 3 until g_i cannot be rewritten; then output g_i and stop.
> 3. If there is a polynomial f in F such that the leading power product of f divides a power product p in g_i, then rewrite g_i as $g_{i+1} = g_i - buf$, where b is the quotient of the coefficient of p by $lcf(f)$ and $u = p/lpp(f)$.

Note that any term of g_i could be rewritten in step 3.

It can be shown that the rewriting algorithm must terminate. Step 3 eliminates a term in g_i, but it may introduce more new terms, so termination is not immediately obvious. However, observe that, since the cancellation is done with the leading term of f, the newly introduced terms in g_{i+1} must precede the term just eliminated from g_i in the term ordering. Thus, to show termination, we must show that the terms introduced in step 3 cannot form an infinite descending chain in the ordering.

Example 7.2: Let $F = \{y^2 + x^2 - 1, xy - x^2 + 1\}$, let $g = 2y^3 + x^2 - xy^2$, and let $x \prec y$. The leading terms are, respectively, y^2, xy, and $2y^3$. We rewrite g in three steps, obtaining g_3 as a normal form of g with respect to F.

$$
\begin{aligned}
g = g_0 \;&=\; 2y^3 - xy^2 + x^2 \\
\rightarrow g_1 \;&=\; g - 2y(y^2 + x^2 - 1) \;&=\; -xy^2 - 2x^2 y + 2y + x^2 \\
\rightarrow g_2 \;&=\; g_1 - (-y)(xy - x^2 + 1) \;&=\; -3x^2 y + 3y + x^2 \\
\rightarrow g_3 \;&=\; g_2 - (-3x)(xy - x^2 + 1) \;&=\; 3y - 3x^3 + x^2 + 3x
\end{aligned}
$$

$\diamondsuit$

Note that the normal form is not necessarily *unique*, since there may be more than one $f \in F$ with which to rewrite g in step 2, leading to different sequences of rewriting steps with possibly different outcomes. For example, when using $y^2 + x^2 - 1$ to rewrite g_1, we obtain eventually the normal form $2y - x^3 + x^2 + x$.

If the normal form arrived at by the preceding algorithm is known to be unique, then it can be shown that g is in the ideal precisely when

$NF(g, F) = 0$. Therefore, we will look for special generating sets with the property that normal forms are unique.

7.3.3 A Membership Test for Ideals

We would like to use the rewriting method for deciding whether g is in the ideal generated by F. Fortunately, there always exists a set G of polynomials that generates the same ideal as F and has the property that the rewriting algorithm produces unique normal forms. Such a set is called a *Gröbner basis* of the ideal $I\langle F\rangle$. Thus, the ideal membership problem is solved as follows:

Input: A set F of polynomials, and a polynomial g.

Output: "Yes" if g is in the ideal generated by F; "No" otherwise.

Method:

  1.   Construct a Gröbner basis from F.
  2.   Compute $h = NF(g, G)$. If $h = 0$, then output "Yes"; otherwise, output "No."

Example 7.3:   Consider the ideal generated by

$$F = \{(x-1)^2 + y^2 - 2, \, (x+1)^2 + y^2 - 2\}$$

where $x \prec y$. We ask whether $x - y$ is in the ideal generated by F. So, we first construct the Gröbner basis G for the ideal, as explained later. The basis is

$$G = \{-x, y^2 - 1\}$$

Then, we compute the normal form of $x - y$ with respect to G. It is y (i.e., not zero); hence, $x - y$ is not in the ideal generated by F. $\diamondsuit$

Geometrically, F defines two circles, and the algebraic set defined by F consists of the intersection points of these circles. We note that the intersection points are easier to compute from the Gröbner basis G than from F. This will generally be the case for Gröbner bases constructed with the lexicographic term ordering.

7.3.4 Buchberger's Theorem and Construction of Gröbner Bases

There are several algorithms for constructing a Gröbner basis from a given set F based on Buchberger's theorem. Technically, they all rewrite the input polynomials, thereby simplifying them and adding certain polynomials that are, roughly speaking, least common multiples of the input polynomials. The polynomials added are called *S-polynomials*. Gröbner bases algorithms are not yet widely available, and for this reason we sketch a simple version that can be implemented without great difficulties. The algorithm to be described consists of two conceptual operations:

1. Consider a polynomial, and bring it into normal form with respect to some set of generators G.

2. From certain generator pairs, compute S-polynomials and add their normal forms to the generator set.

Initially, the set G is the input set F of polynomials. Considering each pair of generators, an S-polynomial is constructed for the pair and is rewritten into normal form. If the normal form is not zero, then it is added to G. Eventually, G is transformed into a Gröbner basis in this way.

Note that all coefficient arithmetic must be exact. Floating-point arithmetic would introduce errors that would effectively change the ideal described by the input polynomials. The sensitivity to such arithmetic errors, and the precise consequences of numerical errors on the algebraic sets described, are not understood at this time.

Definition
Let f and g be two polynomials with respective leading power products u_f and u_g. Let w be the least common multiple of these power products, such that $w = v_f u_f = v_g u_g$ for some power products v_f and v_g. Let c_f be the leading coefficient of f, c_g the leading coefficient of g. Then the polynomial

$$S(f, g) = c_g v_f f - c_f v_g g$$

is the *S-polynomial* of f and g, and is denoted $S(f, g)$.

Example 7.4: Let $f = 2x^2y - x + 1$, $g = 3xy^2 - 2y^2 + x$. Then $u_f = x^2y$, $u_g = xy^2$, $v_f = y$, and $v_g = x$. Hence, $S(f, g) = 3yf - 2xg = 4xy^2 - 3xy + 3y - 2x^2$. $\diamond$

The algorithm for computing a Gröbner basis of F is based on *Buchberger's theorem*.

Theorem
Let G be a set of polynomials in $k[x_1, ..., x_n]$. Then the following are equivalent:

1. G is a Gröbner basis.

2. For all $f, g \in G$ we have $NF(S(f, g), G) = 0$.

Thus, the basic idea is to generate S-polynomials from pairs in the set G, and to add their normal forms to G. It can be proved that this process must terminate. The basis computation is now as follows:

Input: A set F of polynomials.

Output: A Gröbner basis G of the ideal generated by F.

Method:

1.   Set $G := F$, and let B be the set of all pairs $\{f_1, f_2\}$ of polynomials in G, with $f_1 \neq f_2$.

2.   While B is not empty, repeat the following steps. Thereafter stop; G is a Gröbner basis.

3.   Delete a pair $\{f_1, f_2\}$ from B, and compute the normal form $h = NF(S(f_1, f_2), G)$.

4.   If $h \neq 0$, then add to B all pairs of the form $\{f, h\}$, where $f \in G$, and add h to G.

Example 7.5:   We illustrate the algorithm with the set $F = \{f_1, f_2\}$, where

$$f_1 = 2x^2y - x + 1$$
$$f_2 = 3xy^2 - 2y^2 + x$$

We assume $x \prec y$. Initially, $G = \{f_1, f_2\}$ and $B = \{\{f_1, f_2\}\}$. We begin by removing the pair $\{f_1, f_2\}$ from B, and constructing its S-polynomial

$$S(f_1, f_2) = 4xy^2 - 3xy + 3y - 2x^2$$

Now $S(f_1, f_2)$ is reduced using f_2. After clearing denominators, we obtain a normal form

$$f_3 = 8y^2 - 9xy + 9y - 6x^2 - 4x$$

Then f_3 is added to G, and the pairs $\{f_1, f_3\}$ and $\{f_2, f_3\}$ are added to B. Next, we construct $S(f_1, f_3)$. Two reduction steps using f_1 and clearing of denominators bring $S(f_1, f_3)$ into the normal form:

$$f_4 = -8xy + 8y + 12x^4 + 8x^3 + 9x^2 - 18x + 9$$

We add f_4 to G and add to B the pairs $\{f_1, f_4\}, \{f_2, f_4\}, \{f_3, f_4\}$. Next, we construct $S(f_2, f_3)$. Reduction using f_3, f_1, and f_4 results in the new polynomial

$$f_5 = -8y - 20x^4 - 8x^3 - 15x^2 + 34x - 19$$

The next S-polynomial, $S(f_1, f_4)$ yields the normal form

$$f_6 = 4x^5 + 3x^3 - 8x^2 + 7x - 2$$

At this point in the algorithm, we have a set G consisting of $f_1, ..., f_6$, and a set of pairs B containing 11 unprocessed pairs. Each of these unprocessed pairs will generate an S-polynomial, and each of these S-polynomials can be reduced to zero. Thus, no new pairs are generated, and the set $\{f_1, ..., f_6\}$ is a Gröbner basis. $\diamondsuit$

7.3.5 Improved Basis Construction and Reduced Gröbner Bases

Most of the variants of the algorithm given previously concentrate on eliminating certain pairs from B *before* reducing the S-polynomials constructed from them. A pair can be eliminated if we can show that its S-polynomial must reduce to zero. Other modifications order the pairs in B by various strategies that increase the chances of so eliminating pairs. One such strategy is to remove early those pairs from B whose leading power products have a small least common multiple. These heuristics can result in significant speedups and should be implemented.

We give two criteria for eliminating a pair $\{h_1, h_2\}$ from B. The first criterion is as follows. If there is another polynomial h_3 in G with the property that the leading power product of h_3 divides the least common multiple of the leading power products of h_1 and h_2 in G, and if both pairs $\{h_1, h_3\}$ and $\{h_2, h_3\}$ are not in B, then the pair $\{h_1, h_2\}$ does not need to be considered. Intuitively, the presence of h_3 implies that the S-polynomial of h_1 and h_2 will reduce to zero. For example, consider the situation in the basis construction just after processing the pair $\{f_2, f_4\}$. The next pair $\{f_3, f_4\}$ would generate a least common multiple of xy^2. We try to apply the criterion, using for h_3 the polynomial f_2 whose leading power product divides xy^2. Both $\{f_2, f_3\}$ and $\{f_2, f_4\}$ are not in B, so the criterion applies. In our example, the criterion eliminates four more pairs.

The second criterion to eliminate pairs states that, if the leading power products of f_1 and of f_2 are coprime, then the pair $\{f_1, f_2\}$ is redundant. As an example, consider the pair $\{f_5, f_6\}$ whose leading power products are y and x^5, respectively. Since they are coprime, $S(f_5, f_6)$ must reduce to zero.

So far, the algorithm only adds new polynomials to G. It is possible to remove certain other polynomials during the computation. Briefly, if f can be reduced to zero using the polynomials in $G - \{f\}$, then f is redundant and can be deleted. Moreover, if the normal form of f is not zero, then f can be replaced with its normal form. Here, unprocessed pairs involving f are replaced by pairs involving the normal form of f. When these steps are incorporated, we obtain a *reduced* Gröbner basis that is then *unique*, provided the leading coefficients are scaled by some convention. The reduced Gröbner basis in Example 5, without coefficient scaling, is

$$
\begin{aligned}
f_5 &= -8y - 20x^4 - 8x^3 - 15x^2 + 34x - 19 \\
f_6 &= 4x^5 + 3x^3 - 8x^2 + 7x - 2
\end{aligned}
$$

From now on, we consider only reduced Gröbner bases.

7.3.6 Admissible Term Orderings

We have described the Gröbner basis construction with respect to a lexicographic ordering of terms. Other orderings are possible, and the basis-construction algorithm should be implemented such that it works with every suitable ordering. Most generally, the basis calculation can be based on any admissible term ordering.

> **Definition**
> An *admissible* term ordering $\prec_a$ is a total order of power products that satisfies
>
> 1. $1 \prec_a x_i$, for all variables x_i.
> 2. For all power products u, v, and w, $u \prec_a v$ implies $uw \prec_a vw$.

The two major term orderings in current use are the lexicographic and the total degree ordering. Both can be further varied by permuting the variables. For instance, in $k[x, y]$, we can construct either ordering with $x \prec y$ or with $y \prec x$. Moreover, they can be combined in various ways.

The *total degree* ordering, denoted by $\prec_t$, is defined by requiring that all power products of degree n precede the power products of degree $n+1$. Two power products of equal degree are ordered lexicographically. For example, for two variables with $x \prec_t y$, we have

$$
1 \prec_t x \prec_t y \prec_t x^2 \prec_t xy \prec_t y^2 \prec_t x^3 \prec_t \cdots
$$

The *reverse lexicographic total degree* ordering, denoted by $\prec_r$, is defined by requiring that all power products of degree n precede all power products of degree $n + 1$. Two power products of equal degree are ordered in *reverse* lexicographic order. For example, for two variables with $x \prec_r y$, we have

$$1 \prec_r y \prec_r x \prec_r y^2 \prec_r xy \prec_r x^2 \prec_r y^3 \prec_r \cdots$$

Example 7.6: The Gröbner basis of the set F of Example 7.5 with respect to the total degree ordering is

$$4x^3 - 10xy + 4y + 3x - 3$$
$$8y^2 - 9xy - 6x^2 + 9y - 4x$$

$\diamond$

The ordering used can profoundly influence both the time needed to construct a Gröbner basis and the basis size. In most applications, it appears that using the total degree ordering or the reverse lexicographic total degree ordering is much faster and leads to smaller bases than using the lexicographic ordering. On the other hand, the lexicographic ordering has many useful properties that would make it the ordering of choice in most geometric applications.

One consequence of this situation is current research on *basis conversion*. The idea is to construct a Gröbner basis with the total degree ordering, and then transform this basis to another Gröbner basis with respect to the lexicographic ordering. Algorithms for this conversion are discussed in Section 7.8.

7.4 Solving Algebraic Equations

Many geometric applications require solving a system of algebraic equations. If $F = 0$ is a system of algebraic equations, then constructing a Gröbner basis for the ideal generated by F yields an equivalent system $G = 0$ that has the same solution set but is often easier to solve. In this section, we explore this approach.

Given a system F of algebraic equations, it can be shown that F has no solutions iff 1 is in the Gröbner basis G of the ideal generated by F. This theorem does not require that G be constructed with a special term ordering. However, if we wish to determine actual solutions of the system F, then the term ordering used matters.

7.4.1 Triangularizing Algebraic Equations

A Gröbner basis of I constructed with the lexicographic ordering contains information about the elimination ideals of I, and can be used to solve algebraic equations. Let $I \subset k[x_1, ..., x_n]$ be an ideal. Then the set of polynomials in I that contain only the variables $x_1, ..., x_r$ is

$$I_r = \{f \in I \mid f \in k[x_1, ..., x_r]\} = I \cap k[x_1, ..., x_r]$$

In the ring $k[x_1, ..., x_r]$, the set I_r is evidently an ideal, and we call it the rth *elimination ideal* of I. As we shall see, these ideals help in solving an algebraic system $F = 0$, and much information about them is implicit in a Gröbner basis for $I\langle F \rangle$, as stated by the following key theorem.

Theorem
Let F be a set of polynomials in the variables $x_1, ..., x_n$, and G be a Gröbner basis for the ideal I generated by F with respect to the lexicographic ordering based on $x_1 \prec ... \prec x_n$. Then, for $1 \le r < n$, the polynomials $G \cap k[x_1, ..., x_r]$ are a Gröbner basis of the elimination ideal $I_r = I \cap k[x_1, ..., x_r]$.

This theorem implies, roughly, that a lexicographic Gröbner basis is a triangular system of polynomial equations. We use it as follows to solve the system $F = \{f_1 = 0, ..., f_k = 0\}$.

Input: A set $F = \{f_1, ..., f_k\}$ of polynomials in $k[x_1, ..., x_n]$.

Output: All solutions of F in the set X_n if F has finitely many solutions, or a message that F has infinitely many solutions.

Method:

1. Construct a reduced lexicographic Gröbner basis G for $I\langle F \rangle$, with $x_1 \prec x_2 \prec \cdots \prec x_n$.

2. If $1 \in G$, then stop: F does not have any solution.

3. If G does not contain a univariate polynomial g_1 in $k[x_1]$, then stop: The solution to F does not consist of a finite set of points.

4. Let g_1 be a polynomial of lowest degree in $G \cap k[x_1]$, and let $X_1 = \{(\alpha) \mid g_1(\alpha) = 0\}$ be the roots of g_1.

5. Repeat steps 6 and 7 with $i = 2, ..., n$.

6. Initialize X_i to the empty set.

7. For each $(\alpha_1, ..., \alpha_{i-1})$ in X_{i-1}, substitute α_s for x_s in $G \cap k[x_1, ..., x_i]$, where $1 \le s \le i - 1$. From among the resulting univariate polynomials select one of lowest degree that is not identically zero, say p. Then, let $\beta_1, ..., \beta_r$ be the roots of p. Add to X_i all tuples of the form $(\alpha_1, ..., \alpha_{i-1}, \beta_s)$, where $s = 1, ..., r$.

It can be shown that the polynomial g_1 selected in step 4 is unique, and that the algorithm correctly determines all solutions of F. Note that certain polynomials in $G \cap k[x_1, ..., x_i] - k[x_1, ..., x_{i-1}]$ may vanish for specific values in X_i. The examples that follow illustrate this point.

7.4.2 Finding Surface Intersections

We can use the algorithm to solve nonlinear equations for finding the intersection of algebraic surfaces.

Example 7.7: We compute the intersection of the three cylinders

$$\begin{aligned}
x^2 + y^2 - 1 &= 0 \\
x^2 + z^2 - 1 &= 0 \\
y^2 + z^2 - 1 &= 0
\end{aligned}$$

Using the lexicographic ordering with $x \prec y \prec z$, the Gröbner basis G is

$$\{x^2 - 2, y^2 - 2, z^2 - 2\}$$

This system is especially simple since it is diagonal. The roots of the first polynomial are $x = \pm 1/\sqrt{2}$. Substitution into other equations is not necessary, since they do not mention x. The roots of the second and third equation are $y = \pm 1/\sqrt{2}$ and $z = \pm 1/\sqrt{2}$. Thus, we have eight different solutions, given by the eight combinations of solutions to the three equations.
$\diamondsuit$

Example 7.8: We compute the intersection of the surfaces

$$\begin{aligned}
z^2 + 2yz + 2xz + y^2 + 2xy + x^2 - 1 &= 0 \\
z^2 - 2yz - 2xz + y^2 + 2xy + x^2 - 1 &= 0 \\
z^2 - 2yz + 2xz + y^2 - 2xy + x^2 - 1 &= 0 \\
z^2 + 2yz - 2xz + y^2 - 2xy + x^2 - 1 &= 0 \\
z^2 + y^2 - x - 1 &= 0
\end{aligned}$$

Here, the first four quadratic surfaces are pairs of planes bounding an octahedron. The plane pairs intersect in the six points $(\pm 1, 0, 0)$, $(0, \pm 1, 0)$, $(0, 0, \pm 1)$. The fifth surface is a paraboloid of rotation that passes through five of these points but not through the point $(1, 0, 0)$. The Gröbner basis computed for this set is $G = G_1 \cup G_2 \cup G_3$, where

$$G_1 = \{x^2 + x\}$$
$$G_2 = \{xy, \ y^3 - y\}$$
$$G_3 = \{xz, \ yz, \ z^2 + y^2 - x - 1\}$$

The set X_1 consists of the roots of $x^2 + x$, and is

$$X_1 = \{(-1), (0)\}$$

We substitute -1 for x in the basis subset G_2 and obtain $-y$ as the lowest-degree polynomial in y. Its root is 0, so we add the pair $(-1, 0)$ to X_2. Next, we substitute 0 for x and obtain the polynomial $y^3 - y$, with roots 1, -1, and 0, as the lowest-degree nontrivial polynomial. Thus, the final set X_2 is

$$X_2 = \{(-1, 0), (0, 1), (0, -1), (0, 0)\}$$

For the set X_3, we explore the four substitutions for x and y defined by X_2. With three of them, we obtain a linear polynomial in z, with the unique root 0 in each case. The fourth substitution, $(0, 0)$, yields $z^2 - 1$, with roots 1 and -1. Hence, X_3 is

$$X_3 = \{(-1, 0, 0), (0, 1, 0), (0, -1, 0), (0, 0, 1), (0, 0, -1)\}$$

These are all the solutions of the original system of equations. $\diamondsuit$

7.4.3 Locating Singularities

In Section 6.5.5 in Chapter 6, we discussed locating singularities of plane algebraic curves, and we described several methods. If the curve coefficients are known precisely, then we can apply the Gröbner basis method to precompute all singularities by solving the system $\{f = 0, f_x = 0, f_y = 0\}$. We give two examples.

Example 7.9: Consider the cubic curve $f = 28y^3 + 26xy^2 + 28y^2 + 7x^2y + 16xy + 7y + x^3/2 + 3x/2$. We considered parameterizing this curve in Section 5.5.3 of Chapter 5. As a rational cubic, it must have a singular point, which we find by solving the system

$$\{f = 0, f_x = 0, f_y = 0\}$$

With the ordering $y \prec x$, we obtain the Gröbner basis $\{2y + 1, x\}$ Hence, f has one singular point, at $(0, -1/2)$. $\diamond$

Example 7.10: Consider the quartic $g = x^4 + x^2 y^2 - y^2 - 2x^2 + 1$. Using the lexicographic ordering, the Gröbner basis of $\{g, g_x, g_y\}$ is

$$\{x^4 - 2x^2 + 1, y^2 + 2x^2 - 2, x^2 y - y\}$$

Hence, there are four curve singularities, at $(\pm 1, \pm 2)$. $\diamond$

7.4.4 Basis Determination with Symbolic Quantities

The curve g of Example 7.10 is a member of a family of quartics given by

$$f(a) = x^4 + x^2 y^2 - y^2 - 2a^2 x^2 + a^4$$

with $g = f(1)$. It would be attractive to determine the locus of the singularities of the curve $f(a)$ irrespective of the value of a.

The algorithm presented for solving systems of algebraic equations can be used without difficulties in extension fields. If a is transcendental, then we can compute the Gröbner basis for $\{f, f_x, f_y\}$ over $k(a)$. However, the results of this computation are not necessarily valid when a takes on certain values that are algebraic numbers. The problem is that the necessary coefficient arithmetic may entail computing with polynomials in a that could be zero for certain specific values. For transcendentals, this problem does not arise, since a transcendental cannot be the root of any polynomial.

Consider determining the Gröbner basis for $\{f, f_x, f_y\}$ in $k(a)[x, y]$. The input set to the basis computation is

$$
\begin{aligned}
f_{1,1} &= x^2 y^2 - y^2 + x^4 - 2a^2 x^2 + a^4 \\
f_{1,2} &= 2(xy^2 + 2x^3 - 2a^2 x) \\
f_{1,3} &= 2(x^2 y - y)
\end{aligned}
$$

We use the lexicographic ordering with $x \prec y$. Before forming any S-polynomials, we simplify $f_{1,1}$, replacing it with $f_{1,1} - y f_{1,3}/2$, and we eliminate the factor 2 from the other two polynomials. We obtain the set

$$
\begin{aligned}
f_{2,1} &= x^4 - 2a^2 x^2 + a^4 \\
f_{2,2} &= xy^2 + 2x^3 - 2a^2 x \\
f_{2,3} &= x^2 y - y
\end{aligned}
$$

The S-polynomial of $f_{2,2}$ and $f_{2,3}$ is $f_{2,4} = y^2 + 2a^2x^2 - 2a^2$. After adjoining it, we reduce $f_{2,2}$ by replacing it with $f_{2,2} - xf_{2,4} + 2xf_{2,1}$, and we obtain

$$f_{3,2} = 2(1 - a^2)x^3 - 2a^2(1 - a^2)x$$

If a is transcendental, then the structure of $f_{2,3}$ is $x^3 + bx$. If $a = \pm 1$, however, then this polynomial is zero. Hence, for $a = 1$, the Gröbner basis could differ structurally from the one obtained for the transcendental a. This is indeed so. When a is transcendental, we obtain the Gröbner basis

$$\{y, x^2 - a^2\}$$

Substitution of $a = 1$ would yield the set $\{y, x^2\}$. However, as we saw in Example 7.10, the Gröbner basis for $\{f(1), f(1)_x, f(1)_y\}$ is $\{x^4 - 2x^2 + 1, y^2 + 2x^2 - 2, x^2y - y\}$.

So, when considering a family of polynomials with some parameters $a_1, ..., a_m$, the Gröbner basis can be computed over $k(a_1, ..., a_m)$. The results will be valid for transcendental values and for those algebraic values for the a_i for which none of the coefficient polynomials generated during the basis computation vanish. For "exceptional values" for which one or more coefficient polynomials in the a_i vanish, a separate computation is needed.

7.5 Operations on Curves and Surfaces

As we saw, a Gröbner basis for $F \subset k[x_1, ..., x_n]$, constructed with the lexicographic ordering, provides the elimination ideals $I_1, ..., I_{n-1}$ of I at the same time. In the case of zero-dimensional ideals, we used this fact to simplify structurally a set of algebraic equations that we wanted to solve. By triangularizing the system of equations, we reduced the problem to finding the roots of univariate polynomials. We now explore a different aspect of the triangularization procedure using the Gröbner basis construction as a general elimination procedure.

7.5.1 Implicitization and Inversion

If a surface is given parametrically as

$$
\begin{aligned}
x &= h_1(s, t) \\
y &= h_2(s, t) \\
z &= h_3(s, t)
\end{aligned}
$$

then its implicit form can be determined by elimination of s and t. In Section 5.6.1 of Chapter 5, we explored using the Sylvester resultant as an elimination tool, and observed that repeated application leads to extraneous factors. These factors are intrinsic because the method is based on projection. For polynomial functions h_i, the Gröbner basis approach achieves simultaneously the elimination of s and t, as well as a surface inversion. We demonstrate the procedure with an example.

Example 7.11: Consider the parametric surface

$$
\begin{aligned}
x &= st \\
y &= st^2 \\
z &= s^2
\end{aligned}
$$

We construct the Gröbner basis with the lexicographic ordering for the corresponding ideal

$$ F = \{x - st, y - st^2, z - s^2\} $$

Ordering the variables $z \prec y \prec x \prec t \prec s$, we obtain the Gröbner basis

$$
\begin{aligned}
G = \{ \ &x^4 - y^2 z, \\
&tx - y, \ tyz - x^3, \ t^2 z - x^2, \\
&sy - x^2, \ sx - tz, \ st - x, \ s^2 - z \ \}
\end{aligned}
$$

In G, the first polynomial, $x^4 - y^2 z$, is the implicit surface form. Note the absence of extraneous factors. Polynomials $tx - y$ and $sy - x^2$ are the first polynomials in the basis that introduce the variables t and s, respectively. They provide an *inversion* of the surface; that is, given a point (x, y, z) on the surface, we can determine its parametric coordinates (s, t) from these polynomials. Moreover, the linearity of these two polynomials in t and s implies that the surface parameterization is *faithful*; that is, to each point (x, y, z) there corresponds only one point (s, t) in parameter space. $\diamondsuit$

7.5.2 Offset Surfaces

In Section 6.3.3 of Chapter 6, we gave a procedure for determining the offsets of an algebraic surface f. The procedure consisted of formulating a family of spheres of radius equal to the offset distance with centers on the surface f, and determining the envelope of this family of spheres. If the algebraic equation of the offset surface is needed, then we must eliminate the generic coordinates of the sphere centers. The elimination can be done using Gröbner bases constructed with the lexicographic ordering.

Example 7.12:   We consider offsetting the ellipsoid $2x^2 + y^2 + z^2 - 2 = 0$ by the distance 1. Applying the procedure of Section 6.3.3 in Chapter 6, we obtain the following equations.

$$(x - u_1)^2 + (y - u_2)^2 + (z - u_3)^2 - 1 = 0 \qquad (7.1)$$
$$2u_1^2 + u_2^2 + u_3^2 - 2 = 0 \qquad (7.2)$$
$$(x - u_1)u_2 - 2(y - u_2)u_1 = 0 \qquad (7.3)$$
$$(y - u_2)u_3 - (z - u_3)u_2 = 0 \qquad (7.4)$$

Equation (7.1) is the sphere defining the offset distance, and equation (7.2) places the sphere's center on the ellipsoid. The other two equations are the derivatives of the sphere in two linearly independent tangent directions. We order the variables x, y, z, u_1, u_2, u_3, and construct the Gröbner basis for these equations, obtaining an implicit form of degree 9 with 32 terms. ◇

Closer inspection of the surface computed in Example 7.12 reveals an extraneous factor y, which is found to be present because of the problem formulation and is not a consequence of applying the Gröbner basis method. For the directional derivatives (7.3) and (7.4), we used the tangent directions

$$t_1 : \quad (-u_2, 2u_1, 0)$$
$$t_2 : \quad (0, -u_3, u_2)$$

They become linearly dependent when $u_2 = 0$. This condition holds on the intersection curve of the ellipsoid with the plane $y = 0$. Consider the spheres centered on that curve. For every point on that curve, the directional derivatives are in the direction $(0, u, 0)$; hence, all points of a sphere that are in the plane $y = 0$ satisfy the differential conditions (7.3) and (7.4), and since these points cover a two-dimensional region in the $y = 0$ plane, we obtain the extraneous factor y. Choosing for the directional derivatives the tangents

$$t_3 : \quad (2u_2, u_1, 0)$$
$$t_4 : \quad (2u_3, 0, u_1)$$

we obtain the extraneous factor x instead.

We can reformulate the offset problem to avoid the degeneracies. However, since the extraneous factor has such a simple structure, it seems easier just to factor it out.

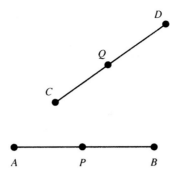

Figure 7.4   Geometric Example Theorem

7.6 Geometric Theorem Proving

Gröbner bases can be used in geometric theorem proving. That is, given a geometric theorem, there are systematic procedures for translating a geometric configuration into an algebraic formula and posing the conclusion of a geometric theorem as a problem of ideal membership whose answer determines whether the theorem holds.

This work is of potential use in robustness problems. As pointed out in Section 4.4 of Chapter 4, coping with numerical uncertainty can be approached as a reasoning problem in that the interpretation of a numerical result is considered to be a logical decision that must be consistent with all other such decisions. Of course, each decision has a geometric meaning — for example, whether two edges intersect, whether a vertex is incident to a face, and so on. If we can account for this geometric meaning, then the symbolic reasoning establishing consistency is related to proving geometric theorems.

In this section, we briefly sketch how the Gröbner basis approach to geometric theorem proving works. We begin with a brief sketch of the method, and illustrate the various technical issues using the following example:

> ### Geometric Example Theorem
> If two line segments $\overline{AB}$ and $\overline{CD}$ are congruent, then so are their halves.

Figure 7.4 shows an instance of this theorem.

7.6.1 Outline of the Proof Method

We will translate the geometric theorem into a logical formula of the form

$$(\forall x_1, ..., x_n)((f_1 = 0 \wedge \cdots \wedge f_r = 0) \Rightarrow g = 0) \tag{7.5}$$

where $g = 0$ and the $f_i = 0$ are polynomial equations in the variables $x_1, ..., x_n$. The x_i are point coordinates. The part $(f_1 = 0 \wedge \cdots \wedge f_r = 0)$ expresses the *hypothesis* of the theorem. In our example, the hypothesis asserts that the line segments $\overline{AB}$ and $\overline{CD}$ are congruent. The part $g = 0$ expresses the theorem's *conclusion* — in our example, the congruence of the segment halves.

Formula (7.5) formally states that, for all values $(x_1, ..., x_n)$ for which every $f_j(x_1, ..., x_n)$ is zero, $g(x_1, ..., x_n)$ is also zero. Abstractly, the set of polynomials $F = \{f_1, ..., f_r\}$ generates an ideal $J = I\langle F \rangle$. Associated with J is the algebraic set $V(J)$ consisting of all points $(x_1, ..., x_n)$ for which all polynomials in J vanish. Formula (7.5) states that the hypersurface $g = 0$ contains the algebraic set $V(J)$. Algebraically, therefore, formula (7.5) says that the polynomial g is in the radical ideal of the algebraic set $V(J)$. See also Section 7.2.6.

We prove that g is in the radical ideal $Rad(V(J))$ by assuming that it is not and deriving a contradiction from this assumption. Suppose we can find a point $(x_1, ..., x_n)$ such that all $f_j \in F$ vanish but g does not. Then, we have proved that g is not in the radical ideal $Rad(V(J))$, and the point is a counterexample of the theorem to be proved. That is, we try to satisfy the formula

$$(\exists x_1, ..., x_n)(f_1 = 0 \wedge \cdots \wedge f_r = 0 \wedge g \neq 0)$$

The inequality $g \neq 0$ is transformed into an equality by introducing a new variable z:

$$(\exists x_1, ..., x_n, z)(f_1 = 0 \wedge \cdots \wedge f_r = 0 \wedge gz - 1 = 0) \qquad (7.6)$$

Clearly, $gz - 1 = 0$ is possible only for points at which g does not vanish.

In view of the preceding discussion, we consider the ideal generated by the set $\tilde{F} = F \cup \{gz - 1\}$ consisting of all the f_j and the polynomial $gz - 1$. This ideal contains a point $(x_1, ..., x_n, z)$ iff formula (7.5) is false; that is, iff formula (7.6) can be satisfied. In that case, the theorem is not valid.

The decision of whether there are points in the algebraic set of the ideal generated by $\tilde{F}$ is made by investigating whether the system of algebraic equations $\tilde{F} = 0$ has a solution. To find that out, we construct a Gröbner basis G for the ideal $I\langle \tilde{F} \rangle$. There is a solution to the system $\tilde{F} = 0$ iff 1 is not in the basis G. See also Section 7.4.

Proving a geometric theorem with the Gröbner basis approach, therefore, proceeds as follows:

1. Translate the geometric theorem into formula (7.5).

2. By introducing a new variable, change the formula into the format of formula (7.6). Let $\tilde{F}$ be the set of polynomials in this formula.

3. Construct a Gröbner basis for the ideal generated by $\tilde{F}$. The geometric theorem is true iff 1 is not in the basis.

Note that the basis can be constructed with respect to any admissible term ordering.

7.6.2 Translating Geometric Configurations

The basic idea of translating a geometric configuration into a set of algebraic formulae is to assign symbolic coordinates to the points and to express the configuration as algebraic equations in these coordinates.

Let the points of the first segment be A, P, B, and let those of the second segment be C, Q, D, as shown in Figure 7.4 before. The hypothesis of the example theorem is rephrased to make its structure more apparent:

- The points A, P, and B are collinear.

- The points C, Q, and D are collinear.

- The segments $\overline{AB}$ and $\overline{CD}$ are congruent.

- P is the midpoint of $\overline{AB}$.

- Q is the midpoint of $\overline{CD}$.

The conclusion is

- The segments $\overline{AP}$ and $\overline{CQ}$ are congruent.

We explain how each assertion is translated.

Consider three points A, P, and B. With point coordinates $A = (x_A, y_A)$, $P = (x_P, y_P)$, $B = (x_B, y_B)$, we express that the points are collinear:

$$\frac{x_A - x_P}{y_A - y_P} = \frac{x_A - x_B}{y_A - y_B}$$

Clearing the denominator, we have stated collinearity by the polynomial equation

$$(x_A - x_P)(y_A - y_B) - (x_A - x_B)(y_A - y_P) = 0 \qquad (7.7)$$

Implicit in the statement "A, P, and B are collinear" is the assumption that at least two of the points A, P, and B are distinct. If this assumption is not expressed by the algebraic formulation, then the translation process is not faithful, and we risk the possibility of "proving" false geometric theorems. We can express that two points are not coincident as

$$x_A - x_P \neq 0 \vee y_A - y_P \neq 0$$

Therefore, the statement "A, P, and B are collinear" can be expressed by the following conjunction

$$(x_A - x_P)(y_A - y_B) - (x_A - x_B)(y_A - y_P) = 0$$
$$\wedge \quad (x_A - x_P \neq 0 \vee y_A - y_P \neq 0)$$
$$\wedge \quad (x_A - x_B \neq 0 \vee y_A - y_B \neq 0)$$

Note that in this formulation we have expressed that A and B are different points, and that A and P are different points, but we have not expressed that P and B are different points. In the following, other constraints will establish that P and B are not coincident, thereby compensating for the asymmetry of the formula.

To express the congruence of the line segments $\overline{AB}$ and $\overline{CD}$, we state that they have equal length:

$$(x_A - x_B)^2 + (y_A - y_B)^2 - (x_C - x_D)^2 - (y_C - y_D)^2 = 0$$

The fact that P is the midpoint of the segment $\overline{AB}$ is expressed by requiring that the segments $\overline{AP}$ and $\overline{PB}$ have equal length:

$$(x_A - x_P)^2 + (y_A - y_P)^2 - (x_P - x_B)^2 - (y_P - y_B)^2 = 0$$

The entire theorem can now be expressed as the following formula, which is universally quantified in all coordinate variables.

$$[(x_A - x_P)(y_A - y_B) - (x_A - x_B)(y_A - y_P) = 0$$
$$\wedge \quad (x_A - x_P \neq 0 \vee y_A - y_P \neq 0)$$
$$\wedge \quad (x_A - x_B \neq 0 \vee y_A - y_B \neq 0)$$
$$\wedge \quad (x_C - x_Q)(y_C - y_D) - (x_C - x_D)(y_C - y_Q) = 0$$
$$\wedge \quad (x_C - x_Q \neq 0 \vee y_C - y_Q \neq 0)$$
$$\wedge \quad (x_C - x_D \neq 0 \vee y_C - y_D \neq 0) \tag{7.8}$$
$$\wedge \quad (x_A - x_B)^2 + (y_A - y_B)^2 - (x_C - x_D)^2 - (y_C - y_D)^2 = 0$$
$$\wedge \quad (x_A - x_P)^2 + (y_A - y_P)^2 - (x_P - x_B)^2 - (y_P - y_B)^2 = 0$$
$$\wedge \quad (x_C - x_Q)^2 + (y_C - y_Q)^2 - (x_Q - x_D)^2 - (y_Q - y_D)^2 = 0]$$
$$\Longrightarrow$$
$$(x_A - x_P)^2 + (y_A - y_P)^2 - (x_C - x_Q)^2 - (y_C - y_Q)^2 = 0$$

7.6.3 Formula Manipulation

Formula (7.8) is not yet in the format of formula (7.5), because of the inequalities and the disjunctions ($\vee$) in the hypothesis part. We change the formula by first replacing the inequalities with equalities, and then replacing the disjunctions with products.

By introducing the additional variables z_i, $i = 1, ..., 8$, we replace all inequalities in the hypothesis part of formula (7.8) with equalities. For example,

$$x_A - x_P \neq 0 \vee y_A - y_P \neq 0$$

is replaced with

$$(x_A - x_P)z_1 - 1 = 0 \vee (y_A - y_P)z_2 - 1 = 0$$

Each disjunction is next replaced with a product. So, for example,

$$(x_A - x_P)z_1 - 1 = 0 \vee (y_A - y_P)z_2 - 1 = 0$$

is changed into

$$((x_A - x_P)z_1 - 1)((y_A - y_P)z_2 - 1) = 0$$

With these changes, the theorem has been expressed in the required format and can be proved as described.

7.6.4 Choice of Coordinate Axes and Other Heuristics

The process of constructing a Gröbner basis from the set $\tilde{F}$ is facilitated by choosing a suitable coordinate system. For example, the origin of the coordinate system can be placed at the point A, and the x axis laid through the segment $\overline{AB}$. Moreover, after suitable scaling, we can assume that $B = (1, 0)$. The effect of these heuristics is that some variables are eliminated and that some of the polynomials simplify.

Other simplifications are possible. For example, having expressed that $A \neq B$ and P is the midpoint of the segment $\overline{AB}$, it follows that $A \neq P$, so the polynomial expressing this inequality can be deleted. Similarly, $C \neq Q$ is implied. Other heuristics can be formulated based on similar basic geometric observations.

7.7 Complexity

Construction of a Gröbner basis is a potentially time-consuming process. It has been shown that the worst-case complexity is doubly exponential. That is, given a set F in $k[x_1, ..., x_n]$ with highest degree m, the Gröbner basis could contain polynomials of degree proportional to 2^{2^m}. In the case of zero-dimensional ideals, the corresponding bound is 2^m, so this case is more favorable.

When F is in $k[x_1, x_2]$ (i.e., contains bivariate polynomials), more specific complexity bounds are available. If m is the highest degree of any polynomial in F, it can be shown that the degree of any polynomial occurring throughout the basis computation is bounded by m^2 for arbitrary admissible orderings, and by $2m - 1$ for the total degree ordering.

For trivariate polynomials, the following bound is known. Let d be the lowest degree, and m be the highest degree, of any polynomial in the input set F. Then any polynomial generated during the basis computation has a degree of at most $2^d(8m + 1)$, when using the total degree ordering.

Practical experience shows that the running time depends heavily on the variable ordering, and on the choice of the coordinate system. Possible coefficient growth can also influence the running time significantly. All these phenomena are demonstrated now.

7.7.1 Simple Basis Experiments

It is instructive to consider the actual running times for the basis computations done in this chapter. First, we consider Examples 7.3 through 7.11. These are relatively small computations in which variable ordering and term ordering affect the running times only insignificantly. The computations were done on a Symbolics 3650 Lisp machine using the Gröbner basis implementation provided with Macsyma 412.45. Table 7.1 summarizes the results. Times are given in seconds for both the lexicographic and the total degree orderings. As the values indicate, no significant difference is observed between the lexicographic ordering and the total degree ordering. In many cases, both orderings lead to the same basis, indicating that the ideals with which we deal are structurally extremely simply. Moreover, the polynomials involved are sparse, due to favorably chosen coordinate systems.

7.7.2 Large Basis Computations

The use of basis computations to eliminate variables in curve and surface operations can lead to significantly longer running times. Here, the effect of term orderings becomes very noticeable. It appears that the ideals defined in these problems have a complicated structure, as evidenced by long running times during which many S-polynomials are formed and reduced.

Table 7.2 shows the timings for several runs of Example 7.12. We ob-

Example	Lexicographic	Total Degree
3	0.05	0.05
5, 6	0.16	0.14
7	0.06	0.06
8	0.32	0.37
9	0.23	0.23
10	0.12	0.10
11	0.27	0.21

Table 7.1 Time in Seconds to Construct the Gröbner Basis

serve that the running times differ dramatically between basis computations using the lexicographic ordering and basis computations using the total degree ordering. Also, when the variables are arranged differently, the running times can vary significantly.

7.7.3 Coefficient Growth

Gröbner bases algorithms assume exact arithmetic and are therefore implemented using rational arithmetic. Much of the observed time can depend on the size of the rationals manipulated. A simple experiment demonstrates this point.

Consider again the three-cylinder intersection of Example 7.7. We order the variables $x \prec y \prec z$ and construct the basis with the lexicographic ordering in a total time of 0.06 seconds. Next, we rotate the cylinders, first about the z axis by an arc of 1, then about the x axis by an arc of 1/2, and, finally, again about the z axis by an arc of 1, using single-precision

Variable Ordering	Total Degree Ordering	Lexicographic Ordering
x, y, z, u_1, u_2, u_3	1.76	216.54
z, x, y, u_1, u_2, u_3	2.19	787.78
y, z, x, u_1, u_2, u_3	5.81	217.82
x, y, z, u_2, u_3, u_1	2.69	1101.99
x, y, z, u_2, u_1, u_3	3.13	252.20

Table 7.2 Time in Seconds to Construct the Gröbner Basis

floating-point arithmetic. The coefficients of the three new equations are then converted to rational numbers by Macsyma's RAT function. The three cylinders are now in general position, and their eight points of intersection are expected to have different x coordinates. Due to numerical errors in rotating and in converting to rationals, the cylinders have become slightly elliptic, but there are still eight intersections. We compute the Gröbner basis for these three equations, now consuming 405 seconds, yielding the basis

$$G_1 = \{h_1(x), y - h_2(x), z - h_3(x)\}$$

where h_1 has degree 8, and h_2 and h_3 both have degree 7. That is, the running time has been prolonged by almost four orders of magnitude.

In the longer computation, 231 polynomial pairs are considered. From 30 pairs, S-polynomials are formed and reduced. Using the first criterion of Section 7.3.5, we eliminate 114 pairs. Applying the second criterion, we reject an additional 87 pairs. In large part, therefore, the longer running time is due to the huge rationals involved, which have numerators and denominators with a magnitude of about 10^{700}.

7.8 Basis Conversion

We have seen that a lexicographic Gröbner basis is a very useful data structure that can yield much information about an ideal and its algebraic set. However, experience shows that, in geometric modeling, the known methods for constructing a lexicographic base often demand excessive resources, both in time and in space. This is a serious limitation that should be addressed.

A basic approach to overcoming the inefficiencies of the lexicographic basis construction would be to reformulate the algorithms that use the bases such that they use instead bases constructed with an ordering that leads to better performance. Indeed, constructing a total degree Gröbner basis is an acceptably efficient computation in many situations. In some cases, we can reformulate the algorithms. For example, there is an algorithm for solving a system of algebraic equations that has finitely many solutions, based on a total degree basis.

Another general idea is to construct first the Gröbner basis using the total degree ordering, and then to *convert* this basis to a Gröbner basis with respect to the lexicographic ordering. If the conversion can be done efficiently, then this method will solve the problem for all algorithms that require a lexicographic basis.

Efficient basis conversion is known to exist for zero-dimensional ideals; that is, for ideals whose algebraic set consists of finitely many points. We explain this method conceptually, and explain a variation of it that can be used for variable elimination.

7.8.1 Computing in the Residue Class Ring

We plan to compute in the residue class ring R_I to reduce certain algebraic computations to linear algebra problems. Recall from Section 7.2.4 that R_I is a vector space over the ground field k. The elements of R_I are equivalence classes; that is, they are sets of polynomials in $k[x_1, ..., x_n]$. Computing with equivalence classes will be reduced to computing with certain *representatives*; that is, in each class, we will identify a unique polynomial and compute with it.

Let p be any polynomial in $k[x_1, ..., x_n]$. The equivalence class of p in R_I is denoted $[p]$. The representative of the class $[p]$ will be denoted by $\bar{p}$.

Given a Gröbner basis G of I, we use $\bar{p} = NF(p, G)$ as the representative of the equivalence class $[p]$ of the polynomial p. It can be shown that

$$NF(p, G) = NF(q, G) \qquad \Longleftrightarrow \qquad [p] = [q]$$

So, for each equivalence class, we have a unique representative. In particular, the representative for the equivalence class of the polynomials in the ideal is zero. We exploited this fact when testing ideal membership in Section 7.3. The following observation is not difficult to prove.

Theorem
Let a and b be numbers in k. Then

$$NF(au + bv, G) = c(aNF(u, G) + bNF(v, G))$$

where c is a nonzero constant.

Applying the theorem repeatedly, we see that, for polynomials u_j and numbers a_j, we have

$$\sum_{j=0}^{m} a_j u_j \in I \Longleftrightarrow \sum_{j=0}^{m} a_j NF(u_j, G) = 0 \qquad (7.9)$$

This is true in particular for power products u_i. The importance of formula (7.9) is that it allows us to test ideal membership incrementally using linear dependence tests.

7.8.2 Basis Conversion for Zero-Dimensional Ideals

We sketch an algorithm for the following problem: Given a Gröbner basis G for a zero-dimensional ideal I in $k[x_1, ..., x_n]$ with respect to some admissible order, construct a lexicographic Gröbner basis G' for I. The algorithm proceeds as follows:

1. For $j = 0, 1, 2, ...$, generate power products $u_j = x_1^{e_{1,j}} x_2^{e_{2,j}} \cdots x_n^{e_{n,j}}$ in a suitable order, and compute $\bar{u}_j = NF(u_j, G)$.

2. For each j, test whether there exists a linear dependence

$$\bar{u}_j - \sum_{i=0}^{j-1} a_i \bar{u}_i = 0$$

If so, add the polynomial p to G', where

$$p = u_j - \sum_{i=0}^{j-1} a_i u_i$$

Two problems must be solved for this algorithm to work. We must generate the power products u_j in such an order that every polynomial p discovered in step 2 is in the lexicographic basis G'. Moreover, we must have a termination criterion. The following theorem addresses the first problem. In conjunction with the fact that, for a zero-dimensional ideal I, the vector space R_I is finite-dimensional, we can then derive a termination criterion.

Theorem
Let U be the set of all power products u that are not a multiple of some leading power product of a polynomial in the Gröbner basis G of I. Then, the equivalence classes $[u]$ of the $u \in U$ are linearly independent and form a basis of R_I.

Note that the theorem does not assume that I is zero-dimensional. However, if I is zero-dimensional, then R_I has finite dimension and the set U is finite.

Conversion Algorithm

We discover the polynomials in G' by generating all power products in increasing lexicographic ordering. Note that this must not be done naively, for then the algorithm would not terminate. For example, there are infinitely many power products x_1^j, $j = 0, 1, 2, ...$, that precede the power product x_2. By the preceding theorem, however, we can skip multiples of leading power products. Let L be the set of leading power products of the polynomials already discovered in the basis G'. Beginning with the power product $x_1^0 \cdots x_n^0 = 1$, we generate the next power product in lexicographic order, but skip all multiples of the power products in L. Deferring the details of power-product generation for the moment, the basis-conversion algorithm is as follows. In it, the function $next(u, L)$ generates the next power product subject to the constraints implied by L.

Input: A Gröbner basis G, with respect to some admissible term ordering, of the zero-dimensional ideal I.

Output: A lexicographic Gröbner basis G'.

Method:

1. Set G', L, U, and U' to empty, and set u to 1.

2. While the basis G' is not complete, do steps 3 through 6. Thereafter, stop; G' is a lexicographic basis for I.

3. Determine $\bar{u} = NF(u, G)$, and test whether $\bar{u}$ is a linear combination of the elements in U'.

4. If $\bar{u}$ is linearly independent, then add u to U, and $\bar{u}$ to U', and skip step 5.

5. Let $\bar{u} = \sum_{j=1}^{m} a_j \bar{u}_j$, for some $\bar{u}_j$ in U'. Add $u - \sum_{j=1}^{m} a_j u_j$ to G', and add u to L.

6. Replace u with $next(u, L)$. The basis G' is complete if $next$ determines that no successor exists.

It can be shown that this algorithm correctly determines the lexicographic basis in a finite number of steps.

Various optimizations should be incorporated in the reduction to normal form and in the determination of linear dependence. With these optimizations, and assuming that G is a reduced basis with respect to the reverse lexicographic total degree ordering, it can be shown that the algorithm requires $O(n^3 D^2 + nD^3)$ steps, where n is the number of variables and D is the size of U, assuming that the arithmetic operations on the coefficients require unit cost. Practical experience shows that using basis conversion is much faster than is constructing the lexicographic basis directly.

The Staircase

We discuss how to implement the function $next(u, L)$ that generates the next power product in the basis conversion. We restrict our discussion to the bivariate case $n = 2$. The general case is relatively straightforward.

Let G' be a reduced lexicographic Gröbner basis for the ideal I in $k[x, y]$. The leading power products of the polynomials in G' must be relatively prime, and therefore form a *staircase pattern*, as shown in Figure 7.5. In the figure, the point (i, j) represents a power product $x^i y^j$. Five leading power products are shown. Each defines a rectangular area whose points represent power products that are multiples of the power product. These areas are shaded. The set U, therefore, consists of the equivalence classes of all power products belonging to points outside any shaded area. In the figure, the basis is of a zero-dimensional ideal and the set U is finite.

The function $next(u, L)$ has to generate the power products in U in increasing lexicographic ordering. Since the leading power products in G'

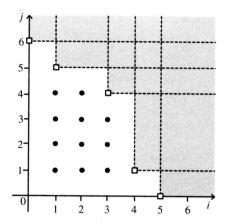

Figure 7.5   Staircase of Leading Power Products

are not known in advance, *next* will generate them also. However, since a linear dependence is discovered, these power products are then added to the set L instead. Figure 7.6 shows the sequence in which the power products will be generated, assuming that the algorithm discovers the leading power products of Figure 7.5. The function $next(u, L)$ is now as follows:

> *Input*: A power product u, a set of power products L.
>
> *Output*: The power product v that is next in lexicographic order and is not a multiple of any $w \in L$.
>
> *Method*:
>
> 1. Set $u_1 = xu$.
>
> 2. If u_1 is not a multiple of any power product in L, then return with $v = u_1$.
>
> 3. If $u_1 = x^a y^b$ is a multiple of some $w = x^i y^j$ in L and $a = 1$, then stop: No successor of u exists that is not a multiple of some w in L. Otherwise, return with $v = y^{b+1}$.

A Basis-Conversion Example

We illustrate basis conversion with a simple example. Consider the ideal in $k[x, y]$ generated by

$$G = \{x^3 + 2xy - x + 1, y^2 + x - 3\}$$

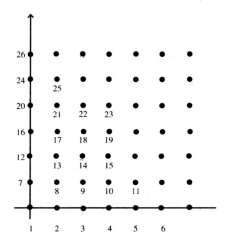

Figure 7.6   Power-Product Generation Sequence

G is already a Gröbner basis with respect to the total degree ordering, and the ideal $I\langle G\rangle$ can be shown to be zero-dimensional. We generate the monomials $1, x, x^2, \ldots$ with the following normal forms.

$$
\begin{aligned}
NF(1, G) &= 1 \\
NF(x, G) &= x \\
NF(x^2, G) &= x^2 \\
NF(x^3, G) &= -2xy + x - 1 \\
NF(x^4, G) &= -2x^2y + x^2 - x \\
NF(x^5, G) &= -4xy - 5x^2 + 2y + 13x - 1 \\
NF(x^6, G) &= -4x^2y + 12xy + 13x^2 - 6x + 5
\end{aligned}
$$

At this point, we discover a linear dependence among the normal forms:

$$
\begin{aligned}
NF(1, G) - 2NF(x, G) - 11NF(x^2, G) \\
+6NF(x^3, G) - 2NF(x^4, G) + NF(x^6, G) &= 0
\end{aligned}
$$

Hence, we have found a polynomial in G'; namely,

$$
1 - 2x - 11x^2 + 6x^3 - 2x^4 + x^6
$$

The set U is, at this point, $\{1, x, x^2, x^3, x^4, x^5\}$. We add the leading power product x^6 of p to L. Since x^7 is a multiple of x^6, the next power product generated is y. The monomial y cannot be simplified and is already in normal form. $y = NF(y, G)$ is not linearly independent because

$$-NF(1, G) - 11NF(x, G) + 5NF(x^2, G)$$
$$-2NF(x^3, G) + NF(x^5, G) - 2NF(y, G) = 0$$

Therefore, the polynomial

$$-1 - 11x + 5x^2 - 2x^3 + x^5 - 2y$$

is also in G'. So, we add the polynomial to G, and add the leading term, y, to L.

At this point, no lexicographic successor to y can be found that is not a multiple of y or of x^6. In consequence, the algorithm terminates, having found the lexicographic basis

$$G' = \{1 - 2x - 11x^2 + 6x^3 - 2x^4 + x^6, -1 - 11x + 5x^2 - 2x^3 + x^5 - 2y\}$$

7.8.3 Variable Elimination

One idea underlying the basis-conversion algorithm is to discover polynomials in I by determining linear dependency relations in R_I. This idea can be applied in a more general way to ideals that are not necessarily zero-dimensional, and it can be used in geometric applications. The general setting is as follows:

> Given an ideal I in $k[x_1, ..., x_n]$ that is known a priori to contain a polynomial p in $k[x_1, ..., x_r]$, for some $r < n$, find such a polynomial p of lowest degree.

Note that we can solve this problem in principle by constructing a lexicographic Gröbner basis. However, constructing a lexicographic basis is often too time consuming, so we seek an alternative. The problem has the following geometric applications:

1. The intersection of two surfaces $f(x, y, z) = 0$ and $g(x, y, z) = 0$ is to be projected onto the (x, y) plane. The ideal I is generated by $\{f, g\}$ in $k[x, y, z]$. The projection p is a polynomial in $k[x, y]$.

2. A parametric surface $x = h_1(s, t)$, $y = h_2(s, t)$, $z = h_3(s, t)$ is to be implicitized. Assuming that the h_i are polynomials, the ideal I is in $k[x, y, z, s, t]$ and is generated by $\{x - h_1, y - h_2, z - h_3\}$. The sought polynomial p is the implicit form of the surface, and is in $k[x, y, z]$.

3. The offset of an implicit surface $f(x, y, z) = 0$ is to be determined. As described in Section 6.3 of Chapter 6, we formulate four polynomial equations defining an ideal I in $k[x, y, z, u, v, w]$. The offset equation is a polynomial p in $k[x, y, z]$.

Other applications are readily formulated in which we are given a system of polynomial equations and seek to eliminate several variables, thus deriving an implied polynomial equation in fewer variables.

The modified algorithm requires a description of the ideal by a Gröbner basis with respect to some admissible term ordering, and is as follows:

Input: A Gröbner basis G for $I \subset k[x_1, ..., x_n]$, and an index $r < n$.

Output: A polynomial $p \in k[x_1, ..., x_r]$ in the ideal, provided such a polynomial exists.

Method:

1. Beginning with 1, generate the power products formed with $x_1, ..., x_r$, in the total degree ordering. For each such power product u, do step 2.

2. Compute $\bar{u} = NF(u, G)$ and test whether there exists a linear dependence between $\bar{u}$ and the normal forms previously generated. If there is a linear dependence, then output the corresponding polynomial defined by this dependence and stop.

Note that this algorithm will not terminate if the ideal does not contain a polynomial p in $k[x_1, ..., x_r]$. Its use is therefore restricted to situations in which p is known to exist. This is the case in many geometric applications.

Example 7.13: Consider the parametric definition of the parabola $x = t$, $y = t^2$. We consider the ideal I generated by $G = \{x - t, y - t^2\}$. With respect to the total degree ordering with $x \prec y \prec t$, G is a Gröbner basis. We seek a polynomial in x and y in I. We generate the following power products and normal forms:

$$
\begin{aligned}
NF(1, G) &= 1 \\
NF(x, G) &= t \\
NF(y, G) &= t^2 \\
NF(x^2, G) &= t^2
\end{aligned}
$$

We discover the linear dependence $NF(x^2, G) - NF(y, G) = 0$, and from it, we obtain the polynomial $y - x^2$ in I. Having found this polynomial, the algorithm stops. $\diamondsuit$

7.9 Notes and References

The algebraic concepts reviewed here are found in most graduate-level texts on algebra and algebraic geometry. However, these texts often present the material in a more concise and abstract form, thereby making it harder for the nonspecialist to access. The algebraic definition of the twisted cubic (t, t^2, t^3) was provided by S. Abhyankar.

The concept of Gröbner bases is due to Buchberger (1965). Buchberger designed and implemented the basis-construction algorithm and investigated many ideal-theoretic applications, including the solvability of systems of algebraic equations, and computations in the residue class ring R_I; see Buchberger (1965 and 1970). For a proof of Buchberger's theorem, see also Buchberger (1976). Buchberger (1985) offers a good survey of Gröbner bases algorithms and their many applications. The chapter contains a very readable introduction to the basis construction and to some of the mathematical applications, including the basis-construction algorithm and the method for solving algebraic equations discussed in this chapter.

Mishra and Yap (1987) analyze the complexity of the basis computation from a computer-science perspective. Buchberger, Collins, and Kutzler (1988) survey applications including geometry theorem proving, and compare Gröbner bases techniques with competing algorithms, such as Wu's method and Collins' quantifier-elimination procedure.

The two criteria given in Section 7.3.5 for avoiding the formation of certain S-polynomials are from Buchberger (1970 and 1976). The theorem on the elimination ideals in Section 7.4.1 is due to Trinks (1978). Kobayashi, Moritsugu, and Hogan (1987) present a modified version to solve systems of algebraic equations with finitely many solutions. Their method determines the next coordinate value from a polynomial of the form $x_i = h(x_1, ..., x_{i-1})$.

In a lecture at Oberwolfach in 1989, V. Weispfenning considered Gröbner bases construction with symbolic quantities and traced the effect of vanishing coefficient polynomials.

Geometric theorem proving is a vigorous research area that is producing a rich spectrum of results. Our brief presentation is adapted from Kutzler (1988). Kutzler takes great care in devising the translation process such that no implicit assumption is forgotten, and considers the connection to the foundational theories of geometry. Inequalities such as those used to formulate collinearity are known as *nondegeneracy conditions*. In Wu's approach to geometric theorem proving, presented by Chou (1988), not all such inequalities are formulated. Instead, the method finds certain subsidiary conditions that express these inequalities. In a sense, therefore, the method can make an "approximate" geometric theorem precise, provided the algebraic form of the nondegeneracy conditions is interpreted geometrically. Kapur and Mundy (1988) present a collection of papers from an international workshop on geometric reasoning.

There have been investigations into the effect of floating-point arithmetic on the basis calculations. Errors introduced by floating-point arithmetic affect the basis construction in the sense that new polynomials added to the basis in the course of the computation may have terms different from those that would be present were exact arithmetic used. This implies that certain S-polynomials do not reduce to zero in the floating-point case, and that the ideal therefore will be altered in ways that are difficult to assess geometrically. The presentation by Auzinger and Stetter (1988 and 1989) seems to be the only published work on this topic. In unpublished work, Chuang and Hoffmann found in 1988 that interval arithmetic techniques were not promising, even in cases where the algebraic problem corresponded to well-conditioned transversal surface intersection.

Significant advances in the wider applicability of Gröbner bases should come from the identification of specific subproblems that permit specializing to highly efficient algorithms. The complexity analyses of the bivariate and trivariate cases, in Buchberger (1983) and Winkler (1984), are the first steps in this direction. Basis conversion and its modification are other examples of progress.

The basis-conversion algorithm for zero-dimensional ideals is described in Faugère, Gianni, Lazard, and Mora (1989). It has very good practical performance and permits us to construct much larger lexicographic Gröbner bases than would otherwise be possible.

The modification of the basis-conversion algorithm for eliminating variables in other ideals was conceived in discussions with B. Buchberger and J. Davenport, in December 1988 and January 1989. An experimental version was implemented by J.-H. Chuang and W. Bouma on top of Kapur's Gröbner basis implementation. Preliminary experiments with the algorithm are very encouraging. Implicit forms of offset surfaces and parametric surfaces have been computed that could not be obtained with the Macsyma implementations of the Sylvester resultant or with the lexicographic Gröbner basis, because of lack of adequate virtual memory.

Bibliography

Abhyankar, S., (1983)
   "Desingularization of Plane Curves," *AMS Proc. of Symposia in Pure Mathematics 40*, 1–45.

Abhyankar, S., and C. Bajaj (1987a)
   "Automatic Rational Parameterization of Curves and Surfaces I: Conics and Conicoids," *Computer Aided Design 19*, 11–14.

Abhyankar, S., and C. Bajaj (1987b)
   "Automatic Rational Parameterization of Curves and Surfaces II: Cubics and Cubicoids," *Computer Aided Design 19*, 499–502.

Abhyankar, S., and C. Bajaj (1987c)
   "Automatic Rational Parameterization of Curves and Surfaces III: Algebraic Plane Curves," *Comp. Aided Geometric Design 5*, 309–321.

Abhyankar, S., and C. Bajaj (1987d)
   "Automatic Rational Parameterization of Curves and Surfaces IV: Algebraic Space Curves," *ACM Trans. on Graphics*, to appear.

Agin, G.J., and T. Binford (1973)
   "Computer Description of Curved Objects," *Proc. 3rd Intl. Joint Conf. Artif. Intell.*, 629–640.

Aho, A.V., J.E. Hopcroft, and J.D. Ullman (1974)
The Design and Analysis of Computer Algorithms, Addison-Wesley, Reading, Mass.

Aleksandrov, P.S., (1956)
Combinatorial Topology, Vol. 1, Graylock Press, Rochester, N.Y.

Ansaldi, S., L. De Floriani and B. Falcidieno (1985)
"Geometric Modeling of Solid Objects by Using a Face Adjacency Graph Representation," *Computer Graphics 19*, 131–140.

Arbab, F., and J.M. Wing (1985)
"Geometric Reasoning: A New Paradigm for Processing Geometric Information," TR 85-333, Comp. Sci., Univ. of Southern California, Los Angeles.

Arner, P.R., (1987)
Another Look at Surface/Surface Intersection, Ph.D. Thesis, Dept. of Math., University of Utah.

Auzinger, W., and H.J. Stetter (1988)
"An Elimination Algorithm for the Computation of All Zeros of A System of Multivariate Polynomial Equations," *Intl. Series Numer. Math. 86*, 11–30.

Auzinger, W., and H.J. Stetter (1989)
"A Study of Numerical Elimination for the Solution of Multivariate Polynomial Systems," Techn. Rept., Inst. Angewandte und Numerische Mathematik, Techn. Univ. Wien, A-1040 Vienna, Austria.

Ayala, D., P.. Brunet, R. Juan, and I. Navazo (1985)
"Object Representation by Means of Nonminimal Division Quadtrees and Octrees," *ACM Trans. on Graphics 4*, 41–59.

Baer, A., C.M. Eastman and M. Henrion (1979)
"Geometric Modeling: A Survey," *Computer Aided Design 11*, 253–272.

Bajaj, C.L., T. Garrity, and J. Warren (1988)
"On the Applications of Multi-Equational Resultants," Rept. TR 88-826, Comp. Sci., Purdue University.

Bajaj, C., C. Hoffmann, J. Hopcroft and R. Lynch (1988)
"Tracing Surface Intersections," *Computer Aided Geometric Design 5*, 285–307.

Bajaj, C., and M.-S. Kim (1988)
"Generation of Configuration Space Obstacles I: The Case of a Moving Sphere," *IEEE J. Robotics and Automation 4*, 94–99.

Barnhill, R.E., and W. Böhm, eds. (1983)
Surfaces in Computer Aided Geometric Design, North-Holland, Amsterdam.

Barnhill, R., G. Farin, M. Jordan, B. Piper (1987)
"Surface/Surface Intersection," *Comp. Aided Geometric Design 4*, 3–16.

Barr, A.H., (1981)
"Superquadrics and Angle Preserving Transformations," *IEEE Computer Graphics Appl.*, 1:1.

Barr, P., R. Krimper, M. Lazaer and C. Stammen (1985)
CAD: Principles and Applications, Prentice-Hall, Englewood Cliffs, N.J.

Bartels, R., J. Beatty and R. Barsky (1987)
An Introduction to Splines for Use in Computer Graphics and Geometric Modeling, Morgan Kaufmann Publishers, Los Altos, Cal.

Baumgart, B., (1975)
"A Polyhedron Representation for Computer Vision," in *National Computer Conference*, AFIPS Conf. Proc., 589–596.

Besant, C.B., (1980)
Computer Aided Design and Manufacture. Ellis Horwood.

Bobrow, J.E., (1985)
"NC Machine Tool Path Generation from CSG Part Representations," *Computer-Aided Design 17*, 69–76.

Böhm, W., G. Farin and J. Kahmann (1984)
"A Survey of Curve and Surface Methods in CAGD," *Computer Aided Geometric Design 1*, 1–60.

Bokowski, J., and B. Sturmfels (1986)
"On the Coordinatization of Oriented Matroids," *Discrete Comp. Geometry 1*, 293–306.

Bokowski, J., and B. Sturmfels (1989)
Computational Synthetic Geometry, Springer Lect. Notes in Math., to appear.

Bokowski, J., J. Richter, and B. Sturmfels (1989)
"Nonrealizability Proofs in Computational Geometry," *Discrete Comp. Geometry*, to appear.

Bowyer, A., and J. Woodwark (1983)
A Programmer's Geometry, Butterworth & Co. Ltd., Sevenoaks, England.

Boyse, J.W., and J.E. Gilchrist (1982)
"GM Solid: Interactive Modeling for Design and Analysis of Solids,"
IEEE Comp. Graphics and Applications 2, 27–40.

Braid, I.C., (1975)
"The Synthesis of Solids Bounded by Many Faces," *Comm. ACM 18*,
209–216.

Braid, I.C., (1979)
Notes on a Geometric Modeller. CAD Group Document 101, Computer
Laboratory, University of Cambridge, England

Braid, I.C., R.C. Hillyard and I.A. Stroud (1980)
"Stepwise Construction of Polyhedra in Geometric Modeling," in
Mathematical Methods in Computer Graphics and Design, K.W. Brodlie,
ed., Academic Press, 123–141.

Brieskorn, E., and H. Knörrer (1986)
Plane Algebraic Curves, Birkhäuser Verlag, Boston.

Bronstein, I.N., and K.A. Semendjajew (1961)
Taschenbuch der Mathematik, Harri Deutsch, Frankfurt, Germany. Sixth
edition.

Brown, C.M., (1982)
"PADL-2: A Technical Summary," *IEEE Comp. Graphics and
Applications 2*, 69–84.

Brüderlin, B, (1986)
"Constructing Three-Dimensional Geometric Objects Defined by
Constraints," *Proc. 1986 ACM Workshop on Interactive 3D Graphics*,
Chapel Hill, NC, October 23-24, 111–129.

Buchberger, B., (1965)
"Ein Algorithmus zum Auffinden der Basiselemente des
Restklassenringes nach einem nulldimensionalen Polynomideal,"
Dissertation, Univ. Innsbruck, Austria.

Buchberger, B., (1970)
"Ein algorithmisches Kriterium für die Lösbarkeit eines algebraischen
Gleichungssystems," *Aequationes Mathematicae 4*, 374–383.

Buchberger, B., (1976)
"A Theoretical Basis for the Reduction of Polynomials to Canonical
Forms," *ACM SIGSAM Bull. 39*, 19–29.

Buchberger, B., (1983)
"A Note on the Complexity of Constructing Gröbner Bases," *EUROCAL
'83*, Springer Lect. Notes in Comp. Sci. 162, 137–145.

Buchberger, B., (1985)
"Gröbner Bases: An Algorithmic Method in Polynomial Ideal Theory,"
in *Multidimensional Systems Theory*, N.K. Bose, ed., D. Reidel
Publishing Co., 184–232.

Buchberger, B., (1987)
"Applications of Gröbner Bases," Summer Program in Robotics,
Instit. for Math. and Applic., Univ. of Minnesota.

Buchberger, B., (1987)
"A Note on Proofs for the Main Theorem in Gröbner Bases Theory,"
Technical Report, Res. Instit. for Symb. Comp., Kepler Unniversity,
Linz, Austria.

Buchberger, B., G. Collins and B. Kutzler (1988)
"Algebraic Methods for Geometric Reasoning," *Annl. Reviews in Comp.
Science*, Vol. 3.

Cameron, S.A., (1984)
Modeling Solids in Motion, Ph.D. Thesis, University of Edinburgh, U.K.

Cameron, S.A., (1985)
"A Study of the Clash Detection Problem in Robotics," *Pröc. Intl. Conf.
Robotics and Automation*, St. Louis, 488–493.

Cameron, S.A., (1989)
"Efficient Intersection Tests for Objects Defined Constructively," *Int. J.
Rob. Res. 8:1*.

Cameron, S.A., and J. Rossignac (1988)
"Relationship between S-Bounds and Active Zones in Constructive Solid
Geometry," *IBM Rept. RC 14246*, IBM Yorktown Heights.

Canny, J., (1986)
"Collision Detection for Moving Polyhedra," *IEEE Trans. on Pattern
Analysis and Machine Intelligence PAMI-8*, 200–209.

Canny, J., (1988)
"Generalized Characteristic Polynomials," *Intl. Symp. Symbolic and Alg.
Comp.*, Rome, Italy.

Carlbom, I., I. Chakravarty, and D. Vanderschel (1985)
"A Hierarchical Data Structure for Representing the Spatial
Decomposition of 3-D Objects," *IEEE Computer Graphics Applications
5*, 24-31.

Chandru, V., D. Dutta, and C. Hoffmann (1989)
"On the Geometry of Dupin Cyclides," TR 88-818, Comp. Sci., Purdue
University.

Chandru, V., D. Dutta, and C. Hoffmann (1989)
"Variable Radius Blending using Dupin Cyclides," TR 89-851, Comp. Sci., Purdue University.

Chistov, A.L., and D. Yu. Grigoryev (1983)
"Subexponential-Time Solving Systems of Algebraic Equations," *Lomi Preprints E-9-83*, Steklov Math. Instit., Univ. of Leningrad, USSR.

Chiyokura, H., (1988)
Solid Modeling with Designbase, Addison-Wesley, Reading, Mass.

Chou, S.C., (1988)
Mechanical Geometry Theorem Proving, D. Reidel Publ., Doordrecht, Holland.

Crapo, H., T. Havel, B. Sturmfels, W. Whiteley, and N. White (1988)
"Symbolic Computations in Geometry," IMA Preprint Series 389, Inst. Math. Applic., University of Minnesota, Minneapolis, MN.

Chuang, J.-H., and C. Hoffmann (1989)
"On Local Implicit Approximations of Curves and Surfaces," *ACM Trans. Comp. Graphics*, to appear.

Cohen, E., T. Lyche and R. Riesenfeld (1980)
"Discrete B-splines and Subdivision Techniques in Computer Aided Geometric Design and Computer Graphics," *Computer Graphics and Image Processing 14*, 87–111.

Collins, G., (1983)
"Quantifier Elimination for Real Closed Fields: A Guide to the Literature," in *Computer Algebra, Symbolic and Algebraic Computation*, 2nd Edition, B. Buchberger, G. Collins, R. Loos, eds., Springer Verlag, 1983, 79–82.

Dennis, J.E., and R.B. Schnabel (1983)
Numerical Methods for Unconstrained Optimization and Nonlinear Equations, Prentice Hall, Englewood Cliffs, N.J.

Dobkin, D., and D. Silver (1988)
"Recipes for Geometry and Numerical Analysis, Part 1: An Empirical Study," 4th *ACM Symp. on Comp. Geometry*, June 1988, Urbana, Ill, 93–105.

Dombre, E., A. Fournier, C. Quaro, and P. Borrel (1986)
"Trends in CAD/CAM Systems for Robotics," *Proc. 1986 IEEE Intl. Conf. on Robotics and Automation*, San Francisco, CA, 1913–1918.

Donald, B.R. (1986)
"Robot Motion Planning with Uncertainty in the Geometric Model of the Robot and Environment: A Formal Framework for Error Detection and Recovery," *Proc. 1986 IEEE Intl. Conf. on Robotics and Automation*, San Francisco, CA, 1588–1593.

Dongarra, J., C. Moler, J. Bunch and G. Stewart (1979)
Linpack User's Guide, SIAM Publications, Philadelphia.

Dufay, B., and C. Laugier (1983)
"Geometrical Reasoning in Automatic Grasping and Contact Analysis," in *Advances in CAD/CAM,*, T.M.R. Ellis and O. Semenkov, eds., North-Holland, Amsterdam, 473–482.

Durrant-Whyte, H.F., (1988)
"Uncertain Geometry in Robotics," *IEEE J. Robotics and Automation 4*, 23–31.

Eastman, C.M., and M. Henrion (1977)
"GLIDE: A Language for Design Information Systems," *Computer Graphics 11*, 24–33

Eastman, C.M., and K. Weiler (1979)
"Geometric Modeling Using the Euler Operators," *Proc. First Annl. Conf. Comp. Graphics in CAD/CAM Systems*, MIT, 248–254

Edelsbrunner, H., and E. Mücke (1988)
"Simulation of Simplicity: A Technique to Cope with Degenerate Cases in Geometric Algorithms," *4th ACM Symp. on Comp. Geometry*, June 1988, Urbana, Ill, 118–133.

Elmagarmid, A., and A. Helal (1988)
"Supporting Updates in Heterogeneous Distributed Database Systems," *IEEE Intl. Conf. Data Engineering*, Los Angeles, 564–569.

Encarnação, J., ed. (1980)
Computer Aided Design – Modeling, Systems Engineering, CAD Systems. Springer Lect. Notes in Comp. Sci. 89

Encarnação, J., and E.G. Schlechtendahl, eds. (1983)
Computer-Aided Design Fundamentals and System Architecture. Springer Verlag, New York.

Farin, G., (1988)
Curves and Surfaces for Computer Aided Geometric Design, Academic Press, Boston.

Farouki, R.T., (1985)
"Exact Offset Procedures for Simple Solids," *Computer-Aided Geometric Design 2*, 257–279.

Farouki, R.T., (1986a)
  "Trimmed Surface Algorithms for the Evaluation and Interrogation of Solid Boundary Representation," *IBM J. Res. and Dev. 31*, 314–334.

Farouki, R.T., (1986b)
  "The Approximation of Nondegenerate Offset Surfaces," *Comp. Aided Geometric Design 3*, 15–43.

Farouki, R.T., (1986c)
  "The Characterization of Parametric Surface Sections," *Comp. Vision, Graphics and Im. Proc. 33*, 209–236.

Farouki, R.T., (1987a)
  "Computational Issues in Solid Boundary Evaluation," IBM Res. Rept. RC–12454.

Farouki, R.T., (1987b)
  "Graphical Methods for Surface Differential Geometry," in *The Mathematics of Surfaces II*, R. Martin, ed., Clarendon Press, Oxford, 363–386.

Farouki, R.T., and C.A. Neff (1989)
  "Some Analytic and Algebraic Properties of Plane Offset Curves," Rept. RC 14364, IBM Yorktown Heights.

Farouki, R.T., and V.T. Rajan (1987)
  "On the Numerical Condition of Algebraic Curves and Surfaces 1. Implicit Equations," IBM Res. Rept. RC–13263.

Faugère, J., P. Gianni, D. Lazard, T. Mora (1989)
  "Efficient Change of Ordering for Gröbner Bases of Zero-Dimensional Ideals," manuscript.

Faux, I.D., and M.J. Pratt (1979)
  Computational Geometry for Design and Manufacture. Ellis Horwood, Chichester.

Filip, D., R. Magedson and R. Markot (1986)
  "Surface Algorithms Using Bounds on Derivatives," *Computer Aided Geometric Design 3*, 295–311.

Garrity, T., and J. Warren (1988)
  "On Computing the Intersection of a Pair of Algebraic Surfaces," *Comp. Aided Geometric Design*, to appear.

Geisow, A., (1983)
  "Surface Interrogation," *Ph.D.Diss.*, School of Computing and Accountancy, Univ. of East Anglia.

Goldstein, R., and L. Malin (1979)
"3-D Modelling with the Synthavision System," *Proc. First Annl. Conf. Comp. Graphics in CAD/CAM Systems*, Cambridge, MA, 244–247.

Golub, G., and C. van Loan (1983)
Matrix Computations, Johns Hopkins Press.

Greene, D., and F. Yao (1986)
"Finite Resolution Computational Geometry," 27th *IEEE Symp. Found. Comp. Sci.*, Toronto, 143–152.

Guibas, L.J., and R. Seidel (1986)
"Computing Convolutions by Reciprocal Search," *Proc. 2nd ACM Symp. on Computational Geometry*, Yorktown Heights, NY.

Halbert, A.R., S.J.P. Todd, and J.R. Woodwark (1988)
"Generalizing Active Zones for Set-Theoretic Solid Models," IBM UK Sci. Center, Rept. UKSC 182, Winchester, UK.

Henderson, M.R., (1985)
"Extraction and Organization of Form Features," *Proc. Prolamat '85*, Paris, France, 131–141.

Hilbert, D., and Cohn-Vossen, S., (1952)
Geometry and the Imagination, Chelsea Publ. Co., New York.

Hillyard, R.C., (1982)
"The Build Group of Solid Modellers," *IEEE Comp. Graphics and Applic. 2*, 43–52.

Hocking, J.G., and G.S. Young (1961)
Topology, Addison-Wesley, Reading, Mass.

Hoffmann, C., (1987)
"Algebraic Curves," in *Mathematical Aspects of Scientific Software*, J. Rice, ed., IMA Volumes in Math. and Applic., Springer Verlag, 101–122.

Hoffmann, C., (1988)
"A Dimensionality Paradigm for Surface Interrogations," TR 88-837, Comp. Sci., Purdue University.

Hoffmann, C., (1989a)
"The Problem of Accuracy and Robustness in Geometric Computation," *IEEE Computer 22*, 31–42.

Hoffmann, C., and J. Hopcroft (1985)
"Automatic Surface Generation in Computer Aided Design," *The Visual Computer 1*, 92–100.

Hoffmann, C., and J. Hopcroft (1986)
"Quadratic Blending Surfaces," *Comp. Aided Design 18*, 301–307.

Hoffmann, C., and J. Hopcroft (1987a)
"The Potential Method for Blending Surfaces and Corners," in *Geometric Modeling*, G. Farin, ed., SIAM Publications, Philadelphia.

Hoffmann, C., and J. Hopcroft (1987b)
";Simulation of Physical Systems from Geometric Models," *IEEE J. Robotics and Autom. RA-3*, 194–206.

Hoffmann, C., and J. Hopcroft (1987c)
"Geometric Ambiguities in Boundary Representations," *Comp. Aided Design 19*, 141–147.

Hoffmann, C., and J. Hopcroft (1988a)
"Projective Blending Surfaces," *Artif. Intelligence 37*, 357-376.

Hoffmann, C., and J. Hopcroft (1988b)
"Model Generation and Modification for Dynamic Systems from Geometric Data," in *CAD Based Programming for Sensory Robots*, B. Ravani, ed., Springer NATO ASI Series F-50, 481–492.

Hoffmann,C., J. Hopcroft and M. Karasick (1987)
"Robust Set Operations on Polyhedral Solids," Tech. Rept. 723, Comp. Sci., Purdue University.

Hoffmann, C., J. Hopcroft and M. Karasick (1988)
"Towards Implementing Robust Geometric Computations," 4th *ACM Symp. on Comp. Geometry*, 106–117.

Holmström, L., (1986)
Piecewise Quadric Blending of Implicitly Defined Surfaces. Report TKK-TKO-B60, Helsinki University of Technology, Espoo, Finland.

Hong, J., (1986)
"Proving by Example and Gap Theorems," 27th *IEEE Symp. Found. of Comp. Sci.*, 107–116.

Houghton, E.G., R.F. Emnett, J.D. Factor, and C.L. Sabharwal (1985)
"Implementation of a Divide-and-Conquer Method for Intersection of Parametric Surfaces," *Computer-Aided Geometric Design 2*, 173–183.

Jackins, C.L., and S.L. Tanimoto (1980)
"Oct-Trees and their Use in Representing Three-Dimensional Objects," *Comp. Graphics and Image Processing 14*, 249–270.

Kapur, D., (1986)
"Using Gröbner Bases to Reason about Geometry," *J. Symbolic Comp. 2*, 399–408.

Kapur, D., and J. Mundy (1988)
"Geometric Reasoning," Proc. Workshop on Geometric Reasoning, Oxford, 1986, special issue, *Artif. Intell. 37.*

Karasick, M., (1988)
"On the Representation and Manipulation of Rigid Solids," Ph.D. Diss., Comp. Sci., McGill University, Montreal, Canada.

Karasick, M., D. Lieber, and L. Nackman (1989)
"Efficient Delaunay Triangulation Using Rational Arithmetic," Rept. RC 14455, IBM Yorktown Heights.

Kimura, F., (1984)
"Geomap-III: Designing Solids With Free-Form Surfaces," *IEEE Computer Graphics Applic. 4,* 58–72

Klein, F., (1925)
Elementarmathematik vom höheren Standpunkte aus, Vol. 2, Springer Verlag, Berlin, Germany.

Kobayashi, H., S. Moritsugu, and R. Hogan (1987)
"On Solving Systems of Algebraic Equations," Rept. 88-001, Dept. Inf. Sci., Univ. Tokyo, Japan.

Kutzler, B., (1988)
Algebraic Approaches to Automated Geometry Proving, Ph.D. Diss., Res. Instit. for Symb. Comp., Rept. 88-74.0, Kepler University, Linz, Austria.

Laidlaw, D.H., W.B. Trumbore and J.F. Hughes (1986)
"Constructive Solid Geometry for Polyhedral Objects," *ACM Computer Graphics 20,* 161–170.

Laning, J.H., and S.J. Madden (1979)
"Capabilities of the SHAPES System for Computer Aided Mechanical Design," *Proc. First Annl. Conf. Computer Graphics in CAD/CAM Systems,* Cambridge, MA, 223–231.

Lazard, D., (1983)
"Gröbner Bases, Gaussian Elimination and Resolution of Systems of Algebraic Equations," *EUROCAL '83,* Springer Lect. Notes in Comp. Sci. 162, 146–156.

Lee, K., and D.C. Gossard (1985)
"A Hierarchical Data Structure for Representing Assemblies: Part I," *Computer-Aided Design 17,* 15–19.

Lee, Y.T., and A.A.G. Requicha (1982a)
"Algorithms for Computing the Volume and Other Integral Properties of Solid Objects. I – Known Methods and Open Issues," *Comm. ACM 25*, 635–641.

Lee, Y.T., and A.A.G. Requicha (1982b)
"Algorithms for Computing the Volume and Other Integral Properties of Solid Objects. II – A Family of Algorithms Based on Representation Conversion and Cellular Approximation," *Comm. ACM 25*, 642–650.

Levin, J., (1979)
"Mathematical Models for Determining the Intersections of Quadric Surfaces," *Comp. Vision, Graphics and Image Processing 11*, 73–87.

Lovász, L., (1986)
An Algorithmic Theory of Numbers, Graphs, and Convexity, SIAM Publications, Philadelphia.

Macaulay, F.S., (1902)
"Some Formulae in Elimination," *Proc. London Math. Soc. 35*, 3–27.

Macaulay, F.S., (1916)
The Algebraic Theory of Modular Systems, Cambridge University Press, 1916.

Mäntylä, M., (1982)
"An Inversion Algorithm for Geometric Models," *Computer Graphics 16*, 51–59.

Mäntylä, M., (1984)
"A Note on the Modeling Space of Euler Operators," *Comp. Vision, Graphics, and Image Processing 26*, 45–60.

Mäntylä, M., (1986)
"Boolean Operations of 2-Manifolds Through Vertex Neighborhood Classification," *ACM Trans. on Graphics 5*, 1–29.

Mäntylä, M., (1988)
An Introduction to Solid Modeling. Computer Science Press, Rockville, Maryland.

Mäntylä, M., and M. Ranta (1986)
"Interactive Solid Modeling in HutDesign," in *Proc. Computer Graphics Tokyo '86*.

Mäntylä, M., and R. Sulonen (1982)
"GWB – a Solid Modeler with Euler Operators," *IEEE Comp. Graphics Applic. 2*, 17–31.

Mäntylä, M., and M. Tamminen (1983)
"Localized Set Operations for Solid Modeling," *Computer Graphics 17*, 279–288.

Martin, R.R., (1987)
The Mathematics of Surfaces II, Clarendon Press, Oxford.

Meagher, D., (1982)
"Geometric Modelling using Octree Encoding," *Comp. Graphics and Image Processing 19*, 129–147.

Mehlhorn, K., (1984)
Data Structures and Algorithms, Vol. 3, Springer Verlag, New York.

Middleditch, A.E., and K.H. Sears (1985)
"Blend Surfaces for Set Theoretic Volume Modelling Systems," *Computer Graphics 19*, 161–170.

Milenkovic, V., (1988)
Verifiable Implementations of Geometric Algorithms Using Finite Precision Arithmetic, Ph.D. Diss., Rept. CS-88-168, Comp. Sci., Carnegie-Mellon Univ.

Mishra, B., and C.K. Yap (1987)
"Notes on Gröbner Bases," to appear.

Montaudouin, Y., (1987)
"Criterion for Terminating Subdivision in the Surface/Surface Intersection Problem. The X Algorithm," manuscript; Center for Appl. of Math., Lehigh University.

Montaudouin, Y., W. Tiller and H. Vold (1986)
"Applications of Power Series in Computational Geometry," *Computer Aided Design 18*, 514–524.

Mora, F., (1982)
"An Algorithm to Compute the Equations of Tangent Cones," *EOROCAM '82*, Springer Lect. Notes in Comp. Science 144, 158–165.

Morgan, A.P., (1987)
Solving Polynomial Systems Using Continuation for Scientific and Engineering Problems, Prentice-Hall, Englewood Cliffs, N.J.

Morgan, A.P., and A. Sommese (1987)
"A Homotopy for Solving General Polynomial Systems That Respects *m*-Homogeneous Structures," *Applied Math. Comput. 24*, 101–113.

Morgan, A.P., and A. Sommese (1987)
"Computing All Solutions to Polynomial Systems Using Homotopy Continuation," *Applied Math. Comput. 24*, 115–138.

Mortenson, M., (1985)
Geometric Modeling, John Wiley & Sons, New York.

Nasri, A., (1984)
Polyhedral Subdivision Methods for Free-Form Surfaces, Ph.D. Diss.,
Comp. Studies and Accountancy, Univ. of East Anglia.

Netto, E., (1892)
Theory of Substitutions and of Integral Functions, The Inland Press, Ann
Arbor, Mich.

Newell, R.G., (1982)
"Solid Modelling and Parametric Design in the Medusa System," in
Computer Graphics 82, 223–235.

Nutbourne, A., and R. Martin (1988)
"Differential Geometry Applied to Curve and Surface Design," Ellis
Horwood Ltd., England.

Ocken, S., J. Schwartz, and M. Sharir (1983)
"Precise Implementation of CAD Primitives using Rational
Parameterizations of Standard Surfaces," *Planning, Geometry and
Complexity of Robot Motion*, Ablex Publishing, Norwood, N.J., 245–266.

Okino, N., Y. Kakazu, and H. Kubo (1973)
"TIPS-1: Technical Information Processing System for Computer Aided
Design and Manufacturing," *Computer Languages for Numerical
Control*, J. Hatvany, ed., North Holland, Amsterdam, 141–150.

Owen, J., and A. Rockwood (1987)
"Intersection of General Implicit Surfaces," in *Geometric Modeling:
Algorithms and Trends*, G. Farin, ed., SIAM Publications, Philadelphia.

Palmer, T., (1982)
Sculptured Surfaces in Volume Modeling Systems, Ph.D. Diss., Comp.
Studies and Accountancy, Univ. of East Anglia.

Paoluzzi, A., M. Ramella, and A. Santarelli (1986)
"Un modellatori geometrico su rappresentazioni triango-alate," Rept. TR
13.86, Dept. of Inf. and Systems, Univ. of Rome, Italy.

Paoluzzi, A., M. Ramella, and A. Santarelli (1988)
"A Boolean Algebra over Linear Polyhedra," manuscript.

Pegna, J., (1988)
"Variable Sweep Geometric Modeling," PhD Diss., Mech. Engr.,
Stanford Univ.

Pogorolev, A.V., (1957)
Differential Geometry, P. Noordhoff, N.V., Groningen, Netherlands.

Ponce, J., and D. Chelberg (1987)
"Localized Intersections Computation for Solid Modeling with Straight Homogeneous Generalized Cylinders," *Proc. IEEE Intl. Conf. on Robotics and Automation*, 1481–1486.

Post, F.H., and F. Klok (1986)
"Deformations of Sweep Objects in Solid Modelling," *Eurographics '86*, North-Holland, Amsterdam.

Prakash, P., and N. Patrikalakis (1988)
"Algebraic and Rational Polynomial Surface Intersections," *Computer Vision, Graphics, and Image Proc.*, to appear.

Pratt, M., (1986)
"Parametric Curves and Surfaces as Used in Computer Aided Design," in *The Mathematics of Surfaces*, J. Gregory, ed., Oxford University Press, 19–46.

Pratt, M., and A. Geisow (1986)
"Surface/Surface Intersection Problems," in *The Mathematics of Surfaces*, J. Gregory, ed., Oxford University Press, 117–142.

Preparata, F.P., and M.I. Shamos (1985)
Computational Geometry, Spring-Verlag, New York.

Ravani, B., (1988)
CAD Based Programming for Sensory Robots, NATO ASI Series F-50, Springer Verlag, New York.

Reddy, D.R., and S. Rubin (1978)
Representation of Three-Dimensional Objects. Report CMU-CS-78-113, Comp. Science, Carnegie-Mellon University, Pittsburgh.

Requicha, A.A.G., (1977)
Mathematical Models of Rigid Solids. Tech. Memo. 28, Production Automation Project, University of Rochester.

Requicha, A.A.G., (1980a)
"Representations for Rigid Solids: Theory, Methods, and Systems," *ACM Comp. Surveys 12*, 437–464.

Requicha, A.A.G., (1980b)
"Representations of Rigid Solid Objects," in *Computer Aided Design*, J. Encarnacao, ed., Springer Lect. Notes in Comp. Sci., 2–78.

Requicha, A.A.G., (1984)
"Representation of Tolerances in Solid Modeling: Issues and Alternative Approaches," in *Solid Modeling by Computers*, M.S. Pickett and J.W. Boyse, eds., Plenum Press, New York, 3–22.

Requicha, A.A.G., (1988)
> "Solid Modeling - A 1988 Update", in *CAD Based Programming for Sensory Robots*, B. Ravani, ed., Springer Verlag, New York, 3–22.

Requicha, A.A.G., and S.C. Chan (1986)
> "Representation of Geometric Features, Tolerances and Attributes in Solid Modellers Based on Constructive Geometry," *IEEE Journal of Robotics and Automation, RA-2*, 156–186.

Requicha, A.A.G., and J.H. Vandenbrande (1987)
> "Automatic Process Planning and Part Programming," in *Artificial Intelligence: Implications for CIM*, A. Kusiak, ed., Springer Verlag, New York, 299–326.

Requicha, A.A.G., and H.B. Voelcker (1977)
> *Constructive Solid Geometry*. Tech. Memo. 25, Production Automation Project, University of Rochester.

Requicha, A.A.G., and H.B. Voelcker (1981)
> "An Introduction to Geometric Modeling and its Applications in Mechanical Design and Production," in *Advances in Information Systems Sciences*, J.Tou, ed., Plenum Publishing Co.

Requicha, A.A.G., and H.B. Voelcker (1982)
> "Solid Modeling: A Historical Summary and Contemporary Assessment," *IEEE Comp. Graphics Applic. 2*, 9–24.

Requicha, A.A.G., and H.B. Voelcker (1983)
> "Solid Modeling: Current Status and Research Directions," *IEEE Comp. Graphics and Applic. 3*, 25–37.

Requicha, A.A.G., and H.B. Voelcker (1985)
> "Boolean Operations in Solid Modeling: Boundary Evaluation and Merging Algorithms," *Proc. IEEE 73*, 30–44

Rockwood, A.P., (1984)
> "Introducing Sculptured Surfaces into a Geometric Modeler," in *Solid Modeling by Computers*, M.S. Pickett and J.W. Boyse, eds., Plenum Press, New York, 237–258.

Rockwood, A.P., and J. Owen (1985)
> "Blending Surfaces in Solid Modeling," in *Geometric Modeling: Algorithms and New Trands*, G. Farin, ed., SIAM Publications, Philadelphia.

Rossignac, J.R., (1985)
> "Blending and Offsetting Solid Models," *Ph.D Diss.*, Dept. of Mech. Engr., Univ. of Rochester.

Rossignac, J.R., (1986)
"Constraints in Constructive Solid Geometry," *Proc. Workshop Interactive 3D Graphics*, ACM Press, F. Crow and S.M. Pize, eds., 93–110.

Rossignac, J.R., and A.A.G. Requicha (1984)
"Constant Radius Blending in Solid Modeling," *Comp. Mech. Engr. 3*, 65–73.

Rossignac, J.R., and A.A.G. Requicha (1986)
"Offsetting Operations in Solid Modeling," *Computer Aided Design 3*, 129–148.

Rossignac, J.R., and H.B. Voelcker (1988)
"Active Zones in CSG for Accelerating Boundary Evaluation, Redundancy Elimination, Interference Detection, and Shading Algorithms," *ACM Trans. Graphics 8*, 51–87.

Sabin, M.A., (1984)
"Geometric modelling – Fundamentals," in *Eurographics Tutorials '83*, P.J.W. ten Hagen, ed., Springer Verlag, 343–390

Sabin, M.A., (1987)
"Envelope Curves and Surfaces," in *The Mathematics of Surfaces II*, R. Martin, ed., Clarendon Press, Oxford, 413–418.

Saia, A., M.S. Bloor, and A. dePennington (1987)
"Sculptured Surfaces in a CSG Based Geometric Modelling System," in *The Mathematics of Surfaces II*, R. Martin, ed., Clarendon Press, Oxford, 321–342.

Samet, H.J., (1989a)
Design and Analysis of Spatial Data Structures: Quadtrees, Octrees, and Other Hierarchical Methods, Addison-Wesley, Redding, Mass.

Samet, H.J., (1989b)
Applications of Spatial Data Structures: Computer Graphics, Image Processing, and GIS, Addison-Wesley, Redding, Mass.

Sarraga, R.F., (1983)
"Algebraic Methods for Intersections of Quadric Surfaces in GM Solid," *Comp. Graphics Image Proc. 22*, 222–238.

Schubert, H., (1964)
Topologie, B. G. Teubner, Stuttgart, Germany

Schwartz, J.T., and M. Sharir (1982)
"On the 'Piano-Movers' Problem; II. General Techniques for Computing Topological Properties of Real Algebraic Manifolds," *Tech. Rept. 41, Courant Instit.*, New York Univ.

Schwartz, J.T., and C.K. Yap (1987)
Algorithmic and Geometric Aspects of Robotics, Vol. 1, Lawrence
Erlbaum Assoc., Hillsdale, N.J.

Sederberg, T.W., (1983)
"Implicit and Parametric Curves and Surfaces for Computer Aided
Geometric Design," *Ph.D. Diss.*, Mech. Engr., Purdue University

Sederberg, T.W., (1985)
"Piecewise Algebraic Surface Patches." *Comp. Aided Geom. Design 2*,
53–59.

Sederberg, T.W., (1988)
"An Algorithm for Algebraic Curve Intersection," Tech. Rept.
ECGL-88-3, Civil Engr., Brigham Young Univ.

Sederberg, T.W., and D.C. Anderson (1985)
"Steiner Surface Patches," *IEEE Comp. Graphics Applic. 5*, 23–36.

Sederberg, T.W., D.C. Anderson, and R.N. Goldman (1984)
"Implicit Representation of Parametric Curves and Surfaces,"
Comp. Vision, Graphics and Im. Proc. 28, 72–84.

Sederberg, T.W., and R.N. Goldman (1986)
"Algebraic Geometry for Computer-Aided Geometric Design," *IEEE
Computer Graphics and Applications 6*, 52–59.

Sederberg, T.W., and T. Nishita (1989)
"Direct Approximation of Surface Patch Intersection Curves,"
manuscript.

Sederberg, T.W., and S. Parry (1986a)
"A Comparison of Curve Intersection Algorithms," *Comp. Aided
Geometric Design 18*, 58–63.

Sederberg, T.W. and S.R. Parry (1986b)
"Free-Form Deformation of Solid Geometric Models," *ACM Computer
Graphics, 20*, 151–160.

Sederberg, T., and J.P. Snively (1987)
"Parameterization of Cubic Algebraic Surfaces," in *The Mathematics of
Surfaces II*, R. Martin, ed., Clarendon Press, Oxford, 299–320.

Segal, M., and C. Séquin (1989)
"Consistent Calculations for Solids Modeling," *Artificial Intelligence*,
special issue on Geometric Reasoning edited by D. Kapur and J. Mundy.

Seifert, H., and W. Threlfall (1947)
Lehrbuch der Topologie, Chelsea, N.Y.

Semple, J.G., and G.T. Kneebone (1952)
Algebraic Projective Geometry, Clarendon Press, Oxford.

Semple, J.G., and G.T. Kneebone (1959)
Algebraic Curves, Clarendon Press, Oxford.

Shamos, M.I., and F. Preparata (1985)
Computational Geometry. Springer Verlag, New York.

Shiroma, Y., N. Okino and Y. Kakazu (1983)
"Research on 3-D Geometric Modelling by Sweep Primitives," *Proc. CAD '82*, Brighton, U.K., 671–680.

Snyder, V., and C. Sisam (1914)
Analytic Geometry of Space, Henry Holt and Company, New York.

Spivak, M., (1975)
A Comprehensive Introduction to Differential Geometry, Publish or Perish, Inc., Wilmington, Del., 5 volumes.

Stewart, G., (1973)
Introduction to Matrix Computations, Academic Press.

Stolfi, J., (1989)
"Primitives for Computational Geometry," Ph.D. Diss., Comp. Sci., Stanford University.

Sugihara, K., (1987)
"On Finite-Precision Representation of Geometric Objects," Memo. RMI 87-06, Dept. Mathematical Engineering and Information Systems, Univ. Tokyo, Japan.

Sugihara, K., (1988)
"A Simple Method for Avoiding Numerical Errors and Degeneracy in Voronoi Diagram Construction," Res. Mem. 88-14, Math. Eng. and Information Physics, University of Tokyo.

Sugihara, K., (1989)
"Symbolically Perturbed Invisibility for Hidden-Line Elimination," Res. Mem. 89-01, Math. Eng. and Information Physics, University of Tokyo.

Sugihara, K., and M. Iri (1988)
"Geometric Algorithms in Finite-Precision Arithmetic," Res. Mem. 88-14, Math. Eng. and Information Physics, University of Tokyo.

Sugihara, K., and M. Iri (1989)
"A Solid Modeling System Free From Topological Inconsistency," manuscript, Math. Eng. and Information Physics, University of Tokyo.

Tan, S.T., M.F. Yuen and K.C. Hui (1987)
"Modelling Solids with Sweep Primitives," *ASME Computers in Mechanical Engineering 6*, 60–73.

Terzopoulos, D., J. Platt, A. Barr and K. Fleischer (1987)
"Elastically Deformable Models," *ACM Computer Graphics 21*, 205–214.

Thibault and Naylor (1987)
"Set Operations on Polyhedra Using Binary Space Partitioning Trees," *ACM Computer Graphics 21*, 153–162.

Tiller, W., (1983)
"Rational B-splines for Curve and Surface Representation," *IEEE Comp. Graphics Applic. 3*.

Tilove, R.B., (1980)
"Set Membership Classification: A Unified Approach to Geometric Intersection Problems," *IEEE Transactions on Computers*, C-29:10, 847–883.

Tilove, R.B., (1981)
Exploiting Spatial and Structural Locality in Geometric Modeling. Ph. D. thesis, University of Rochester

Tilove, R.B., (1984)
"A Null-Object Detection Algorithm for Constructive Solid Geometry," *Comm. ACM 27*, 684–694.

Timmer, H.G., and J.M. Stern (1980)
"Computation of Global Geometric Properties of Solid Objects," *Computer Aided Design 11*.

Trinks, W., (1978)
"On Buchberger's Method for Solving Systems of Algebraic Equations," *J. Number Thy. 10*, 475–488.

Turner, J.U., (1987)
"Tolerances in Computer-Aided Geometric Design," Ph.D. Dissertation, Rensselaer Polytechnic Institute.

van der Waerden, B., (1939)
Einführung in die algebraische Geometrie, Springer Verlag, 2nd edition, 1973.

van der Waerden, B.L., (1967)
Modern Algebra, 2 volumes, Springer Verlag, New York.

van Wijk, J.J., (1985)
  "Ray Tracing Objects Defined by Sweeping a Sphere," *Computers and Graphics 9*, 283–290.

Vaněček Jr., G., (1989)
  Set Operations on Polyhedra Using Decomposition Methods, Ph.D. Diss., Comp. Sci., Univ. of Maryland.

Varady, T., and M.J. Pratt (1984)
  "Design Techniques for the Definition of Solid Objects with Free-Form Geometry," *Comp. Aided Geom. Design 1*, 207–225.

Voelcker, H.B., and A.A.G. Requicha (1977)
  "Geometric Modeling of Physical Parts and Processes," *IEEE Computer 10*, 48–57.

Voelcker, H.B., A.A.G. Requicha, and R.W. Conway (1988)
  "Computer Applications in Manufacturing," *Annl. Rev. Comp. Sci. 3*, 349–387.

Voelcker, H.B., et al., (1974)
  "An Introduction to PADL: Characteristics, Status, and Rationale," *Tech. Memo No. 22, Production Automation Project*, University of Rochester.

Vossler, D.L., (1985)
  "Sweep-to-CSG Conversion Using Pattern Recognition Techniques," *IEEE Computer Graphics Applic. 5*, 61–68.

Walker, R., (1950)
  Algebraic Curves, Springer Verlag, New York.

Waggenspack, W.N., and D. Anderson (1986)
  "Converting Standard bivariate Polynomials to Bernstein Form Over Arbitrary Triangular Regions," *Comp. Aided Design 18*, 529–532

Wang, W.P., and K.K. Wang (1986)
  "Geometric Modeling of Swept Volume of Solids and its Applications," *IEEE Computer Graphics and Applications 6*, 8–17.

Watson, L.T., S.C. Billups, and A.P. Morgan (1987)
  "Algorithm 652, HOMPACK: A Suite of Codes for Globally Convergent Homotopy Algorithms," *ACM Trans. Math. Softw. 13*, 281–310.

Weiler, K.J., (1986)
  "Topological Structures for Geometric Modeling," Ph.D. Thesis, Comp. and Syst. Engr., Rensselaer Polytechnic Inst.

Wesley, M.A., (1980)
"Construction and Use of Geometric Modeling Systems," in *Computer Aided Design – Modeling, Systems Engineering CAD Systems*, J. Encarnação, ed., Springer Verlag

Wesley, M., et al., (1980)
"A Geometric Modeling System for Automated Mechanical Assembly," *IBM J. Res. and Dev. 24*, 64–74.

Wilson, P.R., (1987)
"Conic Representations for Shape Description," *IEEE Computer Graphics Applications 7*, 23–30.

Winkler, F., (1984)
"On the Complexity of the Gr"obner Basis Algorithm over $k[x,y,z]$," *EUROSAM '84*, Springer Lect. Notes in Comp. Sci. 174, 184–194.

Wolfe, R., M. Wesley, J. Kyle, F. Gracer and W. Fitzgerald (1987)
"Solid Modeling for Production Design," *IBM Journal of Res. Dev. 31*, 277–295.

Woo, T.C., (1982)
"Feature Extraction by Volume Decomposition," *Proc. Conf. on CAD-CAM Technology in Mech. Eng.*, Cambridge, Mass., 76–94.

Woo, T.C., and T. Thomasma (1984)
"An Algorithm for Generating Solid Elements in Objects with Holes," *Computers and Structures 8*, 333–342.

Woodwark, J.R., (1986)
Computing Shape. Butterworth & Co. Ltd., England.

Woodwark, J.R., (1987)
"Blends in Geometric Modelling," in *The Mathematics of Surfaces II*, R. Martin, ed., Clarendon Press, Oxford, 255–298.

Woodwark, J.R., and K.M. Quinlan (1982)
"Reducing the Effect of Complexity on Volume Model Evaluation," *Computer-Aided Design 14*, 89–95.

Wördenweber, B., (1984)
"Finite Element Mesh Generation," *Computer Aided Design 16*, 285–291.

Yamaguchi, F., and T. Tokieda (1984a)
"Bridge Edge and Triangulation Approach in Solid Modeling," in *Proc. Computer Graphics Tokyo '84*, T.L. Kunii, ed., Springer Verlag.

Yamaguchi, F., and T. Tokieda (1984b)
"A Unified Algorithm for Boolean Shape Operations," *IEEE Comp. Graphics Applic. 4*, 24–37.

Yap, C.K., (1986)
"Algorithmic Motion Planning," in *Advances in Robotics*, J.T. Schwartz and C.K. Yap, eds., Lawrence Erlbaum Assoc., New York.

Yap, C.K., (1988)
"A Geometric Consistency Theorem for a Symbolic Perturbation Theorem," 4th *ACM Symp. on Comp. Geometry*, Urbana, Ill., June 1988, 134–142.

Yoon, D.H.H., and N.K. Tsao (1989)
"The Integration of Surface and Solid Modeling Using Finite Elements," manuscript, Comp. Sci., Wayne State Univ., Detroit.

Index